HUNGER FIGHTERS

"But it must be borne in mind that all great enterprises are based on work that has been done by individuals whose past is lost in oblivion. Some one has to do the obscure but necessary work of digging a foundation, and if it falls to our part, we must be content with the knowledge that we are playing a necessary part in a great enterprise."

James Mackenzie.

Books by Paul de Kruif

~~~~~

OUR MEDICINE MEN

MICROBE HUNTERS

HUNGER FIGHTERS

SEVEN IRON MEN

MEN AGAINST DEATH

WHY KEEP THEM ALIVE?

THE FIGHT FOR LIFE

HUNGER FIGHTERS

by
Paul de Kruif
AUTHOR OF
MICROBE HUNTERS

Illustrated by ZADIG
NEW YORK · HARCOURT, BRACE
and COMPANY

A C K N O W L E D G M E N T

To Philip S. Rose and Loring A. Schuler—the order of names is purely alphabetical—all my thanks. By their enthusiasm for the deeds of these hunger fighters, by the discipline they exercised on my own too frequent enthusiasms, by their unearthing of several of these obscure heroes whose names were unknown to me, they were more than editors. During the two and a half years of writing of *Hunger Fighters*, Schuler and Rose were my co-workers. What is best of all, they were friends.

Paul de Kruif

CONTENTS

BOOK ONE. WHEAT

CARLETON

CHAPTER ONE. THE WHEAT DREAMER

CARLETON

I.

IT HAS BEEN THE FATE of men who by their dreams and brains have fought hunger for mankind, to die nameless and unknown. Theirs is an earthy science, born ten thousand years before there was such a word as science, beginning in the completely buried days when men first fought nature by their wits. There is no true start to the history of hunger fighters.

There is no question it was Mark Alfred Carleton who brought the magnificent Kubanka wheat from its old home on the Turghai steppe of western Asia to more than four millions of acres of the land of the American Northwest. There is no doubt he died, most miserably neglected and obscure, in a pest-hole in Peru.

There is no recorded beginning of the science of wheat hunters. Nobody remembers the name of the first Turk or Jew or Tartar who tamed the wild wheat of southwest Asia; who, untold thousands of years ago, had the dream to save the seed of this staff of life against the next year's hunger of his tribe. So why not start this story of the adventures of modern hunger fighters with the outlandish deeds of Mark Carleton—who just missed being forgotten?

Of Carleton there is unquestioned record that his solitary explorations brought the tough Kharkov wheat out of wind-swept Starobelsk, Russia, on to twenty millions of acres of the black earth of the plains of the American West. Shortly afterwards he lost one of his children and his home, to say nothing of his teeth, as well as his job. But no one can blame the high authorities and his own underlings who plotted his doom. The strangest part of his grand, melancholy story is this: that the very quality which made him

3

such a fantastic and notable man also brought him to disaster. He was a visionary.

He was a crude dreamer, just as the nameless Egyptian, Assyrian, Chinese, American hunger fighters must have been thinkers, mullers over hunches, when they first of all stored water to make thirsty land grow food for men in magic abundance. So Carleton had the queer notion to put the map of the millions of acres of the American dark land side by side with the picture of the giant band of the Russian black fallow. He looked. He said, "They're no different."

When I say he was a dreamer, that does not mean that Mark Carleton was a loafer, or a genius to sit around concocting revolutions in wheat-growing out of his head. No, first and last he was a dynamo for energy, an American of the Midwest; he was six feet of never tired, slope-shouldered, burly worker. "You know, I'm going to live to be a hundred," Carleton told his friends. But in spite of such energy, he saw visions—some of them foolish—and he was a gambling gazer toward horizons after the manner of a farmer pioneer. His nose was never far from that black earth from which the wheat spike sucks up its starch and gluten; he was always smelling for impossible yields from new soil. That was what helped bring him to his sad end, for he went in over his head trying on his own hook to make a dry farm out of a desert in the Texas Panhandle. "He tried to ride horses going two ways; he tried to mix science and business," said the kindly, white-bearded, professorial Erwin Smith. But who can blame Carleton? Though our Government seemed not to know it, Carleton did need money for his growing family.

He was born in Jerusalem, Ohio; went to the country school there. But in 1876, when he was ten, his family lugged him along with them out to Cloud County, Kansas. By the time he was eleven he began to get a taste of what it means to try to make a living growing wheat in that stern country. The year he was eleven the black stem rust sucked the sap out of the stalks and shriveled the kernels in the spikes of the wheat of the settlers. The rust demon jumped from farm to farm, rode the whistling west wind from one county to another. Carleton said, long afterwards, "Many fields of wheat were destroyed, never harvested." He was still in knee pants then, but he remembered: "Sulphur-like clouds of spores filled the air and irritated the nostrils of the workmen." He hardly knew botany from Bible study, but later he wrote, "A vivid remembrance of the general appearance of the rust inclines me to believe it was *Puccinia graminis* that did the damage." So Carleton came to dread the black stem rust.

It would be romantic claptrap to say that this experience made the eleven-year-old Carleton resolve to free the wheat men from the terror of that black marauding parasite. But the point is that at the swimming, the baseball age, his eyes were open, his nose sniffing, his brain stamped with the look and the smell and the terror of those food-devouring rust spores. He was definitely too old for his age. In 1887, twenty-one years old, he was given that important-looking but so common roll of parchment tied with a nice ribbon to tell the world he was a Bachelor of Science from the Kansas Agricultural College, but he was already way ahead of his teachers. He was an expert botanist, a self-taught lone wolf on whom formal education had none of its usual bad effect. Carleton lived, every spare moment, on those hot flat Kansas lands between the ninety-fifth and ninety-eighth meridians. That endless land was his laboratory.

One day found him on his belly squinting through a magnifying glass at a spot of rust on the leaf of some tiny plant or grass. Next day he sat solemnly clawing into the mysterious black dry earth to see what it was made of. Every day he made notes of every grass or weed he could find in this strange, sad land of his—where the soil is as rich as

5

the parching wind and finicky weather are haphazard and terrible. He was a kind of roving Amundsen, trying to teach botany tamely for a while, but finishing by feeling like bending out and busting the tight walls of his little college. He had to feel the harshness of the hot winds on his face in the summer; to plod the fields so softly, unnaturally green with their young fall wheat in the autumn. He learned for himself how a hardy, good winter wheat plant grows slow, hugs the ground tight in the fall. He was a tramp. He was the kind of bum that a natural-born natural historian can't help being.

There is no record that he thought of anything else in those days but wheat and rust and rust and wheat, but at nights he sat himself down heavily to plug at Greek, Latin —for culture? Not Carleton—but, confound it, he was supposed to be a scientist, and in science these wheats, grasses, rust parasites have those jaw-cracker dead-language names. In less than no time he had shouldered his way through three years of Latin and one of Greek. "He went at everything as if he was driving cattle," said one of his old friends. His country was nothing but wheat. Wheat was his life. To know about wheat, Carleton became a crude kind of language expert and in the end wasn't afraid to try to jabber in their Siberian jargons at the nomads of the Khirgiz steppe.

II.

THE walls of his safe little professorship of Natural History in Wichita University got too tight for him. He threw up his job, went back to the State Experiment Station at Manhattan, Kansas; here by the time he was twenty-seven he made a first-class discovery. In those days everybody, including the highbrow botanists of Europe, believed a rust parasite could jump from oats to rye and from rye to wheat. Carleton, a thin, delicate knife in his hands huge like a teamster's, smeared spores of the black stem rust of oats on

6

to the leaves of oat plants. With care he dug up those young plants, tamped their roots into the black land right in the middle of a plat of wheat.

The oats rusted. The wheat stayed perfectly healthy.

He inoculated the black stem rust that's the death of wheat into baby wheat plants. These youngsters he transplanted into the midst of a plat of oats. The wheat stalks broke out with the deadly black pustules. The oats all around them flourished with never a sign of the fungus sickness so deadly to wheat. By such simple, exact experiments Carleton proved that the different grains have each their special and particular rust enemy; straightened out superstitions of farmers—and scientists—that one kind of rust could hop all over the farm to all kinds of crops.

That got him fame, gave him his job of commanding general of all the U. S. Government work on wheat; and in 1894 this hulking Kansan, absent-minded and with gray eyes filmed by a far-away look, landed in Washington. He found his army of wheat scientists and defenders was made up of a lady clerk and a couple of abominably paid helpers now completely forgotten. But Mark Carleton, who was a man of no humor whatever, never remarked on the ridiculousness of such a department to defend and to improve the scores of millions of acres. After all, this heavy-mustached plainsman was army enough. He set to work.

Now Carleton, who during the thirty-five years of his wheat-hunting was at different times soil expert, Russian scholar, master baker, preacher, strong-arm man for the Government, was first and last a naturalist. He had no faith that men can completely conquer their enemies in Nature. He believed they might trick this kind and savage Dame by obeying her. During his years at Kansas he had tried to *cure* wheat of its black stem rust sickness by spraying this or that kind of chemical on his experimental wheat plats. Always he had to report, "The rust appears in the treated and untreated plats in equal abundance."

7

"But look," Carleton mused. "Out home in Kansas there are billions of dangerous rust spores blowing around. . . . But just the same, billions of bushels of wheat manage to grow, too. Somewhere in the world there's wheat just too tough for any rust parasite to tackle—that's the wheat I've got to look for."

He started a vast experiment, a silly experiment, too big for a whole modern college full of eight-hour-a-day scientists. All over the world he sent for wheat, and in little packages a thousand and more varieties of the proudest grains of the four corners of the earth poured in on him. He sat confused among samples of the bearded Onigara from Japan, the Haffkani from Turkey, the bald Kaiser wheat from Germany, and the bearded Prolifero from Italy, near Rome. He tried to keep all these apart from the winter Ghirka from the land of vodka and the twin wheats Rattling Jack and Rattling Tom from Australia.

Almost a thousand varieties of this strange mix-up, this international congress of wheat sorts, Carleton sowed that year near Garrett Park in Maryland. He planted them in forty-eight-foot rows, hundreds upon hundreds of rows. What will orange leaf rust do to these foreign visitors? Will any of them stand up and laugh at the deadly spores of the black stem rust?

His vast experiment was a discouraging washout.

Look through the dusty files of Carleton's first experiment northwest of Washington, and you ask why Carleton shouldn't have been totally fed up. See our looming Westerner stalking up and down between the experimental rows of his queer international rust-resisting contest, disgusted at the magnificent stands of hundreds of different wheats. Rust? Yes, there is rust, but only the pretty orange-colored dabs of the leaf rust parasite that doesn't hurt wheat so very much anyway. Rust? Where is the bad black stem rust that gnaws at the stalks of wheat plants? There isn't any. . . . Carleton pulls at his magnificent walrus mustache, disgusted. . . . These orange spots aren't the stuff that blasts and murders wheat—no.

"Anyway, what does a fine stand of wheat mean in a nice mild climate like this Maryland one?" There stands Carleton, looking out over his walrus mustache and from under the brim of his big felt hat, away across the soft green hills 'round Garrett Park, out over the dim bulk of the gentle mountains of the Blue Ridge. He looks past those mountains now, straight west and fifteen hundred miles away. . . .

"There's where I ought to be testing these sorts—out there in Kansas. . . ."

From his years of listening to the incessant complaints of farmers, from memories of bleak autumns when he'd watched the winds from the Rockies blow the wheat out of the ground—from such common experiences Carleton came to this fundamental hunch: "It isn't what a wheat yields in the best years—it's how it stands the worst ones. . . ."

He had seen, too often, the tender green of the young winter wheat killed and broken by ice storms, had been in at the bankruptcy of the men who'd planted it, had shaken his head at insanity of their wives driven mad by years of disappointed hopes—and from these sad sights had come this simple science: "I must find the wheat that will stand the worst."

His science was mixed up with his homesickness for those Kansas plains. Many there were in those grim days of the eighties and nineties who asked why any sensible man should try to farm wheat out there in Kansas, anyway. Carleton had reasons. "It is found as a general rule that the wheat sorts which are able to withstand the most rigorous extremes of climate are the sorts making the best bread." So he insisted. There's no doubt he was homesick, and at the end of the summer of 1895 he packed up hundreds of little bags holding the seed of the survivors of the nearly one thousand champion wheats of the world. He

9

took those bags out to Salina, Kansas, near the ninety-eighth meridian, where wheat has to be real wheat to get its head above ground and keep it there.

III.

HERE the enlightened farmer, Stimmel, gave Carleton land free of charge. With all the conditions proper to a field experiment Carleton prepared that dark land, sowed his hundreds of sorts in little twenty-five-foot rows, exactly. He didn't wait to watch his green plant children grow. Restless he went to and fro across the Great Plains, bothering farmers, exploring. And nights, in this horrible little hotel, in that lonely farm house, he read. His nose was in books that told him of wheat with outlandish purple kernels growing in Abyssinia. Or he lay awake, mulling the information that eight inches less of rain falls per year in Ekaterinodar, Russia, than falls in Huron, South Dakota. . . . And he had dreams—strange dreams for a Kansas farmer. . . .

He came back to his new experiment at Salina on the farm of the progressive Stimmel. This was not Maryland, oh, no! He came back to behold a massacre. Even Carleton shivered in the winds of that harsh autumn, and the dreadful winter got into his very bones. It was too cold. It was too dry. The soil blew, the very land disappeared on the west wind. The soil heaved. It turned warm, rained gently, got suddenly cold, and shining pretty ice covered the tender blades of those hundreds of proud varieties of experimental wheats. It was a massacre.

But Carleton was happy. This experiment was meat for him. Carefully in simple tables he set down the slaughter of his wheat sorts by the grizzly Kansas climate—his own climate. Oh, he was a rare searcher, among hundreds of different searchers in these days of faith in all of the abstruse theories, formulas, complicated chemistry, laboratory paraphernalia. Simple child of nature that Carleton was, he had an instinct that one brutal winter would tell him more than a dozen years of highbrow experiments in a warm hothouse or in the average years of a nice normal climate. So now he viewed the remains of his murdered wheats, picked up what was left of them, took them the next year to his old bailiwick at the State Experimental Farm at Manhattan. And again it was a real Kansas winter. It was what Carleton called in his scientific reports "a severe winter." And at the end of the summer of 1897 there were less than a hundred out of those thousand wheat sorts left to tell the story.

"I must go to Russia," Carleton began telling everybody. "I must go out to what they call the black fallow of South Russia, and explore for the toughest wheats that are left there. . . ."

Pretty soon going to Russia became an obsession with him, exactly why, none of his old friends seems to know. I have asked some of them who survive him. They all say: "Carleton was a queer fish. . . . Nobody could tell from his rambling talk how his mind worked. . . . He never told us what put it into his head to go to Russia."

But of one thing there is definite record. While he was roaming up and down through Kansas, one of those days of the many days he stole away from his post of duty, he met certain Russian Mennonites. Strangely successful, wheat-raising, God-fearing Mennonites from Russia they were, well-off even in those bitter bad wheat years of the middle eighteen-nineties. Energetic vagabond that he always was, Carleton left his plats of wheat, roved from the Valley of the Red River of the North as far south as the magnificent rolling desolation of the Texas Panhandle around Amarillo. Everywhere he dug into the dark earth, made crude analyses by his own rough science, of samples of it. Rainfall charts were to be found in his satchel mixed up with his shirts. He visited parched places where there was hardly enough rainfall to make a chart of it. Here he quizzed old-time wheat hounds who had somehow hung on in spite of the

11

devil and all of his hellish wind and weather. And everywhere he found these men raising soft winter wheats, some red, some white. Rather he found men trying to raise such wheat. Rather he watched those men failing, and going, for in those bitter days Old Lady Nature in her temperamental tantrum drove upwards of a quarter of a million settlers out of Kansas. With absent-minded eyes Carleton watched them go—and remembered his God-fearing Mennonites.

These quaint folk weren't chased out; they were building fine houses! Carleton saw those farmers, with twenty-five or thirty English words maybe, get yields of thirty bushels to the acre of tough wheat that weighed sixty-two pounds to the bushel—while ruin raged all 'round them. He made friends with these Mennonites, asked them questions they couldn't understand, pestered them. Carleton had a kind of gentle, cruel persistence when he wanted to find out something. "But this wheat—" he took a bite at a few hard, red kernels of it—"this wheat, where did you get it?" he kept gnawing at the peaceful folk with that one question.

Well, it was called Turkey Wheat. Yes, the first settlers, their old folks, had brought it from Taurida in Russia. It was curious, but when the old folks got into the steerage, every father had carted along a bushel of that wheat with his children and other baggage. That hard wheat was so precious you'd believe those Mennonite patriarchs would every one of them want to be buried with a bushel of it. "It's the old wheat of Russia, and it does wonderful in this new land," they told Carleton.

He kept asking around, and found out how at first the millers wouldn't take this wheat because it was so hard their rollers couldn't crush it or grind it; found out how the noted Mr. Warkentin had first built a mill to grind it. Such was Carleton's science. . . .

He went back to his ruined experiments, sniffed around

in the fields, and among his papers. "That's right—some of my Russian hard wheats *did* stand up better than the others." But Carleton, alas, was never the kind to be impressed with the little exactnesses of experimental science, with the tiny differences between this and that little twenty-five-foot row of wheat. No, there was something rough about him as the first fire bringers and wild horse tamers must a hundred thousand years ago have been rough. The sort of crude fact that brought a flash to Carleton's gray eye was the sight of eighty acres of upstanding Mennonite wheat in the middle of a world of desolation.

There was a rush and a strange sweep to him. And now, born in Jerusalem, Ohio, educated in a little Kansas college of the one-building kind that our smart folks laugh at, Carleton takes a jump. This Jayhawker takes a seven-thousand-mile jump in his dreams from the dark earth of his own plains to the black fallow of the Slavic lands of Kharkov and Kherson. The world is this man's laboratory.

IV.

TWO days before the end of the year 1897, the wheat dreamer married Amanda Elizabeth Faught, who was born in Kingman, Kansas. Carleton was by this time so completely obsessed with going to Russia that it is amazing he found time to get married; but they married, and were happy—though there's something to be said against a wool-gatherer whose pay is two thousand dollars a year, maybe less, getting married and asking fate to let him be happy. You see, practical people might bring arguments against this strange man's marrying, though to the sad end of his life Amanda Carleton remained the most devoted of wives, and bore him four children, whom they both loved. It might even be argued that—but this takes us ahead of our story. . . .

Carleton was married on December 29, 1897. On July 4,

CARLETON BOTHERED THE AUTHORITIES

1898, he left Washington, D. C., for Russia and points east. How he bothered the authorities of the Department of Agriculture to let him go! He interrupted their objections,

14

deluged them with his fantastic imaginings, swamped them with facts, took the map of the Dakotas and Kansas and Nebraska and laid it atop the map of Russia in the region of the Volga. "There, gentlemen," he kept saying, over and over, "you see how exactly they correspond," he repeated in his gentle but dreadfully persistent voice. He made the Authorities believe those maps fitted each other like blocks in a child's game. "There's no real difference between these continents," he kept harping—though I ask you, how could this man have known what Russia looked like?

Mysteriously he seemed to sense what he wrote long afterwards: "A traveler on the plains of Kansas, if suddenly transported while asleep to South Russia and deposited in the Crimea, would discover very little difference in his surroundings except as to the people and the character of the farm improvements and livestock."

"Well, what are you proposing to do about it?" asked the tired authorities.

"Don't you see?" he came back. "On our great plains of the Midwest none of the wheat is *native*. It got there helter-skelter, brought by this or that random settler. The settlers had no notion whether their wheats could live on those fierce prairies. But in Russia—there the wheat is native, has been there since the first savage tamed the wild grass. Don't you see? The wheats that grow there are the ones fit to survive!

"Well—"

"But don't you see—those are the wheats we must try on our western plains that are exactly like the Russian black fallow . . . cold long winters; hot short summers. And rain—why, almost every inch of the little rain falls in the growing season—in both places. And the soils? You can't tell them apart!"

"Well—"

"Well, gentlemen, you must send me to find the best Russian wheats!"

15

It was objected he didn't know the Russian language. He went home, sat down, proceeded to sweat to learn that awful tongue out of a pile of grammars and dictionaries— ponderously. So, on his merits and without any pull and not by any means on a Government joy ride, Mark Carleton went to Russia. Carleton had no pull, being the worst mixer on earth. "He was terrible to talk to," said one of his admirers. "He couldn't see a joke, would look right through the fellow telling it to him and never hear a word of it." Carleton won his point simply by bulldozing everybody, shrewd old Secretary Wilson included, with arguments they couldn't answer.

All the summer and autumn this renegade newly-wed wandered in his fantastic hunt for wheat up and down the mysterious black earth of Holy Russia.

He spent a little time with experts in St. Petersburg and Odessa. He drank vodka—not too much. He ate huge quantities of the admirable hot bread called Kalach in Moscow. But most of that time he was a tall, strange, foreign figure on the endless treeless steppe. He was drawn by a question that was framed on every horizon for him: "What sorts of winter wheats out here are the ones that stand the coldest winds in the most snowless winters?" He was driven forward to ask, in broken laughable Russian sentences, in English, and by sign language: "Which of your spring wheats stand the drought and the rust best?" He kept asking these questions of rich farmers, of agronomists, of peasants who hardly knew their own names. But most of all he looked, kept looking. And his great gray eyes seemed to see something that drew him always farther toward the East, toward that desolate flat land across the Ural where the map gets completely blank for lack of towns and rivers. First and last he was a squinter at nature. Every moment he knew exactly what he was after: a tough wheat you sow in the fall that will stand the blast of winter; a hard wheat to sow in the spring to stand the dryness and the attacks of the black

16

rust. I have no doubt he would have brought home the spring Kubanka and the winter Kharkov without one word of Russian—for he had eyes. As if science and the getting of knowledge by men were such a new thing, such a mystery! Like all first-rate searchers Carleton *knew what he needed and had the eyes to see it when he found it.* . . .

He came at last, on his eastward trek, to the Turghai steppe forty miles to the southeast of Orenburg, which is reasonably far from Manhattan, Kansas. He got his great frame into a droshky and drove out on to that prairie, hot as the Sahara, hot enough to kid you with mirages of trees that don't exist and rivers of phantom water. Gravely he got down out of his carriage, fingered the black earth of those bald plains, so powdery dry they suck up the little rains of the short summer shower like a ten-thousand-square-mile blotter. He stopped by the solitary, skin-covered tents of the sullen yellow-skinned Khirgiz: it is only wild ex-nomads like those Mohammedans who would even try to grow wheat in that cursed land. And here the white-skinned Anglo-Saxon Carleton came to the end of his search —among these heathen yellow tartars.

Here he found the hard wheat, the durum wheat called the Kubanka. It's a wheat that it's hard to tell from barley. Here for God knows how many centuries in western Asia it has been sticking its light green shoots out of ground stirred with a crude tool you'd never take for a plow. It pushes its short sturdy stems upward in weather hot enough to discourage sage-brush. Its flat ripe heads that bristle with long stiff beards are cut by infidel Khirgiz with little sickles in the hottest part of the day. Its glassy hard kernels these ignorant folk thresh out of their chaff by flails, or even by driving cattle or camels round and round on the circular winnows of its straw.

Such is the Kubanka. And here was what Mark Carleton wanted—it was a grain fit for raising in hell by a race of

17

salamanders. It was a wheat for American men who faced hell two years out of six.

Once more dreams for this dreamer. He turned around now and his eyes looked west, seven thousand miles west toward that indefinable front line trench of the American wheat fighters—who are casually lumped together by city folks and smart alecks as dissatisfied farmers. Carleton could see those hot flat lands of the hundredth meridian. Carleton bought a fine lot of seed of this whiskered flinty hard Kubanka and shipped it off towards its new home in the West.

He sent the Arnautka too, and the Gharnovka, the Pererodka, all tough excellent brothers to the Kubanka. Nor was that all he did. Because, on mornings after nights spent with his everlasting rainfall charts and maps, he set out from God-forgotten Russian villages, day after day. He watched the men who wore their shirts outside their pants. He watched those fellows and their wives, their brats, one and all too ignorant to read or write—but how they tilled their ungrateful soil. Cunningly, with the patience of so many glaciers, with a wisdom battered into their hard bodies by uncounted generations of a fight to the death with hunger, they coaxed their unwilling, dry, but so rich soil. Carleton learned their lore, their little cute kinks that were smarter than the shiniest piece of farm machinery. That was his science. These earthy facts this naturalist took back to America.

v.

HOME once more he went to the Authorities—though he must have gone first to his young wife Amanda. But he went to those Authorities, laid a great map of the western plains before their more or less reluctant noses—for wasn't it well known that this Mark Carleton was slightly cracked about his wheats? He made them look at that map, and across it with a rough sweep he drew two giant lines, a few degrees west and a few degrees east of the hundredth meridian, from north in the Dakotas all the way south to the Texas Panhandle. "It is here the Russian durum wheat must grow!" he assured them.

"Yes?" they asked. And Carleton hied himself away from home again and turned himself into an experimenter who did his tests with states for laboratory benches. He became as well, in his own fashion, which folks found so hard to resist, a prophet. Now everywhere over those western plains, but especially in those dun-colored desolations where no sane man would try to raise wheat, you could make out his awkward bulk and his black felt hat. "Take a chance! Try it out! You'll succeed with durum wheat!" he calls out to the tough men, the crack-lipped plainsmen, wind-tanned and with crow's-feet 'round their eyes. "The worse the conditions, the better bread you get from this wheat!" Carleton exhorts them.

But did I say he was an experimenter? His huge test now began to sprawl itself up and down over the prairies. "After all," he admitted, forgetting he'd just been a prophet, "the most convincing evidence that a new crop is or is not adapted to the region to which it is introduced must be found in the results of the actual trials of the crop in that region."

He planted the hardy Kubanka in those dry fringes of our western prairies where you don't know whether to be honest and call the country desert or be polite and call it prairie. But he didn't stop at that. When you think of Carleton's lack of humor you'd swear that by rigid logic he would have doped out just one narrow belt of land where this Russian wheat would grow—one narrow strip to correspond exactly to the dry torrid Siberian home of it. But he was crafty; seemed to sense the million waywardnesses and seeming inconsistencies of mysterious Mother Nature. "I'll trick her!" you can imagine him muttering. So he shipped the seed of the precious Kubanka to every possible region

19

of our great plains, to every latitude from way down 'round Amarillo, Texas, up to the Valley of the Red River of the North, and even back east so far as western Minnesota, where it wasn't so dry, not nearly so dry as that bearded bristly wheat seemed to demand. . . .

So he doubted the logic of his own brain.

Then in the Dakotas the hard wheats from western Asia began to do their stuff. Prof. J. H. Shepperd, exact cool experimenter at the North Dakota station, reported: "Pererodka made a performance of about eight bushels to the acre better than the best Fife and Blue Stem sorts." Professor Saunders from South Dakota told about Kubanka and Arnautka: "They both stood the drought wonderfully well, and yielded in that very unfavorable season about thirty bushels by the side of wheat that yielded two to eight bushels."

But it needed much more than mere scientific reports— it took a knock-down-and-drag-out fight to get American men to grow those Russian wheats. Farmer Paul Landemann from near Scotland, South Dakota, wrote Carleton that the wheat farmers were having to feed this new durum wheat to their pigs. There was no market for this grain. The millers couldn't grind it. Then Carleton lowered one hulking shoulder and started shoving, shoving for a market.

He left nothing to chance, or to friends, or to assistants. Personally and in all directions and utterly without humor he pushed, shoved. Russian durum wheats like the Kubanka and Arnautka were prized in Europe for making macaroni. Folks in the Dakotas began calling the Kubanka—with a faint note of contempt—"macaroni wheat." Carleton became a fantastic sort of macaroni drummer. He wrote to the American consuls at Lyons and Marseilles in France, whooping up our durum wheats, telling them to tell the macaroni-eating Frenchmen that we over here had swell macaroni wheat, equal to Russia's—maybe better. He rushed up to Duluth, harangued the exporters there on the chance they were missing. Strangest of all, he set out to convince America that it should make macaroni a national dish, as widespread a native dish as ham and eggs.

Earnestly Carleton wrote, denouncing our hotels for their abominable macaronis. "The most common form in which macaroni is served in this country is a very white, pasty, doughy mass of sticks, served in dilute tomato sauce. The most enthusiastic lover of macaroni would have little if anything to do with a dish of that kind. . . . It is very little wonder there are very few converts." So he wrote, in those very words. To get the roots of his beloved tough durum Kubanka into our black dry American soil he turned himself into a sincere gulper of macaroni, became a sort of macaroni messiah. This tall macaroni evangelist spent days and weeks gaining macaroni converts. He stuck his nose in cook books now, instead of rainfall charts. He consulted famous chefs. He filled page after page of solemn scientific bulletins—Government bulletins which nobody ever reads—with tasty recipes for semolina made from durum wheat. He gave full directions for concocting semolina fritters; gave the exact temperature for confecting semolina soufflés; praised the exquisite taste of cold semolina pudding, which was particularly toothsome when you garnished it with gooseberry sauce! Such was his science.

But, after all, the chief use of any wheat is for the staff of life, for bread. And now the millers of Minneapolis and the Northwest set up a howl about this new hard wheat that began to show up at their mills. "It's so hard that our machinery won't grind it!" shouted those millers. They began to abuse Carleton. They called the Kubanka bastard wheat and heaven knows what they secretly called Carleton. He went to them. Wide-eyed, he told them of the mills on the far-off Volga—they made the very best bread in Russia from durum wheat. Gently he scolded them. With artless praise of their progressiveness he flattered, encouraged them. "When Carleton was working on durum wheat," said

Professor Shepperd, "I remember of telling him of some miller who was grinding and turning out the durum flour in the southern part of the state. He fired up with enthusiasm. He canceled a month's itinerary of meetings with men of consequence—and started for that mill."

Carleton had twin loaves of bread baked out of his Kubanka durum flour and the flour of No. 1 Hard Spring wheat that the whole American nation prefers for its bread. He sent those loaves out with a questionnaire to two hundred and fifty famous persons, including the renowned cookbook lady, Mrs. Rorer. So he toiled at this delicate tangled job of getting the tough grain from the Siberian steppe on to its legs on the American prairie. He did that whole job *himself.* Never was there a work of science pushed forward with so many strange unscientific human angles by one man; alone, laughed at, cursed at, Carleton dragged the Kubanka grain along toward its strange battle with the black stem rust—toward Nature's grand experiment which Carleton himself never dreamed of predicting.

He hardly slept those first years of the nineteen hundreds, and when he did he dreamed of durum wheat. He was a nuisance even to his best friends in the Government departments at Washington, buttonholing them when they were busy, with shining eyes convincing them of the wonders of Kubanka wheat—when they were already perfectly sure he was right. He became a colossal bore—so immensely boring that he was interesting. Men laughed at him. But Nature came to his aid.

From one farm to another the news of the hardiness of the Kubanka spread. "Why—that damn' stuff grows on next to no rain. . . . Got twenty-five bushel to the acre last year," one hard-bitten Dakota malcontent told another. Men told each other how this wheat ripened early in the Dakota sun, how it grew thick in waste places where rain was worth a million dollars an inch. Farmers grew it in spite of the low money the millers offered them for it, and in spite of its nicknames of Bastard and Goose. But they were cagey, conservative, for every acre of this new stiff-bearded Kubanka grain they grew a couple of acres of their old stand-by wheats, the Fife or the Blue Stem. Side by side with the Kubanka they grew the old wheats, and so not knowing it they got ready a vast experiment for Carleton. That was 1904.

That year the black stem rust came sneaking.

On the farms around Arapahoe in Nebraska, where the sap-sucking parasites of the rust blasted whole farms of the Fife and the Blue Stem, killed them so they weren't even worth cutting—there the sturdy Kubanka nodded its bearded heads, heavy with grain that weighed sixty pounds to the bushel and yielded twenty-five bushels to the acre. So it went through the whole northwestern land, up into the Dakotas and toward the border of Saskatchewan. Where fifty to sixty percent of the crops of Fife and Blue Stem were blasted by the rust, there the fields of the Kubanka durum were hardly so much as touched by it. The farmers were amazed. Even the millers stopped jeering. Carleton himself was flabbergasted. And why not?

He had brought the Kubanka to the great plains to stand drought, to transform the waste lands of the western fringe into farm lands to fill the world's breadbasket. It stayed not because it could stand drought but because it turned back the black onslaught on the stem rust. Such was his science. He had reasoned that the Kubanka would fill the pockets of the farmers of the thirsty land down south 'round Amarillo. But here it caught on, made its great triumph way north in the Dakotas. Only seven hundred miles off was Mark Carleton's theory. Such is all science—not to be judged by the rightness of its guesses but by its grand results for men. . . .

From one cottonwood sheltered lonely house to another throughout the Dakotas went the news of this new tough wheat that would bring in money in the bad years, and the

23

folks of that severe country might have started raising monuments to Carleton or naming their children for him—but he was a bad mixer. He was no hand at personal horn-tooting. He was too much of a wool-gathering queer fish to make a good impression. He was certainly unlucky, in these days when names are blazoned and blatted from one end to the other of the country for deeds which Mark Carleton could have done with the little finger of his left hand. For the bringing of the Kubanka was the least he did.

While the yield of the durum wheat was jumping in five years from next to nothing to twenty millions of bushels, the wheat men of Kansas were, around remote cracker barrels, beginning to swap yarns of that new winter wheat, the hard red Kharkov. Carleton, of whom they'd never heard, had brought them the Kharkov in 1900. All the way back to Russia he had gone—as if he'd forgotten something the first trip—peering his way to places far north of Taurida from which those Kansas God-fearing Mennonites had brought their Turkey wheat. Back in Russia, Carleton wandered to places where the savage winter winds were so much worse than those of Kansas that they made the Kansas blasts seem like a California realtor's description of his own state's gentle zephyrs. He went to Starobelsk, where any wheat man would swear the best wheat would winter-kill. Carleton went there mumbling in his great mustache: "It isn't what a wheat yields the best years; it's what it can stand the worst years." There at Starobelsk, drier than Kansas in the summer, more cold in the winter, he spied a sturdy wheat the peasants sowed in the fall. It was hard, red-kerneled, heavy, grew slowly in the autumn, dug its long roots deep into the black earth, spread its green leaves cunningly flat on the ground to dodge the deadly winter winds. . . .

This was the Kharkov.

With hardly a fight on his part at all, the green fields of this new grain spread like spilled water on a level kitchen floor, over western Kansas, up to Nebraska, down to Oklahoma, way out to Montana. In the summers after hard winters the red-gold fields of it changed the wheat-raising game that was worse than a gamble into a chance, fair enough, for a man who was willing to sweat, to make a fair living. If those Midwest men, building their new houses, buying their first coughing, two-cylinder, chain-drive automobiles, had only realized it was Mark Carleton's eye, and no other, that had found this Kharkov for them—

VI.

BUT he was bad at running his own show. In the midst of the growing triumph for his hard wheats, one of his daughters was stricken with infantile paralysis. "I spent all the money I could get hold of to have her treated," said Carleton. "I spent money in places, with doctors where I had no faith at all, but where Mrs. Carleton had hope." Of course Carleton had to borrow that money. His salary was less than three thousand dollars a year.

It is true that the farm value of the durum wheat crop— of his own precious Kubanka—for 1907 was thirty millions of dollars. That was, for just one year mind you, just three thousand times what it had cost our Government, in all, to introduce it. It was ten thousand times Carleton's salary for that year.

It is also certain there would have been no durum wheat crop whatever if it had not been for Mark Alfred Carleton.

I am not suggesting that the United States Government, through its Congress, should have helped Carleton out of the pitiful mess he'd got himself into, let alone reward him for his gifts to the American nation that were piling up into dollars too many to count. He had only discovered the Kubanka and the Kharkov—in line of duty!

And Carleton, who was no different from any other obscure Government slave, asked no help from his boss, the Government. Idiotically he struggled to free himself. On evenings of the days of his grand battles to dig in his new wheats and make them part of our wealth, he foolishly borrowed money to buy a fruit farm in Florida. He borrowed more money to try to dry-farm it in Texas. Imagine a man thinking he could make enough money dry-farming—without being on the job himself—to pull himself out of the hole of his debts! Was that common sense? But of course his sense wasn't common.

He went from bad to worse and from worse to awful. He even borrowed little sums of money from his colleagues in the Government service. He had to get money from one friend to pay back another 'til it got to be a kind of joke among the ones who were fond of him, who knew the fundamentally honest man he was.

The mess he got himself into was deplorable. He became too worried to properly run the growing staff of wheat hunters his own grand explorations had made possible. But surely he wouldn't be kicked out of his job—no fear of it.

Why—his twenty years of work was bearing fruit ten million fold. The yield of the amber-colored glassy-hard durum wheat from Siberia jumped from twenty up to fifty, sixty, seventy millions of bushels a year. In 1914 it even sold at a premium over the old No. 1 Spring Hard—the Red Fife.

In 1914, half of the yield of hard red winter wheat of the nation was of Carleton's variety—the Kharkov, more than eighty millions of bushels. The front-line men of the hundredth meridian could laugh at those biting fall winds now. The good red grain of the Kharkov filled endless lines of wagons going in dusty cavalcades towards the railroads, in Oklahoma, Montana, Nebraska, and his own state of Kansas. If those men had only known. . . . Or if Carleton had had a press agent. . . . Or if he'd just been a good mixer. . . .

26

VII.

THEN the mortgage was foreclosed on his home in Washington. He moved his family to a shack with chinks to let the wind in—of course fresh air is healthy!—up the Potomac River. But they wouldn't kick him out of his job—no danger. Not Carleton, known all over Europe as the leading plant pathologist of America. So he still could depend on that three thousand dollars.

In 1917, from within his own office, by men whose positions his own incessant searching had made possible, charges were preferred against Cerealist Mark Alfred Carleton.

They were just charges, true charges, let no maudlin sympathizer deny or belittle them. It was charged that his indebtedness and that his interest in his private enterprises —miserable little enterprises!—were interfering with his efficiency as Cerealist in Charge of Grain Investigations in the Bureau of Plant Industry. Let's be fair to the indignant workers in his office. How could their chief do his work with a hundred I.O.U.'s chasing themselves before his eyes, all day long, across the pages of his notebooks, his crop reports?

But of course nobody was going to fire Carleton, the founder of the durum wheat industry, the introducer of the famous Kharkov, the reclaimer of waste western lands. . . .

"We've *got* to save Carleton," said one of the members of the committee appointed to investigate those charges. They tried. Certain of his loyal subordinates—let them be remembered and honored—came forward openly to their chief's defense. And the committee—hats off, they were human—never acted on those charges.

In 1918, one of Carleton's sons was taken to a hospital, operated upon for mastoid disease. While that boy's life hung by a thread, his sister, a lovely girl aged seventeen,

27

took suddenly sick. In five days she was dead. She was cremated to save expense, Carleton was so poor. At this ceremony Carleton, himself afflicted with rheumatism, fainted.

But here is a bright spot! He was relieved of his rheumatism, by experts who pulled seventeen of his teeth.

Now in this last year he made a final effort to clear up his swarm of small debts, by borrowing from a rich friend, a grain man, the vast sum of four thousand dollars, and from two other friends, both grain men, sums not quite so enormous. Let it be made clear in this place that with these grain men Carleton had no dealings that were dishonorable or in any sense unseemly in his position as a Government servant. But it was too bad—for the grain men were of the opposite political party, and besides *it looked very bad* for a wheat man in the Government to borrow from "the grain interests."

In 1918, he was called to the office of the Secretary of Agriculture. The Secretary had been informed by an indignant Congressman, who had been informed by an indignant underling in Carleton's own office, of Carleton the wheat hunter having borrowed from the rich grain man—of the opposite political party.

Carleton, founder of the durum wheat industry, introducer of the hard red winter Kharkov, was given ninety days' furlough, *without pay*, in which time he should pay back in full his debts to the wealthy grain men, or—

VIII.

IN 1919 the acreage of the hard red winter wheat reached twenty-one millions, by far the greater part of it sown with Kharkov, and that was one-third of the total wheat acreage of the American nation.

During the next seven years, certain banks which held notes given by Mark Carleton received checks, signed by him, in whole or partial payment of those notes. They came,

without comment, from Boca del Toro in Panama, from Cuyamel in Honduras, and finally from the Laboratorio de Plagas Algonderas in Peru. So he drifted from one hot little job to another around and below the Equator.

The friends who had put their names on those notes only heard this good news from the banks—Carleton always was a queer fish. Likewise old friends, who had long given his I.O.U.'s up for lost, began to get little payments, without comment.

But it was so hot down there, and he was lonely, what with his wife and children away in the North. The mosquitoes were too thick for him—he was a plainsman, and the air was too steamy and soggy. On the 26th of April, 1925, at Paita in Peru, Mark Alfred Carleton died, aged fifty-nine, of acute malaria.

"And, I may add," said a colleague who respects the memory of that strange man, "of a broken heart."

Is there some talk of a monument, or a small bronze tablet somewhere, or a wreath, made of tin or iron, that would not have to be renewed very soon? It is now three years, and the Official Record of the Department of Agriculture has not yet to my knowledge got around to mentioning the fact of Carleton's death. When he died, of course, Carleton was no longer connected with that Department.

But why a monument? Child of Nature that he was, Carleton himself wouldn't have cared, for surely he knew the transience of things that men carve out of stone. Let his monument be the flat fields of the bright green of the Kharkov, lovely in the spring after harsh winters that before this wheat hunter's coming used to ruin the wheat men. Let his marker be the light gold of the bearded Kubanka, tawny in the time of harvest on those fields that before his coming were blasted by the black rust.

MACKAY—AND OTHERS MORE EMINENT

MACKAY—AND OTHERS MORE EMINENT

I.

IN CONTRAST TO THE BITTER FATE of the wheat hunter Carleton, stands the serene life of Angus Mackay. This square-faced Presbyterian pioneer, not knowing it, made an experiment that took the Canadian pioneers out of the frying pan of the drought. Primitive comparer that he was, Mackay's utterly unexpected and fantastic discovery sent the golden miles of hard red spring wheat marching west, all the immense way from Winnipeg to the foothills of the Rockies.

Profoundly hard-headed, his sharp eye the very opposite to the dreamy eyes of Carleton, Mackay prepared the way for the coming of the sturdy-stemmed Marquis wheat, filler of the breadbasket of the world. Mackay was more than a forerunner—it was this conservative Scotchman's eye that first saw this new early-ripening grain cheat the frost demon. Unlike Carleton's, Mackay's life has had a happy evening, and of him the folks of Saskatchewan say: "There is nothing too good in this world that they can do for him."

Of course Mark Carleton was a stupendous practical dreamer, boggling the little affairs of his own life, but spreading—all by himself—the Kubanka and the Kharkov wheats across the Great Plains, by his energy, by his bulldozing salesmanship, by science. But the surging, red-gold seas of the Marquis wheat came to color the Canadian prairie by no such lonely toil. King of the northwest windy lands, the Marquis dug its roots into that black earth by a most fantastic chain of random happenings. To hear the weird yarn of it you'd swear God was for a moment kind to the wheat gamblers of the North.

Dig through the dusty records, talk to the old-timers of Saskatchewan and Manitoba—you will be astounded at the

WILLIAM SAUNDERS

topsy-turvy birth of the Marquis wheat; you will be amazed
at the mixed-up crew of the Marquis men, who, not clearly
knowing what was what, helped this wheat to get born.

Aside from the two Doctors of Philosophy, Charles and
Percy Saunders, they were not what today would be called
scientists. Chief of the lot stands old William Saunders,
father of these two college boys, an old-fashioned druggist
with a craze for cross-breeding gooseberries. It was old

34

CHARLES SAUNDERS

William who had the basic hunch. For the rest, the wheat
finders were men of the soil, such as Thomas Sharpe, sprung
from the Stuarts of England but himself a wind-bitten
sarcastic pioneer in the Turtle Mountains of southern Manitoba. Sharpe picked the first spike—back in 1892—of what
has since grown into billions of bushels of wheat. The baby
wheat was coddled and tended—with no notion of its

35

value—by the upright apple expert, William Macoun. It was nursed, planted, reaped year after year, by the farm foreman, Fixter of Ottawa, Ontario. Then at last it came to the flat black land near Indian Head, Saskatchewan, into the hands of Angus Mackay in the memorable and dreadful year of 1907. The immensely experienced eyes of that grizzled father of the settlers foresaw this early-ripening grain would take his prairie folks out of the ice-box of the frost. But Mackay denies all credit for himself, laughs, says: "Any other group of men might have found it." Adds the tall old Angus: "It was just the fact of the frost that made Marquis wheat!"

Such, too, is science. . . .

II.

LONG before there was ever a thought of the Marquis wheat, and four years before his discovery of the summer fallow, Mackay was only a prosperous farmer in the Pickering district of Ontario. It was with no idea of making fundamental scientific discoveries that he went west. No— in 1881 this raw-boned Scot put his head together with the head of his farmer friend Williamson. "Let's sell out here . . . go west out to Manitoba," one or the other of them said. "They say there's a big land boom just starting out at Winnipeg." It was gold that pulled Mackay. So the two of them set out, with that mystical confidence common to all pioneers, obscure or famous. They set out feeling the gold already in their pockets—but never reckoned with the August frosts. They saw land red-gold with wheat running fifty bushels to the acre—but never thought of the drought, the searing dry winds that turn heavy yielding wheat to chicken feed.

Mackay got to Winnipeg; the boom—alas—burst in his face. And in 1882 he was only an ox-team wanderer. Three

36

years before he hit on the marvelous trick of making land borrow rain in the good years to use in the dry years, he was only an anonymous one of many now forgotten wanderers, trekking west across prairie interminable like the ocean, strange dun-colored land without a break on all sides sweeping up grandly to meet the horizon rim—like the ocean.

A short way by railroad went Mackay in that spring of 1882, as far as the feeble thread of the C.P.R. then reached into the vast northwestern wilderness. Then he walked, rode behind oxen. "I'll go just as far as I need to go to get good land—land that suits me," he said. But he was modest, honest, never let on that some genius in him made him stop at the lush land of Indian Head, twenty miles southeast of old Fort Qu'Appelle. "No—I had no notion where the best land was. I gave a C.P.R. engineer a lift, made friends with him," said Mackay. "He marked out for me where I'd find the best wheat land in the territories—so I went there." Old now, and able to laugh at all vanities, he smiles to remember the utter chance of his choice.

But it is 1883, he is just past forty, in his prime, powerful and raw-boned, hopeful and idiotically patient. He sticks the point of his plow into the virgin prairie of Assiniboia, turns up, that first year, eighteen acres of strong clay loam into night-black, incredibly smooth and shiny furrows, lays the foundation for his work as a searcher, discoverer—never dreaming of it.

That spring he sows the seed of the hard spring wheat, the Red Fife—itself an accident in Canada—and that year Nature is kind to Mackay as She has a sly way of being to newcomers, one year or another in that grim land. The dark loam of the little eighteen acres gives Mackay back his grain forty fold. Two other Ontario pioneers join him along with the settler, Williamson. Together this band of four men gambles for gold, breaks five hundred acres of the lush earth that's richer than the promised land of Jordan in Bible stories.

37

Sure—Nature will be kind again. Yes, it looks so to Mackay and his three pals peering west. The warm breeze whispers promises. The hot sun conjures up the young green of the Red Fife over those five hundred acres. The quick rains—who cares if the thunder showers are terrible? —pull up the long stems of the wheat as if by magic; fed this wheat is, by an inexhaustible humus never before tapped by plants sown by the hands of men. Then August comes— cool. And September, colder.

"That year all of our crop was frozen," wrote Angus Mackay. "Cutting commenced September 7, but frost came that night."

They were cleaned out. "Of course, this was an exceptional year," said that shaggy-browed hopeful Scot, who was at the beginning of learning that all years up there in the rich land of Saskatchewan are exceptional. He put in his plow, broke more virgin prairie. See this stubborn man in this spring of the year 'eighty-five, plugging along behind a plow that turns up the black gumbo furrows over the disastrous stubble of 'eighty-four. *This* will be *the* year. He hires teams, men to handle them. Into the fields drops the plump deep-troughed wheat seed, while the sun of April daubs the roadsides with the sudden flowers of the northern prairie. . . .

Mackay gets a fine start at getting his crop under the ground—early, to cheat the fall frost. Then disaster, but disaster that means the beginning of as strange an experiment as any in the buried unpublished science—better to call it lore—of pioneers and common people. Part of Mackay's fields, less than half, are safely seeded, when rum flows, riot breaks out, rebellion is reported among the Indians far north. The Authorities clank and rattle into Indian Head, and with no questions asked, grab the teams, the few hired men of Angus and his partners, to haul supplies for the troops of that far-off toy war.

There lie Mackay's fields, all plowed—but half sown.

All that summer—and there are fine rains, too!—there lies more than half of his new broken land, black, useless, fallow. That summer a fine crop of Red Fife wheat turns to ripe red gold by the side of this unsown, useless fallow. Mackay is alone there, with maybe one horse. He can't sow the fallow, but he hates all weeds. He harrows the useless land clean of stink-weed, pig-weed, tumbling mustard. But there it lies, bare and black, its straight furrows mocking him with what might have been.

Comes the next spring, with the men and the teams back safe. Into the stubble of the part of his fields he'd managed to crop the year before, goes the Red Fife seed. Into the fallow land, last year bare and useless, goes the Red Fife as well. Now for a real crop, for the first time—a money crop.

May passes, and the strange unplanned experiment begins. The green down of the young wheat brings hope. June comes, begins to slip by. Every day, each morning, Settler Mackay comes out of his little house, looks west from under his hat for signs of rain, mumbles prayers at night to his old Scotch God for rain. June is gone, and no rain. July is here, and instead of showers, come hot winds that roar with a boisterous whoop all the way from Moose Jaw and the desert place that later gets the famous name of Medicine Hat. These are blasting winds that drive the mercury up into the nineties. Not a drop of rain, and what can this mean but hunger for the Assiniboia men, and failure for Mackay?

No, it means luck—for the next hundred years and more —for the whole northwestern land. . . .

While the wheat of the whole northwest prairie shrivels, day after day of that rainless sizzling August, a miracle happens on Mackay's farm at Indian Head. On the land of the farmers all around him, wheat has been cropped last year and the year before—this year there's not enough to pull the binders out of the sheds for.

39

On Mackay's own land, on the field where the year before he's been able to raise a crop—it's the field he got the seed into before the men went off to the rebellion—on that land he reaps maybe two bushels to the acre. He harvests miserable chicken feed, cooked by that summer of hellish southwest wind.

But on the field right beside it—there stands Angus Mackay, looking, astounded, his gray-blue eyes wide at the wonder of it. Here's the field that lay fallow, black and useless last year. Here's that field, growing a rippling sea of heavy nodding yellow-red spikes of the good Fife wheat. Thirty-five bushels to the acre of good hard wheat Angus reaps off that field.

From that one field—with ruin and failure all around him in Assiniboia.

Fate or luck or chance or God made that experiment for this plain pioneer. But Mackay saw it. Never asking why, he grabbed the fantastic lesson of it, told himself: "It's dangerous in this dry country to try to raise two or three crops one year after another on the same field. . . . Got to plow half of your land in the spring—then let it lie bare all year. . . ." Why? Who could tell? Comparer that he was, Farmer Angus, driven by need, pounced on this strange way of cheating the dry years—this way that the most learned soil physicists, the highest-browed Canadian Professors of Agriculture could never have figured out for him from their formulas or theories. It was too simple, too outlandish, and how could the men of the laboratories know, not being beset by the whims and cruelties of nature? Forty years have passed since that eventful summer; yet the most learned heads still quarrel about why the black fallowed land of one summer raises good wheat the dry next one!

"The farmers came from miles around to see those two fields," said Mackay. "I showed them how the crop on the fallow *compared* with that burned-up stuff on the stubble."

He didn't have to diagram it or put it into two-dollar words. It was a comparison as simple as the one of the first cave man who felt that the warmth of the first fire was better than the dank of his cold cave. It was a comparison as accurate as the most exact test of the modern Pasteur on chickens that had survived a deadly dose of microbes compared to those that were not immune. It was science. It was as old as the brain of man. But who could today improve on it?

So, a simple believer in God, whose Calvinistic God had foreordained all things, Mackay played a trick on God—who never intended men to raise wheat on that rich but nearly arid land. He taught the settlers not to crop all of their land, but to plow part of it, till it, and leave it bare —to store up a mysterious something to cheat the maybe dry next year. "That way it'll be possible every year to reap something," said Angus, the mild prophet. And the settlers 'round him saw, listened, and told their wind-bit friends of the west and north. And now that grim land began really to open up. Now the black fields of the summer fallow made bigger and bigger checkerboards with the gold fields of ripe wheat, north and west on the prairie. The stark treeless land was less cruel; houses came; men laughed; new children saw trees—but in those days only in picture books.

III.

IN the very year of Angus Mackay's fundamental but entirely unofficial discovery of how to cheat the dry years, the official Canadian Government made up its mind it would have to do something about its millions of acres of northwestern land, where the earth was as rich as the weather was stern and malignant. It was 1886; Mackay's experiment was just beginning to be heard of—not by scientists but by the settlers. And all over Manitoba and Assiniboia

41

homesteads built with high hopes stood empty, prairie grass growing up to their doors, their builders beaten by one or another or both of those two demons, the drought and the frost.

Now in 1886 a commission of the Parliament of Canada got the gray-haired, dignified druggist, William Saunders, to start the Dominion Experimental Farms, and for this job you'll admit he was as strange a choice as any. He wasn't an eminent scientist. He knew nothing about wheat farming. Who could have told he was one of those modern animals called "organizing geniuses"? He was already fifty, well off from a prosperous drug business, comfortably fleshy. It is true that he had, as a hobby, done some plum and crab-apple breeding—and it was well known Saunders was responsible for bigger and better gooseberries. In fact old William had a kind of fanatical belief it was good to cross-breed all kinds of crops—not only gooseberries. But of wheat he knew next to nothing. Who was this stately old druggist to help the plainsmen trick the hot wind that blew their seed out of the ground, or to get a wheat that would laugh at the sudden cold mornings of August?

But Saunders was original. He started an experiment farm way back east at Ottawa—but didn't stay there. The very first year of his new job, he jolted off on a journey west. By horse and wagon he bumped, till it was much easier for him to stand up than to sit down, through Brandon, Manitoba, and toward Indian Head. Hundreds of miles he drove, stopping at the poorest little homesteads, asking every settler: "What is it this country needs most?"

The hot winds blew his hat off over the forbidding brown lands 'round the new town of Moose Jaw, and here, and everywhere, the settlers answered his question: "We've got to find some way of reaping something those years when the June and July rains don't come 'til August—or don't come at all." Then William Saunders met Mackay. It is wrong to call this a merely lucky chance, because Saunders, besides being ignorant and original, had an eye for plain original men. He learned from Mackay the miracle of the summer fallow. He looked at the hard-headed Angus, saw he was from top to toe a dirt farmer—with a knack for seeing fundamental facts that lay under his nose. It is to the everlasting merit of Saunders that he cottoned to such men instead of to professorial test-tube agriculturists. He appointed Mackay superintendent of the branch experiment farm at Indian Head, and in the spring of 'eighty-eight the Scot began the building of that rude windswept outdoor laboratory where the Marquis wheat was twenty years later to stand up under its most dreadful ordeal. . . .

Old William Saunders—though he had none of his knowledge—had this in common with Carleton: he thought in continents, not in glass beakers or the fine graduations of laboratory burettes. Way back east at Nappan, in Nova Scotia, he started an experiment farm. At Brandon, Manitoba, only two hundred miles east of Indian Head, he put the experienced settler, Bedford, in charge of a place. "Experiments at Indian Head or Brandon would be no safe guide for our settlers out in British Columbia," said William. So to the fern-covered valley of the Fraser River he sent the eternally disgruntled but shrewd hard-working Thomas Sharpe—the pioneer from the Turtle Mountains. Why? Because Sharpe had discovered on his own hook a grand new heavy-yielding sort of potato, with great shaws that protected the tubers from the hot sun and drought.

Now in all these places old Saunders started experiments on an unheard-of scale. Angus Mackay he buried under six varieties of barley, seven kinds of oats, twenty-three different sorts of potatoes, to say nothing of turnips and mangolds. While Angus toiled to build the farm barns and houses, in winds so boisterous that they blew the uprights over, Saunders sent him trees—twenty-three thousand forest and fruit trees, mind you, to set out in a country the

Lord never meant for so much as a bush, a land bare of trees as the ocean. "Test these carefully," admonished Saunders. This Gargantuan experimenter must try everything, anywhere. That was *his* science. Something deep down in him seemed to say: "Maybe one, two, ten out of these thousands of grains, roots, seeds, and trees will catch on, grow, be of value." Like Nature, Saunders worked— wastefully.

From coast to coast his superintendents sweated.

Years went by. The wheat farms, thanks to the trick of the summer fallow of Angus Mackay, spread north and west, through the toil, the sweat, the strange gambling instinct of foolishly enterprising pioneers. So far the official experiment farms of Saunders had little to do with this growth. It was the brawn of men and the drought-cheating trick of the fallow of Mackay that spread wheat to feed hungry mankind over that impossible wilderness. Squares and oblongs of alternate gold and black, black and gold—a whole day's buggy ride you'd go and see nothing else. And away to the north, new wheat fields and fallows drove back the virgin prairie, back towards Saskatoon where the banners of the northern lights waved over new unpainted shacks of more and more settlers. Hurrah for those optimistic fools! Hurrah for Mackay!

But the farther north those silly settlers went, up beyond latitude fifty-five, tricking the drought with the black fallow—the more danger they ran from the sudden August frosts. Worse luck—the good Red Fife ripened slow on the fallow, ten precious days slower, sometimes, than it ripened on stubble land. So much nearer the chance of the killing frost.

"Give us an early wheat—just a few days ahead of the Red Fife, as strong and as hard as the Fife; and it's got to make the same good white flour!" cried the settlers to old William Saunders.

IV.

LIKE Mark Carleton, Saunders sent the world over—for early wheats, wheats to ripen phenomenally under a hundred days. There he sits, writing letters to the far-off Mr. Goegginger in Riga, Russia, who sends him the Ladoga, a strange yellow-flour wheat that actually ripens in Russia at a latitude six hundred miles north of Winnipeg! He pores over letters, from an obscure Moravian missionary to Archdeacon Denison of England, telling of impossible wheats that ripen in three months in the high Himalayas. He gets those wheats. Then his old cross-breeding mania awakes in him. There he sits nights, in Ottawa, on the tree-girt experiment farm far off from the coyotes and the lonely immensity of the land where it's hell to try to raise wheat.

"Gooseberries I've improved by cross-breeding," mutters old William. He runs his hands through his orderly gray hair, narrows his slanting, light-colored eyes. "Why not wheats?"

It is recorded of this earnest man that he took but a few hours sleep each day, worked in a slow, halting, ponderous and dreadfully persistent way. And for every slow hour he sat and planned, his farm superintendents, Mackay, the grumpy Sharpe, genial Bedford, had to plow, grub, cultivate, and sow a half a dozen hours or more.

"It's only by cross-breeding wheats that our prairie people will get what they *must* have," old William kept saying. "I'll cross-breed the earliest wheats from all over the world with our good Red Fife." He assured the worried settlers it would not be hard. "Breeding wheats consists in bringing together various varieties of grain in the same way you bring together various strains of cattle. Our Red Fife will give strength, yield, the white flour the whole world wants, to the new wheat. The foreign wheats will bring earliness —to dodge the frosts. . . ."

45

As if it would be easy to get what you wanted from those hundreds of thousands of different wheat children, rising helter-skelter through the complicated machinery of heredity.

So it came to pass that in early July of 1892, the proud Red Fife wheat as father married the miserable little early ripening Hard Calcutta as mother, and begat wheat children. It was in the gentle wooded fern-carpeted Valley of the Fraser River, British Columbia, that this momentous act of nature took place, under the eye and care of the bushy-bearded Thomas Sharpe, who was austere, chewed tobacco correctly, spat mightily and notoriously—and was a lover of nature.

"Who knows," pondered Saunders, "wheats might breed different children in the Far West, or on the prairies, than they would do at Ottawa?" So he bred wheats incontinently and promiscuously—all over Canada. So he cut and tried, took innumerable one-million-to-one shots. And so doing, he was scientific! The old enthusiast sent one of his educated sons, Percy, a college boy, on a breeding jaunt across the continent. Percy had learned chemistry, was no botanist, was anything but a plant-breeder. But the trip would be a grand experience for the boy, and before he left Ottawa his sedate father showed him the delicate trick of putting the pollen of one wheat on the pistils of another. So off goes the greenhorn wheat-breeder, Percy Saunders, cross-breeding his way through Brandon, Manitoba; stopping with Angus Mackay at Indian Head in Assiniboia; coming at last to Agassiz to the farm of the able tobacco-chewing Thomas Sharpe. Here is a pioneer, rough-spoken, tireless at his tough work of felling fir trees, grubbing underbrush, clearing the ground of those confounded persistent ferns— and he is a subtle lover and understander of nature.

Percy and Sharpe set to work, side by side in the little experimental wheat plots. With a small pair of forceps— they are the one piece of apparatus in this crude science—

46

they turn back the chaff, still green, of the just flowering Hard Red Calcutta, planted by Sharpe that spring. What earthly good is this little wheat? On the plains north of Moose Jaw it has yielded a miserable five bushels to the acre! It is semi-dwarf—too short for any binder to cut! "Yes—but your father says it ripens airly," growls Thomas Sharpe, to Percy.

Carefully they pull back the green glumes from around this detestable little wheat's secret flowers. Tenderly they pull out the pollen-bearing stamens from those flowers. Emasculated, the Calcutta is now what you can call a female wheat—fit only for motherhood. . . .

Delicately, they take a little of the golden mysterious pollen from a flower of the good Red Fife, growing close by. This life-bearing dust they sprinkle on the feathery pistils of the mother Hard Calcutta. Gently they turn back the green chaff of this mother wheat into place, to protect the pistils they've fertilized. With the finesse of a pair of Swiss watchmakers they wrap thin Manila paper 'round the head of the Calcutta to keep chance pollen, from who knows what other wheat, away. On this paper they mark: "Red Fife, male, x Hard Calcutta, female."

Twenty-three such strange marriages, in all, Thomas Sharpe and Percy Saunders make. Then Percy goes back home—his trip has been a wonderful experience; and Thomas Sharpe stays behind there to watch. Among the always encroaching ferns of that almost tropical northern valley, amid the crash and the boom of the falling fir trees Sharpe works at the thousand jobs old William sets him. "I was like a colt on the end of a rope," grumbles Sharpe —though nobody else would take that independent character for a colt. But he was disgusted to have to be told to do anything. Just the same he did it—and well.

Have the mother wheats conceived? Will they set seed? Sharpe watches; tends those fateful heads; sees that no birds gobble them up; feels gently the hardening kernels

47

and the swelling spikes turning from green to gold under the mild British Columbia sun. The marriages were a great success, were fruitful; many heads of the cross-bred wheats did set seed. Now just at the proper time the bearded superintendent bends down over them, snips off the ripe heads as they nod on the stalks, packs them in a little seed bag, mails them off to William Saunders waiting for them back east in Ottawa.

Which one of these two men, Thomas Sharpe or Percy Saunders, made this one certain cross? "The truth of that," mutters old Thomas, "is lost in oblivion." And he cares not a fig! One with nature, part of nature, this strange man has no more vanity than a bee who marries trees, accidentally getting pollen from one on to the pistils of another, as it buzzes from the blossom of one to the blossom of another.

The momentous seed bag arrives at Ottawa from Agassiz —and by the closest of squeaks escapes an utterly frivolous oblivion. By a hair hangs the future fame of five wheat hunters and the great increase of wealth of the Canadian land. Vastly more important than all these, old Saunders and Mackay come within an ace of failing to cheat the frost —to get the wheat their brown-faced folks of the plains are crying for, failing for.

The little bag, holding the offspring of the Red Fife wheat and his early ripening wives, gets dumped out with the rest of the mail on Saunders' office floor. Two farm boys come in, pick up this little sack, toss it to each other, play catch with it, heave it at each other—heigho, this is fun!— sock it at each other's thick heads, shy it up on the cupboard in the corner, forget it.

Dust gathers on this little bag and nobody remembers having received it. Nobody—excepting old William, who very well knows he ought to have got it, and when he misses his expected precious cross-bred wheats there is the devil to pay. Only a short time ago hasn't Angus from Indian Head written to him:

48

"Early maturing grain is another point of very great importance. I need not remind you, Sir, how safe the field of Ladoga wheat on this farm looked on the morning of 21st August last, nor how cold and green its neighbor, Red Fife, across a twelve-foot road, looked on that eventful morning. . . ."

Oh, Mackay is always the comparer, knows what his settlers need, knows too that this early Ladoga from old William, though a fine early wheat, gives flour too yellow for his folks to sell. And old William knows what his man Angus knows, and now, the wheat's lost, there is hell popping. "Where are those new wheats Thomas Sharpe says he's sent?" roars Saunders.

Amid the hue and cry of looking—everybody scared, scared absolutely, completely, to distraction, of the Old Man on a rampage—some genius looks on top that cupboard. Hoorah for his nameless memory! Now William plants all of the seed children of his new married wheats. Each spring in his back yard he plants them, with a strange undiscriminating industry he amasses hundreds of sorts of cross-bred wheats. Under the soil with his own hands he puts the seeds, just so, pats down the earth over them, with great care puts labels on sticks by each little hill. What will come of them? He knows ahead of time these wheat children will turn out good, bad and indifferent—but mostly indifferent. Shrewd old Saunders knows too that, while the world can use, one way or another, most any kind of human child— with wheat it's another kettle of fish. He reaps his little crops, and tests, ponders.

The men of the plains need a sturdy stemmed wheat. Here's an old yellowing letter, from that indomitable Mackay. He's been trying to start a vegetable garden on that bald farm at Indian Head. Before anything can make a start the infernal wind blows the seeds out of the ground —and Angus finds them growing later a quarter of a mile away. Ha! Ha! Cabbage and cauliflower he sets out four times and they are as often destroyed. . . . Will one or another of these new wheats turn out to have strong enough stems to stand such mighty coughs of the northern storm gods?

What chance has old William, fussing there? Well, he has a chance. . . . But he gnaws at his job, experiments in terms of years, not days, and he thinks in decades. In six short years, helped by his expert right-hand man, William Macoun, the gray-haired ex-druggist tries out more than seven hundred cross-bred grains and hybrid cereals, in his back yard, in the experimental plots of the farm at Ottawa. Any time in the summer you may see him, way past his prime as years go, stooping over little rows of wheat plants, *selecting* from among a strange riot of cross-bred children. He pulls bearded heads from among sorts that are mostly bald. Watch him there! He bends over. His eye has lighted on a head of one single plant that's already turned golden ripe while all of its brothers are green. It's a marvelous early-ripener. Will this be the plant with the seed to cheat the frost? . . . Who knows? William gambles. In his battered notebooks he makes endless signs, entries, apparently meaningless pothooks.

He plants his silly hopes of this year next year but never whines if those hopes are dashed. How many absolutely prize wheats has he actually thrown away? Nobody can tell. And all this time, by a chance that the kind God watches over, each year Saunders and the able apple-expert Macoun, plant, select, reap and don't throw away the seed of the children from the marriage of the Red Fife and the miserable little Hard Calcutta back at Agassiz. What a variety of bad children those wheats have bred! 'Tis always so. 'Tis like the offspring of a fine upstanding human father and a sluttish mother with maybe one good point. . . . And Macoun sticks at his hopeless job, plucking out hundreds of ill-favored wheat plants, bad-yielding children favoring

their mother; late ripening sorts resembling their father.
. . . Where is the perfect wheat?

Oh—it is an abominable science! But always there is
Saunders, single-minded, looking over Macoun's shoulder
for a plant that will be golden when the Red Fife is still
green. Notebooks for ten years these two men fill, exactly
weighing the yields of every new wheat, counting exactly
their days of ripening, testing expertly the strength of their
straw. They do not kid themselves. They know a stalwart
father may sire a litter of dwarfs. But they never quit
hoping. They know, as well, that a mite of a mother may
bring a future heavyweight champion prize-fighter into the
world. Breeding wheat's no different than the blessed random humpty-dumptyness of the begetting of human beings. . . . It is cutting and trying, eternally. It is the sound
old primitive science of the days before there was such a
word as science.

v.

THE century turned. The frost still threatened. At Indian
Head, Angus Mackay, grizzled now, began to get a new
kind of work from William Saunders, got new wheats to
test. Right out there in the open on the experimental farm,
against the assaults of the dozens of devastating demons
that lurk among the natural advantages of Saskatchewan,
the new wheat, Preston, tried its strength. Mackay planted
it, tilled it, watched. There he stood, the very salt of the
prairie, grown up with the prairie since the early 'eighties.
Rough settler no longer, dignified gray sideburns have
grown down before his ears to frame his square-cut face,
but his shaggy eyebrows were still black, thatching comparer's eyes, deep like the eyes of a Faraday. He measured
this new artificial wheat—the Preston bred by William—
against the old Red Fife. . . .

He sent it to the settlers 'round about to try; his was a

communistic sort of science, which every one shared, no matter how little his schooling—everybody who was interested, who might profit. Mackay by now was learned in the lore of the prairie. His brain had become saturated with the sinister chances of that land. Too often he had written, in his beautiful, accurate reports: "The past season was one of bright promise and fair fulfillment. . . . The heavy downpour necessary to rush the growth was absent until mid-July. . . . Excessive hot weather set the grain back but it was then saved by rains. . . . Several drops in temperature dangerously near the freezing-point caused the grain to be blighted. . . ." You see, this steady man's spirits had risen too often in flower-splashed, wheat-green springtimes; just after he had sizzled in too many hot Julys, had fearfully watched the thermometer on too many evenings in August as the sky cleared and the wind turned into the northwest.

He knew every little need of the settlers. He tested this promising early-maturing Preston; had flour made from its abundant yield—but wasn't this flour a mite too dark colored? The Minneapolis and Fort William grain men wouldn't have it, would not pay No. 1 Spring Hard prices for it. . . . To his settlers—with no secretary at all, mind you—he had written better than five thousand letters a year, for years, telling them kinks and tricks to help them dig a real foothold on the soil of their rich but savage land. Meanwhile old Saunders kept sending him new wheats, fancy cross-bred wheats. Mackay tested them.

He was salt of the prairie and had done his share to change it, bring human life to it. These summers, while he was busy testing in weedless plots the new wheats from Ottawa, you might see two thousand settlers come in one day, on Sunday School picnics and excursions to learn his crude science. They have come from places his summer-fallow, his hundred tricks of farming have helped to build, from places where a few years ago there was nothing but a horizon blank like the rim of the ocean. Now these vacant sky-lines were broken by the heads and shoulders of three, four red or yellow painted elevators—waiting to have their bellies filled with Red Fife wheat. Mackay showed the slit-eyed fathers and the rangy sons of these hundreds of families a new bearded wheat, baptized "Huron" by old William. Would it replace the old stand-by, the Red Fife? It was earlier. But didn't the grain of it shatter a bit too easily in the blasts of the southwest wind?

On those festival days of communal science on the Indian Head farm, the children of the learners played—wondering at the sight of a tree—in the shade of the one hundred thousand trees of the avenues, shelter belts, plantations that the persistence of Mackay had made grow on the experimental farm. These children came from new clusters of sod-houses and hovels close by the railroad the wheat land had just opened. Yesterday you might have seen that fourteen-year-old girl, buxom in patched pants, bare feet, brown legs, doing a dance on the black gumbo road beside the new railroad station, south of Saskatoon. Of course it was the energy of that girl, got from the loins of her strong father and mother—it was this kind of energy that helped, maybe more than Mackay or Saunders, these strange people to dare the frost for their own bread, in order to give the world bread. Such was the life of the comparer, Mackay, who with his people brought human company to the wild ducks and gray geese of the prairie.

Dressed up in a neat ministerial long black coat and a stand-up collar, Angus took crowds of plainsmen in their store clothes out onto his experimental fields. "Here is a piece of stubble land that has been plowed in the fall, sown with Red Fife the following spring," he told them. "Here is another plot, gang-plowed in the *spring* at the time of seeding. Here's another, sown by drill without being worked before or after seeding." The farmers looked at the stands of wheat on each field. Not so bad—but not much difference between them. . . . "But alongside here," ended up Mackay, "is a piece of fallow land, plowed spring of *last* year and kept bare all summer, that I've sown for comparison."

The farmers compared, saw for themselves; their eyes saw that fallow land heavy and golden with a magnificent thirty-five, maybe forty bushels to the acre. For better than fifteen years Mackay did that old chance experiment of 'eighty-five, over and over. Did the magic of it hold for all years? "The past season, like all others preceding it, has been an exceptional one," Mackay wrote dryly—and with wisdom topping that of the highest-paid official government weatherman. Well, he would try out the virtues of his summer fallow in every kind of exceptional season! Never was a fact more firmly grounded—though it's maybe too simple a fact to be called a fact of science. . . .

Yet from this deliberate trying, Mackay learned the grief and the trouble that comes of the trick of leaving your land bare to cheat next year's dryness. Baldly honest, he gathered the settlers 'round him to tell them the disadvantages of his invention. While their wives, under the trees, spanked their children for getting into the poor defiant little flower beds of that farm, and whispered women's secrets, out in the sun on a bare black field stood Angus, telling the husbands: "It is worthy to notice the effect fallowed land has on the crop . . . it having prolonged the ripening process fully eight days over that which has been fall-plowed. . . ." He reminded them of the promise of last year's crop—and the sudden wrecking of that hope by the August snowstorm, catching wheat made late by the fallow.

The settlers all over that country knew they could bank on Mackay.

VI.

COMES now a fantastic event to hurry us towards the more or less happy ending of this comedy of wheat. Back at

Ottawa, wise William Saunders goes on seventy, sits somewhat confused but never discouraged among better than a
hundred new sorts of spring wheats. Now he hires his son,
Dr. Charles E. Saunders, brother of the chemist Percy, to
fuss with these new wheats, select them, improve them—
who knows? Charles Saunders freely admitted he didn't
have any particular yen to be a wheat hunter, never thought
of being a wheat farmer, never planned to be a wheat
scientist—though it is true he was highly educated, and
held the degree of Doctor of Philosophy. His father, old
William, appointed him, insisted that he take it, even after
he had turned down this new job! All in all he seems an
outlandish companion and co-worker for Sharpe whose
beard was stained brown, for Mackay with face brown from
the prairie sun and wind, for Macoun who knew all of
Canada.

But Charles Saunders had patience, and marvelously
clever and knowing fingers, and with these he went at picking out heads—even solitary kernels—of the mixed-up
children of cross-bred wheats. Slender, tall, not healthy,
Charles cared much for the refined things of life. He was a
good chemist, but hadn't entirely wanted to be one—that
too had been his stern father's idea. For years he had studied
singing, in New York and even in London. He had taught
the art of song to the young ladies of St. Margaret's College
in Toronto. Professor Buller, who has written a book about
his deeds, says that Charles Saunders was masterly on the
flute and took a keen pleasure in song. Getting over an illness that weakened him, he had taken up, become a wizard
at a most delicate sort of French fancy-work. How could
this man be a wheat hunter? And yet, if William Saunders
hadn't picked out his son for this job, there's an excellent
chance the Marquis wheat would never have been born.
But this comedy is a scherzo of ifs and buts!

In the ten years that had gone by since the time the Red
Fife and the Hard Calcutta had been bred by Percy and

Thomas Sharpe out at Agassiz, many adventures, deaths, and losses had come to the children of those two wheats. The two Williams, Saunders and Macoun, had toiled, torn out rogues, incessantly thrown away the less promising wheat plants—with an expert cruelty it would be beneficial to apply to human children, if they only weren't human. (At least such is the theory of folks who hold with eugenics.) A vast amount of trash in the descendants of the Red Fife and the Hard Calcutta had been got rid of. In fact, these new wheat families were now pretty respectable. The very fact that they had kicked 'round—obscurely—for ten years in the experiment plots had given these new wheat varieties time to stop sporting, to stop reverting to their mother type. They no longer shot such a bewildering number of hopeless bad varieties. And among these children of that marriage, long ago, out in British Columbia, was one wheat sort that old William Saunders had baptized with the name of "Markham."

Why now did Charles Saunders, new at his strange job, begin to pick out early ripening plants from the plots of this Markham? Heaven knows! Out of ninety-three different kinds of wheats on the Ottawa farm, this Markham was a miserable yielder—stood eighty-fifth in the list, only eight from the bottom. Its kernels were light, chaffy, compared to its old ancestor the Red Fife. Why, that wheat only weighed fifty-eight pounds to the bushel. And out on the prairies a wheat to be called good should do better than sixty! Of course it ripened six days ahead of its father, the Red Fife. . . . But then there were forty other wheats, that year, which ripened well ahead of this Markham. . . .

It is a complete mystery to me why Charles Saunders should have picked out that mediocre kind of wheat called the Markham at all. Excepting that he always was saying this piece of wisdom: "Animal breeders know the best looking animal does not always prove the most satisfactory parent." So maybe this gentle, delicate man, with sunken cheeks and great sad eyes protected by a white cotton hat, sits on a folding stool by the side of a garden of nodding heads of this maybe good, maybe bad Markham wheat, cutting off heads of it.

"Wheat can be improved fastest by picking out one extra good plant and multiplying seed from that," says Charles. But how does he know a plant is extra good? And in how many ways is it extra good? Alas—not the greatest wheat genius in the world could foretell it. Does Saunders not know that here he deals with the same grand lottery of mixed-up strength and weakness that two human parents deal with when they mix and multiply their seed? Who dares to prophesy the issue? It is a sad magnificent business of heads and tails—this breeding of any living thing!

But here you see Charles Saunders next spring, sowing the seed of this extremely medium-yielding Markham wheat. He looks delicate, looks like anything but an outdoor worker, not at all like a wheat farmer, but his friends say that for thirty-five years he has looked that way—and still lives. New stools of the Markham shot up, ripened in the year of 1904. "Will our wheats make strong flour?" That was what old William Saunders was always telling his son to look for. Too many times, fine early-ripening frost-dodging grains had gone out to try their luck on those grim plains and turned out—starchy.

From hundreds of different varieties of these newly crossed wheats, Charles Saunders picks out a few kernels, puts them solemnly in his mouth, chews them carefully without swallowing them—wads them up in a ball in his mouth, like chewing gum. Along with all these other sorts he chews the seed of the fair-to-middling Markham. This chewing business is no invention of his—it's an old trick of practical wheat men, who say the gummier your wheat the stronger, more glutinous, the flour from it. The kernels of the Markham make a good gum. They're high in protein, in gluten as the prairie wheat has got to be. But what of their flour? "You could chew wheat till you choked and you'd never know whether the flour from it would be light or dark," says an old-timer from Saskatchewan.

But the kernels of the Markham were good and gummy, and next spring Charles Saunders planted them once more, and that fall he gave the wheat that grew from them the noble name of "Marquis,"—nobody knows why. And now his father, old William, does his last simple stroke of horse sense, makes his last simple crude experiment—who dares call it science? Wise from twenty years of failure, from exactly twenty years of getting fooled by wheats that ripened early, that yielded heavy, that stood up under the hot blasts of the afternoons and the cold dews of the Manitoba and Saskatchewan mornings only to make poor flour—old Saunders says to his son Charles: "We'll get a roller mill. We'll buy a little roller mill and make flour right here —*before* we send our wheats out to the prairie."

In a series, in the course of a hundred tests with a hundred wheats, Charles Saunders puts the red plump kernels of the grain of the new Marquis wheat into the Allis-Chalmers toy roller mill, writes: "Marquis wheat . . . ripens a few days before Red Fife. Produces very strong flour of very good color." That's all. And what of it? Dig into Charles Saunders' reports of that year and you'll find no bands playing nor fireworks fired about this Marquis wheat. Why, out of thirty-seven sorts of wheat, this Marquis was twenty-first in the list of yielders! And it wasn't so tremendously fast to ripen—only three days ahead of the Red Fife, called "H," did Charles Saunders reap it. What would the prairie men do with such a wheat? Why change from the Red Fife at all?

Together with his son, Charles, William Saunders lets his old eye wander up and down this list of laboratory wheats. Here's the Chelsea. It too has fine flour. And it yields much heavier here on the experiment plots than the

Marquis. Here's the new wheat, named "Gatineau" after the beautiful river that comes down to Ottawa from the north country—this Gatineau has a dozen excellent points, that stand out here on this sheltered Ottawa farm. There you see this faithful, steady old William Saunders, sitting looking at his list of wheats that have grown so lustily behind the pretty shelter belts of the Ottawa farm. "Yes—but what will the prairies do to them?" he ponders. Inwardly doesn't this wise old man, wise through experience of failure, curse these pretty experimental plots? His hair, his heavy brows over his slanting strange light eyes, are white now. How can he any longer hope for the miracle of a new wheat—to take the western men out of their frost fear? He has learned enough not to trust those fine breeding experiments. He is wise enough to gamble.

"Let's try out all of our strongest, highest gluten wheats on the western farms," says old William. So out west in bags goes the seed of the Chelsea, the Gatineau, the excellent early Red Fife, called "H"—and the red plump kernels of the Marquis which the expert Charles Saunders has chewed and not found wanting.

VII.

IT was the year of 1907, and what a year that was. To Angus Mackay all years were exceptional, but this was the champion of all exceptional years—for exceptional badness. All through April, even the last part of April when the Saskatchewan men should have been getting their seed under ground, that ground stayed hard as granite under cold gray skies. No seed at all could be got in 'til the seventh of May, weeks late—hardly a settler got his wheat drills out of the barn 'til the middle of May, a month late. Manitoba, Saskatchewan, Alberta—three provinces are nervous. The lean tanned men of a thousand miles from West to East kick their toes into the hard black earth, look

59

at their houses and barns—not yet paid for—think of their wives and children. "We're a month late getting the grain in," that's the spoken thought and the worry of wakeful nights. "This means we can't begin to harvest 'til September—and what of September?"

Every northwest man knows September may be anything in the humpty-dumpty weather of that land—anything from a mild Indian summer to roaring winter. . . .

The seeding is a month late. And at Indian Head Angus Mackay puts under the earth the seeds of the wheat Charles and William Saunders have sent him, sows them carefully, in the line of duty—Mackay's too old for great expectations. He sows, tends, cultivates the fields of the early Red Fife, called "H," of the Gatineau, the fine-yielding Chelsea —and the just fair-to-middling yielding Marquis. What will August, September be like?

What a summer! June was not a bad month; there were rains, and some sun; in July there was enough hot sun to shoot up the late grain on all of the fields. Mackay walks up and down his fields. Here is the grain on his fields that last year have lain fallow. A fine heavy stand here on these fallowed fields—but late. Still green on the fallow fields is the grain, and here it's the last of July—that's as always the trouble with his trick of the summer fallow, cheating the drought, but holding back the fine heavy stand of the wheat just long enough for the danger of those cold mornings. . . .

Mackay walks serenely through these experimental fields, looking for the beginnings of that change of the grain from green to the ripening yellow—and looking at the sky. What an August! The sun seems to lose his force. Squadrons of gray clouds sweep up from the West, riding low. Morning of the first of August—thermometer, thirty-five degrees! A little warm spell, and then, morning of the twentieth of August, Angus steps out, buttons his coat to his chin, looks: temperature this morning—thirty-three above zero, Fahrenheit.

Recorder that he is, Mackay sets these figures down—not for a day in these twenty years has he failed to report them. They are the simple data of a gigantic experiment. But what of the wheat? On this morning of the twentieth of August, the heads of the still-green Red Fife on the fields of the settlers on low land around Indian Head are nipped while forming. "Well—maybe there'll be a turn for the better," Mackay tells the worried neighbors.

There is a turn—for the worse. Cold rain comes, plastering the fields with slippery glaze of black gumbo glue. The Red Fife, staff of life of Saskatchewan? It has barely begun to turn from green to yellow. Mackay goes to his record book and writes down: "It is the worst season known since this country was settled in 1882."

September is here. The skies clear. And on the night of the twelfth of September it really freezes. Throughout the northeastern land there is a massacre of wheat. What was feared last spring has come true this autumn; there'll be patches on the pants of the farm boys this winter, and no new shoes for the girls. Yes, you may ask: why do these hardy fools *try* to raise grain in this terrible land? I'll give you no answer.

But Mackay walks out towards his fields on this morning of the twelfth of September, up as always, at six, the sad story of the frost set down in his eternal record book. Methodical, a philosopher who seems always to accept what God sends, his eye is as clear as ever it was in that memorable dry year of 'eighty-six when he learned how to cheat the threat of the drought. He walks out to his fields. His gray eyes look about him. Yes, here's the Red Fife, cold and green. Yes, the frost has killed it. Here's the wheat called the Huron, there's a patch of the Preston, and close by it the Pringle's Champlain—old William had great hopes of that one. But here they all are in ruins—worse off than the Red Fife, if anything. No—this year has left no wheat alive, no hope of anything. . . .

But what's this? Here is a little patch, just one-fifth of an acre in a great frame of desolation. Here's a little field of a new wheat, standing straight, with plump beardless spikes that nod a little, still a wee bit on the green side maybe—but ready to cut for all that. Mackay's old gray eyes look at this bald stiff-strawed wheat, its head a peculiar lovely red-gold. His experienced hand pulls a head of it—picks out a few kernels. Yes, they're hard, good and plump. Here by all that's outlandish stands a wheat that's ripe and fit to cut among the ruins of all the others.

Here's the Marquis. . . .

On the fifteenth of September Mackay cuts it, measures and weighs the grain of it. Yield: forty-one bushels to the acre. Here is his second miracle. There stands old Angus, once more with an experiment done for him—by the frost. Out of his immense experience with the shortcomings of a hundred of old William's wheats in a dozen bad years, now in a flash, without a chain of thought, he sees the marvelous sturdiness of the Marquis in this worst of years. The Saskatchewan men were right in their faith in him: never fear, when a real early-ripening wheat came, said they, Angus Mackay would be the man to know it. Now the Marquis has come.

VIII.

In that sad fall of 1907 when too many prairie families had no threshing at all to do, Mackay set off for the Exhibition at Regina with a bushel of fine red wheat. It would have been hard for the eye of the most expert inspector to have told that seed from the seed of the old Red Fife. To a great crowd of settlers, down at the mouth with the frost, the grizzled Angus showed the seed of that strange marriage of the Red Fife father and the poor little short-stemmed Hard Calcutta mother. " 'Tis the new Marquis wheat—here's the wheat for our prairies."

62

The settlers stepped on each other's toes, jostled 'round the tall patriarch to get a look.

"On pea land this new Marquis ripened nine or ten days ahead of the Red Fife, stood the cold, beat the frost. It was six days ahead of that killing frost," said Angus. "Even on our summer fallow—where wheat's always late—it ripens as fast as the Red Fife does on stubble. . . ."

There was a babble of questions from this crowd of weather-gamblers. In a moment they seemed to forget last year's disaster. "Where can we get this wheat, Angus?" they pressed him, demanded of him. Mooney, the seed dealer, offered ten dollars for the lone bushel of it. Now over the prairie ran the news of this heavy-yielding, sturdy grain—ripening days and days earlier than the Red Fife. Angus Mackay had done the test, found it so. And who doubted the word of Mackay?

In five short years, in that fantastic way new strong life has of increasing, the frost-cheating Marquis spread from Indian Head, everywhere replacing the old stand-by, Red Fife. From a scant half-bushel sent out to Angus from Ottawa, sown by him in that gloomy spring of 1907, this red wheat multiplied to millions of bushels by 1912. Marquis became the overwhelming fact of that land, from the lakes of Manitoba to the Alberta frontier where the ragged peaks of the Rockies throw their giant shadows over the last western wheat fields. As fast as Donald Mackay, lean tall expert son of Angus, could multiply the seed of it on his own farm, northward marched the Marquis wheat. Enthusiastic settlers saved out part of their year's crop, sold seed to each other: like a benevolent pestilence the Marquis spread, to silly wheat growers who once more dared the cold Augusts north of Saskatoon. In that strange land there was now one work: the sowing and reaping of Marquis wheat, ripening earlier, yielding heavier than ever the Red Fife, its father. Go to that strange land in August.

63

Stand in the fields of it: you'll stand in the middle of a land that's a bowl for God to eat wheat out of. And from the middle of it at night you'll see the beams of the headlights of Fords twenty-five miles away on the horizon rim.

But is there now no more danger from the frost for these northern men? Never fear—there are years when the cold still comes too soon: after all it's only a few days earlier that the settlers can reap the new wheat—in a land where it's the droll custom of summer to switch seasons with winter. But those few days do help. You see, it's like this with those folk up there: some years the Marquis just does manage to get cut ahead of those sudden cold August mornings, and that's the fun of their life. Marquis has made this difference: up north there, where wave after wave of raggedy lean men and their wives and children have in past years been driven back by the frost, some can now hang on, even make good livings—frozen out not quite so often.

That is all those strange Canadian folk seem to ask: the chance to be frozen out not quite so often. Like men who go down to the sea in ships, these wheat growers are poker players with an absolutely unconquerable nature. Here is Marquis, giving them a new stack of chips. After all it's these men, and the husky children their stern land breeds, more than any science or any new wheat or new-fangled discovery, that have made that Canadian land.

Here's the happy end of this story, not at all like the shameful fate of Mark Alfred Carleton who helped the wheat men far to the South. For his part in the finding of the Marquis—and everybody must admit it was important —Charles Saunders, the artistic son of old William, was given a pension of five thousand dollars a year, for life, by the people of Canada. Cheated of health, he can now devote himself to the delights he had always craved: to the music of the flute, the art of song, the reading of French classics.

Of the eminence of his father, old William Saunders, there is no question. Founder of the Dominion Experimental

AGASSIZ—WHERE MARQUIS WAS BORN

Farms system, father of Canadian Agriculture, he lived to see his Marquis wheat sweep over the prairie, build bold little homes there, and even great stone Universities like the one that startles you on the bare land west of Saskatoon. Will the searching and science that now buzzes in those laboratories bring a wheat to beat the Marquis that was born in part of the crude cross-breeding dreams of the stout old druggist?

As for Angus, he lives out his life at Indian Head, comfortable in a square brick house—under trees. Angus admires most of all good settlers who make an expert summer fallow, who hate weeds. Philosopher that he is, he remembers best the facts of the invading armies of grasshoppers, the hot winds, the hail that wipes out the work of a year in five minutes. With a smile he recalls the drought that presided over the experiment fate made for him back in 'eighty-six, and the cold that killed all of his wheats—save the Marquis—in 1907. Strangest of facts, the fields of those two experiments were hardly a mile apart!

As for men . . . "Oh, of course," says old Mackay, "it

was all due to the foresight of William Saunders. He saw the need of an early wheat."

Mackay himself? In his own honest view he is nothing—why should anybody make a hero of him? He smiles, this man who has welcomed the cruel facts of nature, bent himself to them, taken such enormous advantage of them. He smiles, then says:

"It was the fact of the frost that made the Marquis wheat."

BOOK TWO. MEAT

DORSET

CHAPTER THREE. THE SCIENTIFIC BOLSHEVIK

DORSET

I.

AFTER ALL, the dangers besetting Angus Mackay in his fight against hunger were nothing to the troubles hounding Marion Dorset in his hunt for truth.

The killing frost of an August morning was just a fact of nature, not trying to fool Mackay nor muddle him up; Jack Frost was only doing his honest best to drive Mackay clean out of a country where a man has to use his brains as well as his muscle to get started and keep going.

Now Dorset, a small man with a limp and brown eyes, was in danger from science itself. Sent out to southwest Iowa to fight a most terrifying malady of pigs—it was making headlines in the newspapers about the danger to the bacon supply and the threat to our reserves of hams— Dorset had to grapple with a trouble a million times more subtle than the simple facts of drought or frost—and that trouble was the mistakenness of science. He was sent out to Iowa with the notion planted in his head that the cause of this pig-death was known, the science of it nicely sewed up, that his job was just to push the plunger of his syringe so many thousands of times and presto!—this pig death would die. Mackay had only the drought and the frost for his teachers, his authorities; but Dorset—and he was a most mild little man—had to unlearn the official dope of Governmental Pooh-Bahs on this plague of pigs, had to disbelieve the science of Theobald Smith himself. More, he had to prove that William Welch of the Johns Hopkins University—then the holy of holies of American science—had gone off the track about this devastating death of hogs.

In short, Marion Dorset—and who was he, anyway?— had to start all over from facts farmers knew, facts the scientists had forgotten to see maybe because they weren't farmers enough. Isn't it hard for the best man to see with his eyes when his brain already knows what his eyes should see? There was something in Dorset's stubbornness as splendid as the simple comparisons of Mackay.

Dorset was only twenty-three years old in 1897, one of the most terrible years in the unwritten history of pigs—a year when better than one hundred and thirty out of every thousand American hogs died from the cholera. The men of the corn belt—this time with justice—sent up a cry for help to Washington; and Washington sent Dorset, who knew at that time nothing whatever about the lives and lore of swine, and very little about their sicknesses. But he was equipped with what Washington told the farmers was an excellent preventive for their threatened bankruptcy. Armed with bottles of serum, filled with notions of science, eager with the enthusiasm of a stripling hunger fighter, Dorset arrived at the town of Sydney among the Iowa hills along the river that used to have the right to be called the Wild Missourai. He looked out of his hotel room window. He went downstairs, asked: "What's the glare of all of those fires, out over the hills?"

The hotel keeper said: "Them's the fires of the carcasses of their dead hogs the farmers hereabout can't do nothing else but burn."

Next morning Doctor Marion Dorset set out with his serum bottles, to scotch a death that slithered from farm to farm with all the mystery of the Black Death that killed half the humans of Europe at the end of the Middle Ages.

II.

DORSET was born in Tennessee and before he was old enough to start studying at the University of Tennessee, good old Doctor Salmon of the United States Department of Agriculture, and his right-hand young man, Theobald Smith, were pretty certain they had collared the microbe that caused this deadly hog cholera. That was in the middle eighteen eighties, when the fashions of studying the ills of humans and animals were imported from abroad just as women's frills are now—and in Europe it was just then the fashion to find a microbe for every ill of man or beast.

Theobald Smith, and his boss, Doctor Salmon, started off on the right track—in three years' time they fished in the carcasses of five hundred pigs miserably dead of this strange plague. In four hundred out of that five hundred they found one and the same kind of microbe, a stick-shaped beggar, five hundred thousandths of an inch long, that swam about lustily. In those first days of microbe hunting this was considered mighty strong evidence that here was the criminal. But then, alas, Theobald Smith left pigs and began trying to give the hog cholera to rabbits. He stayed away from the study of the natural disease.

It was amazing how few of those fast-swimming microbes you needed to bowl over a rabbit. One four-millionth of a thimbleful of a soup of those bugs spelled death for a healthy creature in eight days or less, and the insides of the perished rabbit looked something like the insides of a doomed pig—though not exactly. Smith kept this new germ in tubes of clotted beef blood for a year and a half, and at the end of that time it would still kill mice. While Dorset was brightly learning his three R's in Tennessee—where science is supposed to be wicked—Theobald Smith was pouring soups of his new microbes into sterilized soil in flower pots, letting them stand, then shooting tablespoonsful of this earth into rabbits—who once in a while died. "Since rabbits are most susceptible of any animals to the hog cholera virus, it was not thought necessary to experiment with pigs after the rabbits had taken the disease," wrote Doctor Salmon and his right-hand man, Doctor Smith.

But at last they did try their new bacillus on pigs—with very queer results. While Dorset was hardly old enough to hold a good lively shote, Theobald Smith fed his new microbe, grown to billions in a rich beef soup, to healthy hogs. Alas, the beasts seemed to like it; they thrived on this bug-soup until Smith—he must prove his point!—fed them a whole half pint of it. Then the pigs up and died—in three days, which was queer—when you remember it takes an ordinary pig nearly two weeks to show signs of toppling over when you put him in a pen with some cholera-doomed friends. That wasn't like the hog cholera—in nature.

And then too, why did it take so many billions of their bugs to kill a pig? In nature a single drop of blood of a sick beast, on the end of a needle, will doom a healthy one. . . .

But here came Doctor William Welch, fresh from the front-line trenches of microbe hunting in Europe—he had been in the very same laboratory with the great Robert Koch. Professor Welch, in the interests of scientific exactness, did Theobald Smith's work over, found this very same bacillus in dead pigs, said: "It's the cause of hog cholera." And Doctor Welch rightly had such a reputation that his opinion about a given bug and its badness was as good as the promise to pay on a United States Treasury note.

This was years before Marion Dorset blinked his eyes at the glare of the burning-ghats of stricken animals on the land of impoverished farmers in Iowa, but already the Washington authorities sent out a word of good cheer to the men of the then new corn belt. Earnestly Salmon and Smith tried to find cures for this swift death. Sick pigs they purged with calomel and jalap; others they physicked with Epsom salts and the aloes from Barbados; yet others they dosed with castor oil, and even turpentine. One and all of these sad creatures were griped—then died. To no avail they drenched their beasts with the ancient medicines of horse doctors and the modern medicines of science. . . . But in the midst of this fruitless physicking, Theobald Smith made an amazing discovery—like so many of the finds of this extraordinary man, it was the first of its kind in all of microbe hunting. Those fast moving microbes from the sick hogs he could take, grow them in soup, grind them up, filter them and throw away everything excepting the juice of them: but this extract was potent to protect against the real living microbes!

It was momentous. This chemical stuff from his ground-up bugs, shot into pigeons, started strange doings in those pigeons' bodies. These fortunate vaccinated doves were proof against death from the microbe that came from the sick pigs. It was superb. But what about pigs themselves? After all it's pigs whose lives are snuffed out by hog cholera, whose death was threatening their owners with the poor-house. It's pigs, not pigeons—pigeons do not have this plague, in nature. Well, with pigs this vaccination did not go so good, as the plain folks say. But just the same, here it was 1897, with the burning heaps of the bodies of pigs lighting up the eager face of Dorset, and the real microbe of the plague was thought to be known; and Salmon, Dorset's chief, had written about this germ discovered by himself and Theobald Smith: "These discoveries solve the most important problems of swine epizoötics."

The morning after the first night out there at Sydney, when the hotel keeper had told him what those fires in the hills were made of, Dorset saw the real plague of hog cholera—not some laboratory disease of rabbits or mice or doves. For the first time he saw the mystery, the explosive-ness of this strange ill. Back of the barn of a worried farmer —whose herd of swine had, good luck, so far been safe— Marion Dorset saw a healthy hog suddenly refuse his food, watched him stagger strangely, begin to turn red and then purple on his sides and belly—die in two or three hours after the first symptoms were noticed!

But what could it profit young Dorset—or more impor-tant still the threatened porkers, or most important of all the farmers whose families live from corn and pigs—to see

73

this terror? He was not a veterinarian; a few years before, his father had died, leaving him six hundred dollars, on which he'd set out to take a medical course at the University of Pennsylvania. It was a lot of money in those days of the nineties, but just when he should have had two-thirds of it left, that six hundred was gone—such is life. And Dorset had got himself a job in Washington, as chemist in the Department of Agriculture; and he went to a night school to finish his medical course—those were the days when medicine was not thought too important to study in night schools or with some good old country doctor. And now here stood Marion Dorset, amid dying pigs, paid by the Government to fight their death.

But a man who plugs to get ahead as Dorset had done is a worker, no mistake about it—and now he set out to obey his orders. Here were his bottles of serum, made from the blood of horses into whose bodies had been shot the microbe discovered by Dorset's boss, Doctor Salmon, and Theobald Smith. With this serum and his degree of M.D. entitling him to treat human beings—but not pigs—Dorset faced worried farmers. "Save this lot of shotes for me, Doc, with this here Government serum—and you can have all the rest of my hogs," said one Iowa hill man.

With this farmer holding his still-healthy shotes, Dorset shot great doses of the official Government serum under their hides. A few days went by, with Dorset bumping about over gumbo roads, peddling his serum from one threatened farm to another, then he came back to the first farm. Alas—here were those supposedly immune shotes, huddled in their nests with their eyes glued shut, standing around with their noses strangely wrinkled as if they had headache, staggering about with grunts and groans until their hind legs began to cave in under them and they died. Dorset watched them all die—in spite of the serum. So it went, from one farm to another.

This was the first time that Marion Dorset, trained in

74

the words of book science and the test-tube juggling of laboratories, had met up with fundamentals. He looked at his serum that was just about as powerful as so much pink-tea to ward off the death that exploded among these Iowa herds. He looked at the dead bodies of swine at his feet, looked away toward the hills where rose the smoke from funeral pyres of dead bodies of animals his serum had failed to save. He became as hard-headed as any farmer, turned Bolshevik against his science, forgot the authority of his chief, the good Doctor Salmon, refused to be awed by the deserved eminence of Theobald Smith. He asked himself: "If the microbe of Salmon and Smith is the real cause of hog cholera, why doesn't the serum made from it stop this frightfulness?"

Without telling the Washington folks anything about it —after all they were committed officially to this serum business and to that fast-swimming little bacillus—Dorset staged a one-man revolution. To look at him, fussing perplexed among pigs those days of 'ninety-seven in the hills near Sydney, you would have taken him for nothing more than an earnest young pig-inspector—who was confused. Hardly more than five feet four in height, his smile was so pleasant it would be impossible—so you'd say—for him to do anything more than agree with everybody. Only there was this quirk to him: back in Washington it had been observed by Doctor De Schweinitz, one of his superiors, that Dorset had a funny way of poking about, experimenting, testing, experimenting—making experiments on questions that everybody considered to be absolutely settled. "It looks as if you don't believe a single thing unless you do it yourself, or see it yourself!" said De Schweinitz, in a huff.

"No, I don't believe I do, Doctor," and from Dorset's smile you'd have sworn he wanted to apologize for such unexpected mulishness—that his efficient chief knew was simply wasting the Government's time. The idea of doing experiments over! Today we know better, and the National

Research Council has brainy men who see to it that two searchers don't do the same experiment at the same time.

III.

ALONE amid this pestilence that was sending hard-working men to the poor-house, Dorset kissed his hand good-by to the official bacillus that the Government had declared to be the murderer of pigs. He became a secret outlaw, started his own private science. He went about buying hopelessly sick pigs, marked for death, from farmers who had uselessly plowed their black fields, planted the yellow maize, cultivated it, cut it, shocked it, husked it by the sweat of their brows to feed beasts—which were now worth nothing. "The Government authorizes me to pay you seventy-five cents for a sick pig," said Dorset.

"They're all yours," answered a hill man of the Missouri, tickled to death at this chance of six bits in a world from which this plague had seemed to chase all chance of making a dollar.

On the spot Dorset would kill a beast, bend his small body over its carcass, slash it open with a dull knife that was all the knife he had, peer into every corner of that pig with his inexperienced eyes. With little or none of the sort of dentist's skill that microbe hunters have to have, he even tried to find microbes—other kinds than that confounded Government bacillus. Among smells of the barnyard, in pens so dirty you'd swear every microbe in Iowa would crawl in to contaminate his bottles of soup, Dorset failed utterly to find any microbe. Then he would wash his hands streaked with blood—to make notes, always notes.

"Now will you please sign this receipt for the seventy-five cents I've paid you?" he asked the farmer.

"Reckon I'd better not," said the good hog-raiser. "Ain't a hand at puttin' my name to papers I don't know nothing about." So Dorset—you will see what an economical man he was—paid for his new pig-knowledge out of his own pocket. The farmer was too cussedly ignorant to sign a simple receipt for six bits that he'd as good as found for his doomed pig, but it was from this fellow and a hundred others no more educated, that Dorset learned the earthy fundamentals about the murder that was taking the bread out of the mouths of the families of the corn-belt men. From these men—called rubes—Dorset learned the mysterious slow-fuse action of the terror. Said one: "You buy a sick pig into your herd, or say one strays in. In a couple of days he dies. Don't nothin' happen to your own swine for ten, twelve days maybe. Then, bang!—your critters up and come down sick all over the place. . . ."

Dorset listened, remembered the way pigs had died back in Washington, when they were dosed with half a pint of the soup holding billions of the official Government bacillus. Those pigs hadn't died that way; there was no time-fuse to that disease; they turned up their toes in two, three days! How did that fact jibe with this disease out here in nature?

From these farmers, whose very dirtiness would be accused by scientific sanitarians of breeding the terror that now starved them, Dorset took lessons. "Sometimes they die right quick, other times slow. You'll see one of your hogs start bleeding at the nose—that means he's going to croak. But, by golly—there's one that ain't got a nose bleed at all. All the same you'll find him dead next morning. . . ."

"And catching! Say, Doc—this stuff run through my herd like measles through school kids. Any feller gets a single one of his shotes down with it—he can say good-by to a new dress for the Missus this fall." Dorset listened, saw this man was right. Then he tried to remember back to the death died by the experimental pigs at Washington after their meal of soup of the official Government microbe. Was that catching? Did healthy pigs die when they were stuck in a pen along with one of those artificially sick beasts? No. . . .

"Anyhow, Doc, you never lose 'em all," said a stalwart who spoke in gurgles through a chew of Peerless that bulged out his face. "It came into my hogs, 'n' believe me, we had a funeral here. Look at them ashes. But d'y'see those half dozen shotes over there in the feed lot? Well, they had it. . . . Some even got as far as the staggers. But there they are—okay now. Cholera-proof—that's what we call 'em. Wish to God I had a whole herd of 'em. . . ."

Again Marion Dorset thought back to the experimental disease at Washington. Yes—some of the pigs that had sickened from the enormous doses of the official bacillus had got better too. But were they proof against catching hog cholera? On the contrary, hadn't they up and died when they were merely put in a pen with beasts with the natural sickness?

So these men—called yokels—taught school without ever a thought of it to Dorset who was their pupil, and knew it. So Dorset learned the gaunt facts of this death before which he stood helpless. Autumn came, the flare of the fires in the hills died down, Dorset stood with his mouth open before the grandest fact of all, for suddenly the plague began to fade away. His scientific serum had stopped the epidemic just as efficiently as the Naples Fire Department would have put out Vesuvius by squirting streams into its crater. But now, as the November days turned the black earth hard with the frost and the first snowflakes swirled around the corn-shocks, the beasts of the Iowa men stopped dying. Such is the impotence of men, and the mercy of Nature. It is by such secret medicine of Nature, working from the days when there first were pigs, that pigs still live and make this story possible. It is by the same mysterious power—and not by tricks born in their feeble brains—that men remain on this earth to worry whether or no they will have meat to eat. With the green of the spring, death had come threatening hunger; with the frozen road-ruts of early winter it vanished. Dorset packed his few poor tools and went back to Washington—knowing the real disease of hog cholera.

IV.

DORSET, you'll remember, was not an obviously forceful man, not in any sense a Bolshevik getting himself into trouble with Authorities for his opinions. He went back to Washington, nursing his doubts about the whole official science. But he didn't face his chief and recommend that the Government supply of this silly hog-cholera serum be poured into the Potomac forthwith. No—for the time being the menace of the hog plague was over, and they put him to work at other jobs, as any efficient Government Department has to. After all it has to fight hunger where hunger threatens most, so here's Marion Dorset, deep in the chemistry of the tubercle microbe, finding a food for it, getting his name in the scientific magazines by inventing a food, made of the mixed yolks and whites of eggs, that the horrible tubercle bacillus relishes very much. And to this day most of the few who know Dorset's name know it because he is the inventor of what is called "Dorset's Egg Medium for the culture of the Tubercle Bacillus."

But in 1903 his real chance came. On the prairies and in the hills of the Midwest the fires destroying bodies of stricken pigs began to burn once more. Dorset was put back on the job. The thing that has always stuck out in my memory of Dorset, as a person, is the curious preciseness of his talk. You can see the commas in his nicely grammatical spoken sentences; now and again your eyes will open at a perfectly placed semicolon. His speech has the exactness of an epigram of the austere old Duke of La Rochefoucauld; no different is his way of experimenting. From the new epidemic in Iowa came unfortunate pigs by fast express to Washington, pigs with doom under their hides, pigs who had been shot with a small part of an ounce of the blood of a hog at its last gasp with the natural hog cholera.

"If this is the real hog cholera—it must be catching," Dorset told the boys working with him. Never during those five years had he forgotten what the Iowa hill folks had taught him. He went a jaunt out into gentle country 'round Washington—so different from the stern Iowa land where the great plains begin—and picked up pigs, personally saw to it that he got absolutely healthy pigs from farms where hog cholera had never been known. These critters he put in a pen along with the sick ones that had just come from the West—but he saved a few of these healthy ones out, kept them in a pen by themselves, under strict guard like so many convicts. That was all there was to his first experiment. That was all there was to his test, but that was enough. Eight days, ten, twelve days—and the healthy Washington shotes who ran with the dying hogs from Iowa caught their death. Thirty days—and the healthy Washington pigs kept in the clean pen by themselves stayed well.

Here was the real stuff: it was catching.

Alive now—in body after body of martyr after martyr pig—Dorset kept the unknown virus. A fresh supply of this flaming plague he kept to hand in his laboratory. There is Dorset, punctually on the job as a smitten pig gives up the ghost, with a slash, with the expert stab of a long, thin glass tube into the creature's steaming heart. A short suck at the safe end of the tube: up wells the blood, alive with hidden poison for heaven knows how many innocent future squealing porkers. In a glass jar, with a curious little broom made of glass, Dorset shakes out the clot. Into the next healthy brute goes a bit of this blood—and so on, *ad infinitum*. The deadliness of that original bit of blood never grows less. Mysteriously, though diluted through the bodies of a hundred swine, it renews itself, multiplies as all life unseen or visible must multiply. Starting out from that first doomed visitor from Iowa, Marion Dorset, if his arm hadn't dropped from his shoulder with tiredness, might have killed every hog in the world, excepting—

That was it! Excepting a few who for some completely unknown whim of God or Nature, decided to get better.

"If this is the real hog cholera, these few beasts that almost die, but come out of it—must be immune," Dorset told his boys. Never for a moment had he forgotten this second fundamental lesson the hog-raisers taught him. "Cholera-proof," that was the word they had used—a simple, rather inaccurate word like water-proof or fire-proof. Here grunted a beast—death had been under his hide but he'd refused to die. Here another—and over in that corner of the field maybe one more. "Are they cholera-proof?" asked Dorset. He did his second simple experiment.

He took these strangely recovered beasts, drove them amid their guttural protests to a pen, a special pen, a dangerous paddock, where a few of their brothers sick with the genuine hog cholera coughed, and staggered, and drearily waited the flight of their souls to the pig heaven. Into this same pen at the same time he drove the same number of healthy shotes who'd never had hog cholera, nor been anywhere near it. It was beautiful as a clear-cut experiment can be beautiful. The healthy pigs, who were now for the first time exposed to the pestilence, were in twenty days every one of them dead. Months went by—and not a single one of the creatures who'd recovered from the cholera turned so much as a hair, with death all 'round them.

Here was the real stuff: here were cholera-proof pigs: here was the fact the farmers knew—disguised in a word they'd maybe never heard: here was immunity.

"Yes, there's now no doubt we have the right thing to work with," Dorset said to his boys. But here's another thing that makes him stick in my memory: just as he didn't believe any so-called fact at all until he'd tried it out for himself, so also he still didn't believe an experiment even after he himself had done it. "You see," it was his wont to say, with a kind of self-knocking smile of apology, "I've always been afraid I might be wrong." That was the one difference between Dorset and his farmer teachers: all of them lived in a world filled with facts and superstitions but Dorset was always trying never to swallow a fact 'til it absolutely overwhelmed him. That is the one difference between the vast tangled common sense of human experience and *experiment*, or science—which will never be more than a wee part of that experience.

"Here are these so-called cholera-proof pigs," said Dorset to his boys. "There's no doubt they are proof against the natural disease, but how much of the disease *will* they stand?"

v.

you would say that this precise little man with the brown eyes was only trying to pile up details, details—great heaps of useless facts. What the devil did it matter, anyway, how much of the living poison of this pestilence an immune pig could stand? Dorset then had no notion of how it might matter, but he picked out Hog No. 844—who deserves to be famous—put her in a little pen all by herself. She had shown herself cholera-proof. But how cholera-proof? On the 24th of July, 1903, Dorset started, helped by the able young Doctor Schroeder. And from then on, every fortnight, this fantastic No. 844 was caught and pinned down to a solo of protesting grunts, and each time under her hide this pig got bigger and yet bigger doses of deadly hog-cholera blood. At last, on the 29th of October, Dorset and Schroeder did their level best to kill this stubborn No. 844 by shooting under her skin one whole pint of the blood of a brother pig just dying from the flaming death. That was enough blood to kill one hundred and twenty millions of non-immune animals.

No. 844? She only grunted.

Here was Dorset's first new fact, and it was something unheard of in the whole history of the plagues that threaten beasts or men. In his famous evangelical experiment at Pouilly-le-Fort, Louis Pasteur had had to be mighty careful to give his sheep, vaccinated against anthrax, only a little bit more than one fatal dose of the anthrax microbes. Their immunity was a wabbly thing, a delicate thing—and when Pasteur's experiment turned out so well, there were scientists who even hinted he had crooked it. Our immunity to this plague or that one is hardly ever what you'd call solid. What human being, no matter how well vaccinated, would dare to submit himself to the injection of a pint of the virus of the black small-pox? But here stood Dorset, as usual not quite able to believe it, looking at an absolute immunity, as absolute as the sickness itself was dreadful.

At this astounding moment Dorset showed a stubbornness, a contrariness that was as much a part of him as his mild brown eyes or his trick of talking in sentences whose perfect punctuation marks stuck out at you. Here was No. 844 and here were several other creatures, so amazingly immune—surely there must be hope of using their immunity in the cure of the plague that was every year threatening the folks out there. What were the men of the Bureau of Animal Industry, if they weren't hunger fighters? Here was Dorset, paid to be a hunger fighter, with his three or four tremendously immune pigs, listening to the appeals from the Midwest farms. Already, in these early days of the nineteen hundreds, our people were being led to believe in science, to think searchers can invent preventions for diseases like magicians bringing rabbits out of plug hats. Even Dorset's bosses seemed to believe that, told him: "Get out a serum as fast as you can."

But Dorset had an exact conscience that refused to be budged by the moans of the farmers or orders from above.

There was that old business of the bacillus that had been discovered by his boss, the good Doctor Salmon, and the now famous Theobald Smith. In every first-class laboratory the world over lived cultures and happy colonies of this microbe, feared and respected by all and rejoicing in the name "Hog Cholera Bacillus." Long ago, in the epidemic of 'ninety-seven, Dorset had become Bolshevik against this official microbe. And now he told Schroeder and the rest of his boys: "We know we are working with the genuine natural disease of hog cholera at last. Here is our chance to see whether the bacillus has anything at all to do with it."

Taking a whole year of valuable time at it, with a cruelty you would say was entirely foreign to his nature, Dorset proceeded to explode any claim this official microbe might have, of being the criminal cause of hog cholera. Into the warm bodies of beasts just dead of the real hog-cholera disease Dorset fished. Yes, no doubt of it—those microbes could be found in these beasts. So far Theobald Smith was undoubtedly right. Dorset brewed cultures of these microbes, fast-swimming devils that measured five hundred thousandths of an inch long. "Half a pint of a soup of these creatures is supposed to give hogs their death of the cholera," said Dorset. To healthy hogs Dorset fed meals of this broth of the official bacillus. Some of them died; others got sick but got better. While all of them were sick Dorset chased innocent healthy pigs who'd never been near the cholera into the pen with these sick ones—but not one of the healthy ones caught their death! But the real disease was catching. . . .

"Here are some that have got better. Are they immune?" asked Dorset. Into the exposure pen, the dread paddock where lurked the natural cholera in an unending succession of martyr pigs—into this pen Dorset drove the beasts that had got better from the bacillus. Promptly they caught the hog cholera; in less than twenty days they were dead.

But from the real disease, pigs get immunity—

Dorset dared to talk out loud now, to say: "This official bacillus has nothing to do with hog cholera. It's no wonder the old serum I used back in 'ninety-seven failed to stop the epidemic. The bacillus may lurk around in the body of a pig who is sick from the real disease. It may be poisonous enough to give him a last kick when he's already dying— but the bacillus alone . . . ?"

Now you see him, with his trusty assistant Niles, struggling to get blood out of a coughing poor creature who has just fallen sick with the hog cholera. If the official bacillus has nothing at all to do with this pestilence, then there must be a time, maybe early in the pig's sickness, when his blood contains never a single one of these microbes. So here are Dorset and Niles, annoyed almost to the point of taking the name of the Lord in vain. They wrestle with a slippery and entirely unwilling shote, trying to get blood out of him without killing him. He's still well enough to put up a battle—it is a dirty scrimmage. They get the critter pinned for a moment, stick the needle of a syringe under his hide here and there—where is a vein? A grunt! He's out of their grip again, amid their—no, certainly not amid their curses, for Dorset is methodical, persistent, and mild, and it is impossible to conceive of his permitting himself more than a whispered "dammit!" But they must get blood, this very day, from this sick shote. . . .

Niles is a veterinarian, a practical pig doctor as well as a searcher. Niles knows a way. Here you see that infernal shote—though we must excuse his cussedness, for how can he know that his discomfort and doom are for the salvation of millions of future unborn porkers? Here you see him trussed up, with his absurd quirk of a tail straightened out and tenderly laid across a block, washed thoroughly with soap and then alcohol. An inch from the end of that tail Niles sets a good sharp chisel. Bang! down comes the hammer. Out spurts a hot stream of red blood into the sterilized bottle Dorset holds ready. Day after day, as the shote

85

grows sicker, nearing his end from the unseen death that breeds and multiplies within him, piece after piece Dorset and his chiselman Niles chop off that tail, to draw blood. And now once more Dorset can speak out loud.

Because—when they tried it, the blood of that shote from the very beginning of his sickness was fatal to a healthy hog. But where was the official hog-cholera microbe? Every day went a few drops of that blood into a well-made soup— but not a microbe grew in it; not until the sixth day of the animal's illness, just before he died, could they find so much as a microbe there—but his blood? In that blood there was death the second day. And yet Dorset was not entirely ready to talk. From the heart of the dead beast he drew blood, watched it clot, drew the clear serum off the clot through a long glass tube. This blood held plenty, now, of the official bacilli. But through a close-grained porcelain filter he pumped the serum, through a filter so fine that the tiniest microbe couldn't sneak through it. The light-colored innocent-looking fluid that did come through was alive with unseen death, toppled healthy pigs over with an ill that was unmistakably the natural hog cholera.

Thus died the fame of the official bacillus of hog cholera —that had nothing to do with the cause of hog cholera. Eight years, off and on, Dorset had worked to learn what was *not* so about this red plague. It was not any grand array of facts he had learned that made him ready now to save meat, fight hunger, lift suffering and failure from farmers. It was the strong-brained way that he kept before him two or three simple facts learned years before under circumstances nobody would call scientific. And now hats off to Doctor Salmon. His own science of the official bacillus wrecked by his underling, with an open-mindedness rare in science, he told Dorset: "Go ahead!"

THE SCIENTIFIC BOLSHEVIK

VI.

EIGHT years after his first ignorant journey Dorset went back to Iowa. With him this time went Niles, the practical chopper-off of pigs' tails, and McBryde, who was so accurate he could hardly believe a fact after Dorset himself had found it and proved it. The small general with his absurd army of two men arrived without ceremony on the banks of the Skunk River, near Ames, where the endless forests of the maize and the grunting legions of beasts turning themselves into meat from this maize are the two dominant facts. Here men are as nothing amid the straight-rowed jungles of maize they grow each year for the one uncouth purpose of producing living meat on four legs. Hidden in the green of their maize, outnumbered by their beasts, all men are slaves to these lovely plants and those dirty animals—all men live by them. Here, as Dorset comes in 1905, death walks once more through the pig population, and the Iowa men are down in the mouth. The Government has made optimistic prophecies about this death—promises that haven't come true. With brains that care little for explanations by words, with eyes wide open to cruel facts, the farmers have lost faith in the power of the Government science to save their herds. They've been fooled by bulletins and bottles of serum that turned out to be bogus. Through their herds death sneaks. What now can they hope from insignificant Dorset, who talks little, listens a lot, and promises absolutely nothing?

On a fifty-acre patch of ground by the Skunk River, Dorset and his two men built a shed, not much bigger than two corn cribs. "It was a first-class shed," said Dorset. "It had two windows, a door, and there was a kitchen chair out in front where the three of us could sit down, by turns." This shed was their Institute for Hog Cholera Research, and a beautifully equipped laboratory it was, it having a

87

gasoline stove, a rickety table and on that table a few
bottles, a syringe or two, and a hammer and chisel—for
the use of the expert Niles. In this preposterous little chapel
of science Dorset got ready to try to smuggle resistance to
the worst of plagues into the bodies of the most susceptible
hogs. Looking at his miserable outfit, what hope could have
been more foolish, and do you wonder the corn-belt men
snickered bitterly?

What hope, indeed, could Marion Dorset have possibly
had? It is true that one of the two fundamental facts he'd
learned from the farmers in 'ninety-seven was the fact that
there is immunity to this death. But what possible use
could this immunity be? What possible way was there to
guard beasts, except by turning the real disease loose among
them—and watching eighty or ninety out of a hundred of
them die? It was ridiculous. Of course this survival of the
fittest is Nature's way of keeping men as well as beasts alive
on this earth, and who knows, in the end, it isn't the best
way? But Dorset couldn't believe that, no hunger fighter
worth the name can believe it. Good hunger fighters follow
Nature just so far—then try to trick her.

In his shed by the Skunk River, Dorset started hatching
his trick. But what chance was there of borrowing from
beasts that had passed through the Valley of the Shadow
their blessed immunity to give to the threatened millions of
the Midwest herds? Back at Washington Dorset had fumbled at it, tried it. He had drawn blood from the chopped-
off tails of hogs who'd come through after running nine
chances out of ten of perishing. Alas, their *blood* seemed to
have no power to protect healthy creatures put into the
deadly exposure pens.

But then Dorset had remembered that entirely remarkable beast, No. 844, who, recovered from her cholera, had
never minded at all a shot of red-hot virus big enough to
kill one hundred and twenty million pigs. Was this creature's blood different from the blood of a pig who had just

simply stood the natural disease? Well—why should it be?
"But is it?" asked Dorset, foolishly.

He drew blood from the tail of this famous No. 844, so
appallingly immune. He mixed this blood with a fatal dose
of the blood of a dying hog—blood that teemed with unseen
murder. He put this mixture into an innocent beast who'd
never been near hog cholera. "By George! it doesn't feaze
him!" said Dorset.

Then by accident—or by design, I can't tell which, only
knowing that it was a random small experiment, this pig
was chased into the dangerous exposure pen, amid his dying
colleagues. This pig who had got at the same time under
his hide the tremendously immune blood and the terribly
dangerous virus settled down to live there—and lived, ate,
drank, and was merry. It was remarkable.

"Can it be that we have smuggled immunity into this
pig?" Dorset asked his boys.

"Don't you see?" persisted Dorset. "This beast here certainly got enough of the virus to kill any ten ordinary creatures. But he got No. 844's immune blood at the same time.
The virus undoubtedly started off trying to kill him—but
844's blood saved him. . . . We've given him the disease
—and cured him at the same time. And look—here he is,
healthy and happy with beasts dying all 'round him. . . .
We've smuggled immunity under his hide!"

It was a strange, even a fantastic thought. It was founded
on one experiment—one of that Lorelei kind of experiments that lures searchers on. Again and again back at
Washington Dorset and his men had tried it—but things
kept going wrong and the survival of that one curious pig,
immune without danger, might very well have been considered just a chance, and been forgotten.

Except here was Dorset by the banks of the Skunk
River, led by that one happy little result, driven on by his
notion that you might give beasts life without their paying
for it by taking nine chances out of ten of dying. He began

again his fantastic attempts at smuggling. On to his fifty acres near the Skunk River he brought four full-grown hogs who had each one passed through an epidemic that had as good as ruined his owner. Each one of these beasts had been a miserable consolation to his master. Each one was immune —God alone knew why.

But how immune? Dorset took a chance; he would see right off the bat how cholera-proof these creatures might be; he ditched his old scheme of shooting in gradually bigger and bigger doses of deadly blood, as he'd done in the case of famous old No. 844. Here is Dorset, timid-looking, yes —and the possessor of only four precious immune pigs in all. Into the shade in front of his comfortable shed he drags one of these pigs, whose laboratory name is "Q No. 2." Here are Niles and McBryde—they have just gotten a great quantity of deadly blood out of the heart of a beast dying on one of those stricken farms near Ames. "Just how immune *is* this Q No. 2?" asks Dorset.

By the method the elegant French searchers call "the brutal method" Dorset tests poor Q No. 2. Surely there's nothing gentle about it. Into Q No. 2 Dorset pumps a quart and a half of the blood of the dying hog—one nine-millionth of a thimbleful of that blood is enough to lay an ordinary hog low! He does the same thing to Q No. 2's naturally immune brothers, shoots this enormous dose of death into all four of his valuable beasts.

"In view of the virulence of this blood, the behavior of the immunes after injection seems truly remarkable," writes Dorset in his notebook. "For not one of them showed any ill effects besides a transitory stiffness."

For a few days Q No. 2 was a little bit stiff. In less than two weeks he was cavorting, grubbing, rooting, and grunting about as any good pig should—as if he'd never in the world been host to a billion living messengers of death. Before the brutal test his *body* had been strangely immune to the natural cholera. What now of his blood?

Thud! Down came the chisel of the trusty Niles. Here was crude science, with no splitting of hairs or finely calibrated apparatus. Out spurted the good red blood from this fantastically resistant Q No. 2—it was a science no more delicate than the age-old art of butchering! What of the blood of Q No. 2 who so bravely stands Dorset's brutal dose of this death?

Into ordinary swine, carefully brought in, swine who'd never been near the cholera, Dorset injected serum that rose off the clotted blood of Q No. 2, turned these swine loose in pens where staggered hogs doomed with the natural malady. For two or three weeks everything went swimmingly. The injected beasts snorted and wallowed, oblivious. Uninjected companions put in with them at the same time passed away. It was a lovely test. The blood of Q No. 2 held magic, held mysterious weapons against the unseen virus. But wait—a month the injected pigs stayed in that pen, then began to cough, to stagger, to pop off one by one. The protection didn't last. The effect of the serum of Q No. 2—hats off to that noble beast!—had worn away. It was only a borrowed immunity the new beasts had got, and what good would that do the Midwest farmers—to protect their herds for three weeks against pestilence that lurked 'round all summer?

"No," said Dorset, to McBryde and Niles, "we must give them the real hog cholera. Only we must smuggle it into them—without hurting them."

Who can blame Dorset for trying everything else before going back to that impossible plan of smuggling? What would one of these farmers say, one of these practical men around Ames, if Dorset came to him proposing to save his hogs by shooting under every one of their hides a shot of the dangerous blood of a dying animal? Wouldn't all farmers give him the horse-laugh—even if he assured them their beasts would get life-guarding serum at the same time? He tried to get around this business of the dangerous injection. He tried to take the kick out of the virus by heating it a little—or by adding chemicals that might take the deadly sting out of it a little. It was no go. By that little shed on the Skunk a hundred pigs were murdered, were wasted. The chemicals either knocked out the invisible life of the virus so that it had no effect on a critter at all, or it didn't hit the virus hard enough—and then nine out of ten of the hogs he was trying to immunize kicked the bucket. It was no go. "We must smuggle it in!" insisted Dorset.

VII.

ACCORDINGLY, one hot Iowa morning, in front of the shed out under the cottonwood trees, a lively sixty-pound shote got—in spite of most vigorous protests—a little injection, in his left thigh, of hot hog-cholera blood fit to do to death three hundred thousand swine. A moment later, under the skin of his right thigh he gets half an ounce of the life-guarding serum of the remarkably immune hog, Q No. 2—but he squeals just as loudly. Three more shotes, each of them forty-five to sixty pounds of squirming cussedness, get the same strange injection of fatal virus in one leg—of life-saving serum in the other.

Dorset, and Niles who knows how to get blood, and the doubting McBryde, wait. Every morning they come to look at their four fateful beasts—who have no notion of what's going on inside them. Which will win? Will the terrible assassins—too small for the strongest microscope to see— multiply, poison them, choke them, overcome them? Or will the straw-colored sap from the body of the wonderful Q No. 2 kill the wee devils before they get started? It's a gamble, a tight-rope walk—Dorset's plan is a thousand-to-one shot. "If we've given them too much of the immune serum—then the virus won't hit them hard enough to immunize them!" complained Dorset to Niles and

McBryde. But who knew what was just enough, or too much?

They wait. Three weeks, and the four shotes are full of vim—but maybe that's only because the fatal half of their injection hasn't hit them hard enough. But it's three weeks, and this fine morning when the prairie wind makes ripples on the waters of that creek politely called the Skunk River, these four shotes are driven, called, dragged and pushed into a pen where sundry smitten swine stand shivering, dying. Here is a simple outdoor science—no more complicated than herding any drove of hogs. Along with these injected ones—that are carefully marked—go six ordinary pigs, of the same weight and healthy, but with no serum nor virus under their hides.

They wait, do Dorset and his army of two. It's like all experimenting with living stuff that takes its own time to multiply, to develop—it's a long business of one little experiment for every thousand thoughts, 'til you're near wild with the fidgets or 'til you're bored and forget all about what you've done.

They wait. One morning a pig is found dead. They look for his mark. Ha! It's one of the checks, one of the controls, one of the critters that had got no injection. That afternoon another beast lies dying—again it's a check, uninjected. The next day a third lies stark and stiff—overcome with that devastating suddenness by this cholera that's like the Black Death. Again it's a check pig, and by Jove! here's another of those check beasts turning up his toes. Here's luck. But what about the ones we've given the hot virus and the serum of Q No. 2? We hardly dare to look for them, among this gang of sick beasts. But we do, we must, we wade around in the wallow of that muddy pen. Dammit! they're hard to catch, slippery, lively. Yes—here's one— he's in fine shape. This from the good Niles. Here's another —nothing wrong with this one. This from McBryde. In short, here are all four, safe in the midst of dreadful danger.

In fact, there stayed all four vaccinated beasts, frisking, grunting, biting sidewise at each other in that queer way pigs have of fighting. They ate, and wallowed, and were utterly safe—with every other pig in the pen sick or dead or dying.

VIII.

IF all searchers were as severe on themselves, as pessimistic as Marion Dorset, there would be no exploded hopes for sufferers from cancer or tuberculosis—who every year are led astray by newspaper hints of great discoveries, coming even from the most celebrated laboratories. Dorset was certainly the opposite in character to Louis Pasteur, who rushed out his vaccine to the farmers of France on the strength of one fine experiment. But Dorset was wise to Nature, immensely distrustful of Her, aware of the bag of nasty tricks She has up her sleeve for the hunger fighter who plumes himself on having got 'round Her. He was as thorough as ever was Angus Mackay, with his fifteen years of testing what might be wrong with his drought-cheating summer-fallow. To the corn-fed men around Ames in Storey County—who would have snickered at him anyway—he said nothing about his four magically guarded shotes. Seared into his brain was the sight of the burning carcasses down by the Missouri in 'ninety-seven, bodies of beasts the serum made from the official bacillus had failed to save.

All the next year he worked, trying to defeat himself and to prove his simultaneous injections of death-bringing virus and life-saving serum were nonsense. How long would the protection last? Did the jolt that pigs got from getting such a dose of dangerous stuff under their hides, weaken them, stop their growing? Would pigs, with this vaccine under their skins—remember they actually had the living dreadful stuff of the disease itself in their bodies—would those pigs spread the disease to unvaccinated ones? Could suckling pigs stand the dreadful dose? What about that first

94

triumphal experiment, where all four of the vaccinated pigs had lived so prettily—were those figures correct? He knew Nature is cranky, hates to submit Herself to figures, loves to upset and make nonsense out of prophecies based on pretty scientific tables.

One hundred and thirty-six beasts who had got in one thigh the hot killing virus, in the other the serum, were driven a few at a time into a terrible exposure pen. Four of them died. Sixty-eight unvaccinated shotes he drove in there —fifty-six perished. What a pen that was! What a shambles! But that was Dorset's way. "The conditions in this exposure pen were not conducive to thriftiness, for no attempt was made to disinfect or clean the pen, as this might have defeated its object, which was to furnish a certain and severe exposure to hog cholera."

No Iowa men who were there in 1907 will forget the wonders that happened that year—the year the Marquis wheat first defied the frost. Here was the cholera, here was the threat of it, hanging like a sword over the prairie men, whose fate it is to grow corn to raise hogs to feed the people of the cities. Here was the pestilence, "depressing" the industry—to use the mild word the newspapers use, after our optimistic American manner. The richer the land, the more men, the more corn, the more swine and prosperity—until death breaks out among the close crowded beasts. That seems the rule of Nature. That is the reason for the toil of the men who fight to keep meat on the plates of mankind. Here was the pestilence—but here too was the strange trick of Dorset.

Here was the trusty Niles, with his twin bottles; with the dangerous bottle holding death and the benevolent bottle that carried proof against it. On forty-seven farms Niles toiled, shooting his two simultaneous doses of death and life into more than two thousand creatures. "But we must be sure, we must have checks!" insisted the overcareful Dorset. And every farmer whose herd was vaccinated had to leave a certain number of beasts unprotected to make those check experiments Dorset was obsessed with. On forty-seven farms Niles toiled, and the result was unheard of, unhoped for. On the farms where the creatures had not yet been exposed to the plague, not a single vaccinated creature died. On those same farms, when the plague did get there, sixty-eight out of every hundred—not injected—turned up their toes. Where the herds had already been exposed, the twin injections saved ninety-six out of every hundred, while eighty-nine out of every hundred of the check beasts died.

At last Dorset published his long report, called the experts of the States to a congress to tell them the simple way to get ready to guard our herds. He ended with an excessive caution—which was like him—as follows:

"If this serum is widely used, there is every reason to believe that the enormous losses that yearly result from hog cholera will be materially reduced."

He permitted himself that mild prophecy. The losses were reduced all right—to a point where the hog cholera nearly died out, to a point where laboratories for making the serum had to go out of business because no more serum was needed, to a point where immunization was neglected, to a point where—in 1926—when a new epidemic flamed up, there was the devil of a time to find serum to stop it.

So Dorset helped the prairie men to buy dresses for their women, shoes for their kids, Fords for the whole family, and saved the country—as the newspaper will have it—untold millions of dollars. He has stayed obscure, but happily so. When asked, during a meeting of the National Academy of Sciences, why he wasn't attending, he smiled, and said: "Oh, I do not belong. That is a body composed of real scientists!"

He limps around his laboratory, gray-haired now but young-brained, smoking cigarettes, working incessantly, failing to find new tricks to fight hunger, save meat, but what of it? He is searching. He may not find another simple trick to cheat Nature—but what hunger fighter has found more than one? He can look the world in the face. If his rheumatism should floor him so that he could no longer work, it is true that the Government would pay him only sixty dollars a month, which is a silly pension, indeed, for a man who has saved us those "untold millions of dollars."

But that doesn't worry Dorset a bit. Long ago, in the days when he was first sent out to southwest Iowa, this precise man started two bank accounts. One was the checking account of Marion Dorset, which owed—and there was no getting out of it—the account of a certain very stingy M. Dorset so much each month. And now, should his rheumatism get him, he wouldn't even need that miserable sixty dollars.

"No one else was going to look out for me, so I decided to look out for myself," said Dorset.

MOHLER

CHAPTER FOUR. A MAN FOR FUNDAMENTALS

MOHLER

I.

THE SMALL MAN with brown eyes and the limp stands out in the annals of hunger fighters for being clear-headed enough to see that farmers are sometimes sounder than scientists. But there is no general rule for fighting hunger; every job is a thing in itself. In certain ways Dorset had a much easier time of it than burly John Mohler, who by a vast and terrible experiment drove the foot-and-mouth sickness under the ground—with a thoroughness unheard of in the whole history of death fighting.

Once he'd exploded the official science—certainly no fool's job—Dorset had had Nature on his side, had beasts, to start out with, that the natural cholera had made tremendously immune. That's a rare thing—so rare that there's not a single ill from which men can be guarded in the simple way Dorset could protect his pigs from the red death of the cholera. But from the very beginning of John Mohler's struggle there wasn't a chance of such a neat life-saving vaccination of the threatened millions of American calves, cows, and bulls—to say nothing of sheep. Among the pathetic creatures having the bad luck to live through the foot-and-mouth sickness there's no such immunity.

Strange are the traps the gods put in the way of each hunger fighter. Having got rid of bum science, Dorset went at his meat-saving job with every bit of true science he could make. But look at Mohler, perplexed in hot California valleys, his heavy figure slumped in the saddle as he rode back home in the dusk of hectic days in the High Sierra. In that gigantic laboratory—it was cruder even than Dorset's shed by the Skunk—he had to ignore science, to face a pestilence that could be everywhere at once, like a ghost, and that swept over the ranges with the speed of a prairie fire.

Mohler had to throw overboard nine-tenths of the true science that was known, and there was plenty known about this ill of the feet and the mouths of cattle. Pretty facts, absolutely accurate, he had learned over beer seidels in Germany from Friedrich Loeffler—who had mustaches like a pair of curved whiskbrooms. Mohler had to ask himself what was the use of his knowing all about the cause of this plague if knowing it didn't help him to do anything about it! That's where he was clear-headed. But you'd think he hadn't a jot or tittle of the curiosity that's supposed to drive searchers to their discoveries. Watching Mohler's vast experiment you'd swear he didn't care a cuss about old Loeffler's discovery of the immense tininess of the foot-and-mouth assassins—so weirdly small that the eye of man will never see them through the strongest lens man could possibly invent.

Yet there was at the back of Mohler's brain an elemental science. It cared nothing whether microbes were as small as atoms or as big as angle-worms. His science consisted in one crude fact, and banking on this, Mohler had the impudence to believe he could wipe out this threat of hunger—completely. You would be polite to call his work under the dry California sky an experiment—more accurate you'd be to call it a shambles. He was unquestionably a man for fundamentals.

II.

FRIEDRICH LOEFFLER—for whom Mohler always expressed the greatest respect—was a fundamental man too, only his ideas were much more sophisticated by science. Like Mohler in America, Loeffler in Germany was called by his Government to fight the peril of the sores on the feet and the blisters in the mouths of German cattle—it was a plain case of having to fight hunger. On thousands of tidy German farms where the barn is more important than the house and built right into it and where the manure pile is most important of all, there had smoldered for years this curious plague of the rotting hooves and the ropy spittle. Good times, fat times were abroad in Germany in the eighteen-nineties; more babies were born, more cattle were raised, the clean stables and the little pastures were crowded, more thousands of cows were bartered, sent from place to place. Now this is just what the foot-and-mouth devils feed on—and the danger burst from a smolder into the flare, and the high bureaucrats of the empire called on Loeffler.

It was no business of pure science; there was no time for pure science in these days when something unknown was raising blisters the size of dollars in the mouths of German cows, was reducing sleek-sided beef cattle to bags of bones, was drying the grand heavy-hanging udders of thousands of heavy-milking Holsteins. Looking at Loeffler, as he stalked around stables, stiff as a field marshal and with the whole barn force standing around at salute and scared half to death, you'd certainly feel confident that here was the man to put out this fire. Loeffler was a terrific man— that best describes him. It wasn't only the ferocious sweep of his proud mustaches which had more hair in them than the beards of three prophets. It was his whole rough appearance; his sharp eyes, guttural curses, blocky shoulders, gave him the look of a kind of scientific Charlemagne. As he unlimbered his microscope it wouldn't have surprised you if the very germs of the foot-and-mouth plague had turned their tails and fled out of Germany.

Loeffler stooped his enormous body to keep his head from bumping the rafters, in stables so spotless the finest lady wouldn't have to pick her way. He peered into the mouths of cows—cows that opened and shut their mouths with a curious smack, a kind of ominous smack that lets you know the foot-and-mouth sickness is close by. "I must find a beast who's just getting the disease—one with fresh unbroken blisters in her mouth," ordered Loeffler, to farmers who said: "At your command, Your Excellency!" That's what Loeffler was after—the sickness at its very beginning, and there he was shrewd. Of course he was shrewd, this man who had learned his microbe hunting from Robert Koch himself in the bold days of the discovery of the tubercle bacillus, days so busy that Loeffler himself records there was hardly time to go to the bathroom. Never was there a microbe hunter who made so few mistakes as Loeffler, who had himself discovered the germs of diphtheria, of glanders, of swine erysipelas and the typhoid fever of mice!

Those were certainly true fundamental tricks he had turned, and who can blame him if he believed, that to fight the hunger of the foot-and-mouth sickness, you should first find the cause of it? Loeffler had a special religion, of which his stringy-bearded little master, Robert Koch, was the god, and the simple creed of his religion was this: that for every contagious disease there must be a microbe cause, and if you once spot that cause then it ought to be simple to scotch the sickness.

Each morning Loeffler went out into the country from Berlin, plodded through pastures, among herds of hundreds of cattle in which every last beast was slobbering, hanging its head, refusing to eat, and walking gingerly as if this were a pasture of red-hot iron instead of grass. "We must find blisters that are not broken!" he kept insisting in gruff gutturals. "Let a blister in a cow's mouth break and every bug in the world will get into it!"

Through scores of sick sore mouths looked Loeffler and his respectful little procession of assistants, stablehands, and discouraged cattle-owners. Ah! here is one—with two or three nice round welts on its tongue, and on the margin of its gums! Here's the ill at its very beginning. And while the beast is tied and thrown Loeffler's dark eyes blink and snap behind his spectacles. Now his fat body bends over the

LOEFFLER

animal. . . . There is a smell of strong alcohol and a gleam
of glass to astonish the open-mouthed peasants. Loeffler
hurries back to Berlin with a few drops of clear yellow
fluid sealed up in glass. Here'll be the microbe!

That night he looked—and found nothing.

He brought the disease into his laboratory to get a more
convenient whack at it. With great trouble and at expense

105

he gathered cows and several heifers from a far-off farm where the health-sapping ill of the sore feet had never been known. He put them in a stable where only horses had ever been kept, and confided them to the care of a moral and respectable stable man, married, accustomed to stay at home with his wife, not given to mixing with dairy-maids. For, you see, Loeffler already had a hunch of the swift contagiousness of this ill. Now he would grow this disease— under his own hands in his laboratory.

To these innocent animals Loeffler brought the pest, and had all the fresh unbroken blisters he could possibly want, to look into. Here he must find the microbe. Here he looked —and found gray blank emptiness under his lens. He stained that blister fluid with a rainbow assortment of aniline dyes; he took pictures of it when there was no visible thing in it to take pictures of, tried every last trick his master Koch had taught him. He looked—and found nothing. And yet, one ten-thousandth of a drop of that blister fluid was enough to make the ropy saliva drool from the mouth of a healthy calf, to bring it down to its knees off from feet that were too terribly sore to stand on; to kill that calf, like as not. . . .

But his very strongest microscope showed him nothing. What was wrong with the science of Robert Koch? For Loeffler, Koch's teaching was truth itself. Never was there a more loyal disciple, and once, at a solemn congress on tuberculosis, at Brussels, where French, English, and American searchers were taking pot-shots at Koch's doctrines, Loeffler mounted to the scientific pulpit, pounded it with his thick fist, opened his speech by shouting through his epic mustache: "*Aber—Koch hat Recht!*" He was full of wine, it's true, that day—but drunk or sober, for Loeffler, Koch was right. And now here was a catching disease— without a microbe!

III.

BUT he had to do something, had the honest Loeffler. Here he was, head of the Commission for the study of what the Germans call "Snout-and-Claw" sickness. Now in Germany, then, just as in our country today, the notion was widely held that given a celebrated searcher, money, guinea-pigs, and test-tubes—the riddle of any sickness will be solved, and that right quickly. It was such a notion of the authorities that forced Robert Koch into going off half-cocked with the tuberculin, into making his one terrible mistake that resulted in the death of nobody knows how many people who otherwise might have got over their consumption without any dosing whatever. Now the German farmers were clamoring, pinched by this unknown evil that wasn't actually killing all of their beef cattle but that mysteriously melted the flesh off them, that didn't necessarily put their cows under the ground but instead left abscesses in their udders and ruined them for keeps as milkers. Who can blame the plug-hatted authorities? They were responsible to the worried farmers. Who blames them if they, from their swivel chairs, ordered Loeffler to produce a preventive?

Even the burly Loeffler, so appallingly slow and exact, was overwhelmed by the cries of a nation. He began looking for a preventive, a vaccine—without having found any germ at all in that poisonous blister fluid. Of course he had the best of examples to follow there. He could imitate the fundamental wisdom of the English dairy-maids here: after all, *they'd* never seen a smallpox germ when they discovered the smallpox vaccine. Not even knowing there were such imps as microbes, they just knew that if you caught cowpox from the blisters on cows you wouldn't get smallpox. So Loeffler tried to follow the example of old Doctor Jenner—the most famous pupil of those milkmaids. He started trying to invent a vaccine against the virus of the foot-and-mouth sickness by taking the clear poisonous water from the blisters in the mouths of those sick laboratory cattle who were so well chaperoned by the moral stableman.

Alas, Loeffler got himself into a holy mess. Beginning with all the shrewd sense of a Dorset, he went asking around among stockmen and horse doctors—who also ministered to the needs of cows: "Are cattle proof against this sickness after they pass through an attack of it?"

Alas, to this simple question he got all sorts of answers. Some said a calf who'd minced around on sore hooves would be proof against this ill for two years after; others said it might come back in six weeks like a cold in the head. You'd think this confusion among the plain people would have steered him off this plan, for the superstitions of folks are rarely true unless all folks believe them—and then you still can't be sure until those beliefs are put to the test of experiment. But Loeffler started at it, trying to weaken the hidden poison in the blister fluid by diluting it with water, by drying it in an oven, by mixing it—as Dorset did with the hog-cholera virus—with the blood of a calf that had got better. In short he tried to give creatures a little mild sickness to protect them against the real villainous stuff that lay in wait for them in nature.

Before he was at all sure of his vaccine he went out to the farm of prosperous Frau Becker, at Greifswald—among her draft-oxen this sturdy woman farmer had heard the sinister smacking of lips that she knew threatened her prosperity. The honest Loeffler came—just as the vile trouble had sneaked over from Frau Becker's draft oxen into her one hundred and fifty-three cows. But there were the bulls and steers, still safe. "We'll try to protect them!" Loeffler told the good woman. Loeffler, a man of the laboratory from his great feet to the bald dome of his head, was never cut out for a cow-boy. Under his eyes, peering from behind spectacles, the fractious beasts were driven into a corner of the pasture and caught by throwing lassos around their

horns, by helpers who got tangled up in their own ropes.
Loeffler summed the entire hurly-burly up by writing:
"There was no lack of disagreeable incidents caused by the
wildness of the animals. Luckily there were no serious acci-
dents to the servants—except during the injection of two
very angry bulls. . . ."

It seemed as if the bulls knew poor Loeffler's vaccine was
a frost. A few days later the bulls got sick, and so did the
steers—was it only a light attack, or was it the real foot-
and-mouth demon that was making them slobber so? Was it
the vaccine or had these funny German cow-boys contami-
nated the bulls by the virus carried on their hands from the
already sick cows? Nobody knew: Loeffler couldn't tell.
Here were some three-weeks-old calves, seven of them.
Loeffler gave them a shot of vaccine. Nothing happened. He
gave them a second shot to make sure they'd be guarded—
and they all came down with virulent foot-and-mouth disease. It was a mess, no less. Loeffler brushed the dirt of the
fields off the knees of his pants—imagine it: he'd actually
shot his vaccine into the veins in the necks of those resentful
bulls roped by the amateur cow-boys. Imagine having to
vaccinate all the cows of Germany by that delicate business
of putting stuff into a vein. . . . But Loeffler brushed off
his trousers and tried something else, and failed to save
cows, but tumbled into an utterly strange new world of
science. . . .

He was driven into his discovery, not by what's called
genius, not by vision—but simply by a silly sense of duty.
Such a hard-headed fellow as Loeffler knew very well by
this time it was nonsense to try to shoot that dangerous
blister fluid—so mysteriously free of any microbes at all—
into healthy cattle. He was continually spreading the disease into new farms in Germany, instead of keeping it out,
but he wouldn't give up, and the walls of his laboratory
vibrated to the pacing to and fro of his body, bulky as a
barrel. Evening, and he tried to find a way out—but like as

not had to drown his futile thoughts in the kindly amber fluid that left flecks of silky foam on his magnificent mustaches. He patted his shiny pate, he mused: "If only I could use the pure blister juice, without the disease virus in it—freed from the living poison. . . ."

Of course he'd failed to see any microbe whatever in the fluid from the most villainous blisters in a freshly sick calf —but surely microbes were there. . . . Koch couldn't be wrong—maybe here was a new kind of germ no dye would stain. . . .

But if he could take that poisonous *life* out of the fluid, so there wouldn't be that confounded danger of infecting new herds of cattle all over Prussia—when he'd meant to make them immune! If he could only remove the virus, there might be left in that blister water some chemical remnant of the germs, some stuff that might make calves immune—safely. . . .

Never famous for imagination, reveries like these racked the brain of this conservative man. Now he knew one thing, it was common knowledge and all searchers knew it: there was a way to clean every microbe no matter how tiny out of any fluid. This trick was the invention of the bearded Chamberland, who smoked pipes to the disgust of his master, Pasteur, and whose science had a way of being forgotten in the hoorahs for Pasteur. Loeffler grabbed the idea: he could clean his foot-and-mouth virus out by filtering it. He bought a quantity of Chamberland's little porcelain filters, neat they were, about the size and shape of little candles you used to see on Christmas trees, only these candles were hollow, but their walls were so fine-meshed that the tiniest microscopic particle would get stuck in them. Only fluid could pass.

Here stands Loeffler—unaware of any fantastic surprise —before a battery of the white filter candles, sterile, tight, and neatly screwed into glass cylinders by his helper, Froesch. From a calf just down sick, with pretty blisters the size of a quarter, they've got enough liquid poison to put a dozen large herds out of business for months. There is a glint and gleam of glass, a clink and tinkle of glass on glass; heavy Friedrich Loeffler makes sundry delicate passes with his hands that are like a stevedore's paws.

From behind his absurd little oval spectacles and over the tips of his mustache he peers at the deadly juice as it trickles out of the spout of the filter—no longer harmful. . . .

He is super-careful. The French guarantee no microbe can get through these filters—but who are the French? So to make sure, on his own hook and for his private satisfaction, he adds to the stuff from the blisters, just before he pours it on to the filter-candles, a broth swarming with the very tiniest visible harmless bacilli that he's got in his laboratory. If *those* creatures don't get by the filter—then the foot-and-mouth virus certainly can't! The last drop dribbles from the end of the filter spout, limpid—surely harmless. . . .

Heigho for the test! No—wait! Annoyingly thorough, appallingly pernickety—twice more he pours that already perfectly filtered stuff through porcelain candles. . . . No life must get through. Now for the test. But wait! Is the blister juice from the sick calf—before the fluid was filtered —is it properly dangerous? Is the virus there? Easy to find that out, easy enough. Now for the experiment.

Four calves are ready, sound, healthy little critters, brought up by that stableman famous for his sobriety and steadfast character. A grunt, a little struggle, a swift thrust of a syringe in Loeffler's hand—the light touch of this giant is incredible, grotesque. A minute, at the most two minutes, and it's all over. Here are four calves. Two have got into their veins the terrible blister fluid—before it was filtered. Two of them harbor the limpid juice that has gone three times through the filter—harmless, surely. And maybe there's a chance it'll make them immune!

Two days pass—and hell pops and bursts wide open in Loeffler's laboratory. Never a gentle man, he breaks now into a stream of Gargantuan guttural remarks never mentioned at family firesides. All four calves are sick! All four of them hang their heads, are off their feed, smack their lips with that ominous smack. And yes, the good stableman shows him—here are blisters the size of peas on their tongues; it's unmistakable. All four of them have foot-and-mouth disease! It is impossible. . . .

But it is true. Not believing his senses, and doubting all filters, Loeffler does the experiment over, and over, and over once more. Through one filter after another he passes this dangerous fluid—that stays dangerous. . . . Calf after calf comes down sick from a tiny dose of the filtered stuff, and here's a husky seventy-five-pound hog—in two days he can hardly walk, in four he's pitifully walking on his knees; all from a little shot of fluid that's gone through porcelain that'll let no microbe pass. . . .

Loeffler has stumbled into a new world. Two hundred years and more after Leeuwenhoek first saw microbes—and couldn't believe his eyes—Loeffler realizes there is life, poisonous life tinier than the smallest visible microbe, undreamed-of life that lurks in a dark cellar of nature in a murk that's below the visible. Here are infinitesimal dots and points of deadliness—tinier they are than the theoretical size of the wave-lengths of light itself. Powerful enough they are to make pitiful bags of bones out of lusty bulls, to ruin the power of broad-rumped cows to bring forth calves —sinister enough to take meat out of the mouths of men in future hard times when maybe there'll be hardly enough meat for mankind. Loeffler the solid man stands in awe. Do they swim about—these savage living things that are so near nothing? Or are they motionless? Are they spheres, or corkscrews, or shaped like sticks? Or are they nebulous constellations of electrons like their lifeless brothers—the atoms? Loeffler had no idea, was never a man to propound scientific fantasies; what his eyes couldn't see he would not describe. All he knew was that here was a new world of life—whose existence he could tell only by the fact that, starting with a drop of it, he could bring every calf, cow, and bull in the world down with foot-and-mouth sickness.

He permitted himself a careful little prophecy: "The causes of many other contagious diseases are still unknown. They have hid from the sharpest eyes and defied the most skillful hands. It is possible that the microbes of typhus fever, rinderpest, measles—perhaps too those of infantile paralysis and yellow fever, are all of them too small to be seen." A solid man, Loeffler! Thirty years have gone by. The living poison of not one of these plagues has been seen for sure. The poison of each one steals through fine filters. So Loeffler dug down to a new fundamental.

But, as the sage Ring Lardner would say: "What of it?"

What's the use of knowing all about the fantastic tininess of the cause of foot-and-mouth sickness—if you can't do anything about the sickness itself? There's a question for philosophers, for those who defend what's called "pure science." But let's hurry back to our threatened farmers— our totally disgusted German farmers. Here is Loeffler, helping not a bit to lift this curse from German livestock. While he so accurately finds out the details of this invisible life, how sneaking it is, tough it is, how it can live in hundred-proof alcohol without getting a bun on—that very same virus escapes from his laboratory! By hidden ways it gets into new herds of German cattle, bankrupts farmers, costs the Government, that has spent hundreds of thousands of marks for Loeffler, additional millions of marks to appease the farmers. Getting out of Loeffler's workshop, despite the care of the estimable stableman, past quarantines enforced by the German Army, it runs over Germany like some invisible quicksilver. In 1911, one out of seven of the cattle of the realm is hit by it!

Poor old Loeffler, his pointed beard turned gray but his

mustache still defiantly black, is stowed away with his terrible ultra-microscopic microbes on the Island of Riems in the Baltic Sea—for the safety of the beef, pork, and mutton of Europe. . . .

Loeffler went to the Great War, a bespangled general of sanitary troops, in 1914. In 1915 he died, and it is recorded of him that he muttered of microbes—visible and invisible —in his last delirium.

IV.

IN the very year Loeffler was assisting in the invasion of Belgium and France, the plague that had baffled him invaded America, stealing past the excellent quarantine in some way that's completely mysterious. In the very heart of the American land, it exploded in a drove of hogs, on a farm near Niles, in Michigan. Into Michigan it had stolen across ocean and mountains from God knows where.

The very next day, late at night, John Mohler was bending over these beasts in the feed lot of that Michigan farm, peering at their feet by the glow of his flashlight. Six days, Mohler and his men found cattle smacking their lips on thirty-nine Michigan farms. Thirty days, and this trouble that dried the milk and emptied the wombs of cows, that melted good fat from the flanks of steers, was aflare in twenty-two states of the Union. It was Mohler's job not to study this plague but to stamp it out. Five times before the virus had gotten into the American land, only to be blotted out pronto; and now Mohler squirted, dowsed, and swabbed farms with carbolic acid, fumigated himself and his men with formaldehyde, quarantined, butchered hugely. He used the despairing tactics of firemen who dynamite buildings in conflagrations where water fails them. He fought. He failed.

He watched the virus slip through his fingers and slide between his legs. A rat-tat-tat of epidemics broke out across six states, sown in a single day by mere wisps of straw and bits of manure that blew out of cattle cars clanking across the Midwest flat lands. In one place he had set up what he was sure was a perfect quarantine—only to have infinitesimal mites of the living poison carried to neighboring farms on the feet of night-prowling dogs. Who'd have thought to tie up the dogs? In another place the pestilence hops a hundred and fifty miles—carried heaven knows how on the clothes or the shoes or the hands of a farmer who has gone from his own stricken farm, dressed in his best, to attend a funeral. In yet another place Mohler has stopped all traffic, of cattle, of dogs, of men—only to watch vagrant crows feed in tainted farmyards. "Oh—we forgot about crows," says Mohler, and shotguns are brought, and loaded, and aimed, and the crows flap up with taunting caws, carrying death through the air to farms thirty miles away. . . .

What good could the subtle science of Friedrich Loeffler do John Mohler, as he slugged at this death? Loeffler, too, had begun by seeing the terrible fact of the pestilence as it slipped from farm to farm, but then he'd bored down, down, into the mystery of the invisible cause of it until he stood in a world of intangible but murderous beings with no more body, no more weight, hardly any more reality than the theoretical electrons of the modern physicists. Yes, Mohler admired Loeffler, admired such deep fundamental science— but what of it? How did that help him to rid the American stockmen of their fear, what did all this have to do with the fighting of hunger? Here was one gigantic fact: American meat was threatened with the most contagious of any of the ills of beasts or men. Where was the fundamental to fight it?

There was only one thing to do: get it under the ground, get every last speck of it under the ground—but would that rid American stockmen of this terror? Mohler butchered; the Government and the states paid—nine million dollars they paid to cattle owners for allowing Mohler to ply his uncouth experiment. Farmers denounced him; whole states hated him; but he argued slaughter, talked slaughter, in barns, in smelly mass meetings where farmers had to dip their feet into tubs of disinfectant before they came into the hall—to keep any sly hellishness they might carry about with them from getting onto their neighbors' shoes. . . .

Who blamed these cow- and dairymen for their anger, their despair? At a scientific conference in Chicago in 1915 arose Farmer Smith. "Here's a fellow with a herd of fifty nice fourteen hundred-pound steers that would have liked to have gone to market that day. Four miles away the foot-and-mouth breaks out in a dairy herd. Quarantine! They held those steers for three weeks—then one of 'em showed it. They drove the other forty-nine into a trench, shot them down, put lime over 'em. . . . That's the kind of hard luck farmers have. . . ."

But there were sensible men too—who helped Mohler build his crude science. Davidson from West Virginia gets up. "I'm a farmer," says he. "Foot-and-mouth disease raises the hair on a man's head, if he is in the cattle business, every time you speak of it. It's the greatest menace—we should not have any haggling. We've got to get the country clear of it at any cost. . . ."

Who would blame Mohler for despairing of that—with confusion in the whole livestock industry, with fear, with bitterness among the Pennsylvania and Kentucky men, who will kill their cattle, against the stubborn Illinois men who won't? To defend the obstinate men of the Sucker State, T. Williams lumbers to his feet. "We have a couple of herds quarantined in Illinois. Has anybody heard of foot-and-mouth disease coming from one of those herds?"

Bayard of Pennsylvania jumps up: "I don't know anything about that. . . . But I do know that we in Pennsylvania are very much afraid of any territory that allows this disease to remain above ground. You can't expect to keep your diseased animals above ground and expect your stock to come into Pennsylvania." (Applause.)

For a moment, silence in this scientific conference, where the best hunger fighters in the land are met, only to find there's no science with which to fight the worst terror that's ever threatened American meat. Silence—broken by an unscientific man who halts and stutters, but manages to ask for the floor. He gets it. His name is Farmer Brown, he's from heaven only knows where, he's now forgotten. In a little sentence, that's got no grammar, that contradicts itself, that doesn't mean anything at all, this Brown drawls out the one fundamental:

"It is impossible to have foot-and-mouth disease unless there is foot-and-mouth disease!"

Farmer Brown has stated Mohler's whole science, and he's resurrected the old war-cry of Louis Pasteur, that's been buried and forgotten for forty years among the refinements of modern bacteriology. It's really not science, but faith. It was Pasteur's religion. It was Pasteur who shouted on every possible occasion—on the evidence of certain experiments with brews of meat broth and stews of hay—that there's no such thing as the spontaneous generation of life. All life must come from life, and pestilence cannot arise by itself out of nothing. Here is the one stark fundamental truth—if it's true! The only way to fight this foot-and-mouth plague is to kill every last critter that has it—or that's even been near it. . . . Farmer Brown fades out of the picture. The meeting goes to its various homes. Mohler plugs and slugs for two years—and the foot-and-mouth fades away, disappears, somehow. For nine years John Mohler has a breathing spell, gets ready for his final test with a terrible thoroughness on the vast scale of canal-building engineers with whom he has so much in common. . . . It is impossible to have foot-and-mouth disease unless there is foot-and-mouth disease. . . .

How different are Mohler and Loeffler, after all—though

they look somewhat alike, both having bald-domed heads surmounting Teutonic faces that are pleasantly open and round. But Loeffler has scientist's eyes that flash and dream behind professor's spectacles, and in spite of those cavalry-man's mustaches his one proper battlefield is the bench of his laboratory. Mohler has a close-cropped mustache respectably turned downward, and in further contrast he has the cold eye—very light gray—of a man who's more at home in mountains, of a man who has the nerve to try to bore great holes through hills.

V.

ON the 10th of December, 1923, a funny lameness is noticed among six hundred pigs, owned by Mr. Winslow of Vallejo. They've been excellent creatures. They are fat. They've been fed on what was left of the food from the Mare Island Navy Yard in San Francisco Bay. Ships tie up there, and among the remnants of the food from those ships is meat that's been taken aboard in Manila, in Hong-Kong, in towns on the Straits of Malacca, and in harbors of the unprofitable isles of the sea. Mr. Winslow's pigs have eaten bits of this meat from the Orient, now they're lame, now their hooves begin to drop off, finally here are dozens of these pathetic beasts—walking on their knees!

Just after New Year of 1924, shipments of these pigs—among them a few of those broken-down unhappy ones—were made to a packing company in West Berkeley. On the 16th of February the excellent horse doctor, Hogarty, of Oakland, whose sharp eye and good sense should not be forgotten, saw a small herd of six cows who were drooling at the mouth and smacking their lips—it was certainly suspicious. On the 18th several out of three hundred and fifty fine cattle, twenty-five miles away from Oakland at Hayward, were certainly off their feed. Early the next morning the Chief of the Bureau of Animal Industry of the State of

California wires the Big Chief, John Mohler—at Washington. In an hour a wire comes back: INJECT HOGS CALVES SHEEP GUINEA-PIGS AND HORSES FOR TEST. On the 23d of February these tests have given a sure yes to the suspicion of peril and that morning Mohler acts. "Veterinarians and other employees were directed to proceed to Oakland . . . by a plan worked out in advance many men were en route on transcontinental trains before the close of that day," he writes. By a plan worked out in advance—those words smack of war, and here is war, there's no doubt. Here is the foot-and-mouth danger, not smoldering in the civilized Midwest where there's a good chance to spot it and scotch it. Here it is, aflame on the edge of the limitless American ranges, within two looks and a holler of the wilds of the High Sierras—if it gets loose into the stray cattle of those impenetrable hills, who'll ever get it under the ground?

Mohler acts. Heavy ditching machinery begins to clank and rumble over the roads, hard roads, newly paved roads. There's a law no ditching or other heavy machinery may travel by these roads, and the sheriffs, imposing with stars and formidable with guns, come out to stop this disobedience. The ditching machines pay no attention, bang and clank along like so many tanks in the war. Here is a ranch. That morning, inspectors—fantastic scientists on horseback —have sat looking at a long line of cows, driven past them in single file. Wait—here are two that limp. Yes, and there's one that's slobbering and with its mouth red and white with blisters. Only three out of two hundred maybe. The ditching machine stops, and on that farm—miraculously—a cavern opens, eighteen feet wide, nine feet deep, five hundred feet long.

And here come Mohler's laboratory workers, rolling into the ranch yard in a fleet of Fords, twenty-four good men and strong, armed with a delicate apparatus of science, consisting of manure forks, scrapers, brooms, crow bars, axes, and milk cans. Out of the trucks they drag other instruments of precision, a tangle of pipe-wrenches, one hundred feet of hose, shovels, hoes, rakes, picks, wrecking bars, hatchets, pails, and spray guns. They don their laboratory uniforms—overalls and rubber boots. They bring out their chemical reagents—chloride of lime, cresol and formalin.

Into that five-hundred-foot long ditch goes the fine herd of steers, cows, calves and bulls—only three of them sick. Down they go, struggling, mooing, bellowing, and protesting, and above them there kneels a grotesque row of scientific investigators. The 25-20 rifles are loaded from the piles of clips, they're cocked, they're aimed. The air is split by a not very loud, but harsh, dry, crack-crack-crack-crack-crack. In ten minutes that ditch is a shambles. In a half hour it's a grave for every last one of that magnificent herd of hundreds of cattle. Now rough anatomists, armed with knives, jump down into this ditch, and go at their devilish work of slash, slash, slashing the hides of the carcasses of grade cows, of proud pure-bred bulls, of pretty calves that yesterday were the pets of the stockman's children. Yes—this ranchman is honest—but there's just a chance that some ghoul might dig up this grave at night and try to salvage the hides of his cattle, and who would blame the rancher if he did it himself? Into the gashes in this terrible heap of bodies the chemists pour gallons of quick-lime—there's no fooling with this foot-and-mouth virus, strongest and toughest of all invisible life.

Meanwhile 'round the barns and outhouses there goes on an epic scrubbing, a hectic raking, a stinking burning of piles of straw and manure and a gigantic dowsing with disinfectant. Then this little part of Mohler's experiment is done; the appraisers have settled with the ranch owner; the tears of his children—for their pet lamb—are dried. Here are some of those outdoor scientists loading their murderous tackle into the Fords; here are others standing, looking like Ku-Kluxers with their hoods off, absurd in long white rubber capes—under their capes 'round their bodies play the fumes of formaldehyde. There's no fooling with the tough sneaking virus of the foot-and-mouth. Every pinpoint speck of this life, whether it's on the hand of a horse-doctor or in the mouth of a champion dairy cow, or on the foot of some poor old bag of bones of a stray—means danger to the two hundreds of millions of cattle, goats, and swine of the American land.

By March 22d—it was hardly a month—John Mohler wrote: "The situation is under control." He'd done the impossible—for who excepting the mad prophet Pasteur would dare to say you could get every speck of the virus of any disease under the ground? Thousands of cattle had been shot, slashed, limed, buried. The last mangers and stanchions had been scrubbed with hot sal soda, and the last dogs, cats, and chickens had been killed—or more kindly dipped, to their great disgust, in cresol. Mohler's tired veterinarians had given their own bodies their last bath in corrosive sublimate. The situation was under control.

But on that very day a cattle-buyer, upright and innocent of any sinister intention, had gone up into the rough country in Merced, near the Yosemite, to buy some calves. . . .

In less than ten days after, the pestilence was racing through that rough hilly country, where the fences were poor, where many herds used the same salt licks; in less than ten days eight thousand cattle were hit a dreadful invisible blow by the virus. The game was up; what chance was there now ever to put the virus under ground? High California authorities threw up their hands, made long faces, wrote unctious reports that ended: "The fight was lost when the disease penetrated the domain of the wilderness."

But here is Mohler, riding the rough hills, through the brush, cold nights after dry hot days. His moustache is close-cropped and not fanciful like Loeffler's it is true; indeed, to look at him, it's hard to find anything fanciful, unless it may be that funny little wedge-shaped beard of his, that has its base under his lip and runs off into a point at the crack of his chin. But Mohler too has his fancies. There he rides, his cold eye looking off at inaccessible ranges from under his sombrero—infected strays have just been reported to have limped off into those hills. What are his thoughts? Can it be that he thinks of that entirely hair-brained prophecy of Louis Pasteur:

"It is in the power of man to make parasitic maladies disappear from the face of the globe, if the doctrine of spontaneous generation is wrong, as I am sure it is."

No, Mohler would never use fine words like that. He's probably thinking, like good Farmer Brown: "It is impossible to have foot-and-mouth disease unless there is foot-and-mouth disease." Or he's maybe not thinking at all— excepting to invent details, everlasting practical details. Authorities come to him, tell him:

"You can't get the disease under the ground here. The country's too rough and rocky for the ditching machines. You'll have to cut down whole forests to dig graves. The fight is lost."

Mohler gives a grunt, has never a scientific word to answer them with. He rides among his crack-lipped men, as they drive great herds into abandoned railway cuts, into little canyons—where man couldn't make ditches Mohler found ditches made by God. In these ditches thousands of cattle mill around—under that dry stuttering crack-crack —crack-crack-crack of the 25-20 rifles. Their volleys are magnified to the rolling fire of a regiment by the echoes that bound back from the lonely hills. . . . "Yes—but these beasts are not under the ground. . . . You haven't buried the sickness!"

Mohler grunts, cocks his ear for his answer. There's a dull, muffled, boom . . . boom . . . boom . . . Mohler's men are blasting in the sides of the cuts and the canyons to cover forever the bodies where the pestilence still might lurk. In two short weeks thousands of stricken cattle are shot, slashed and limed, along with more thousands of still healthy critters whose one fault it was to lick the same salt or drink from the same water holes with the sick ones. . . .

Mohler's experiment is like all real science: its theme is simple—but its details are endlessly complicated. Mohler has to turn his hand to every kind of trick. Here comes an inspector, with his face a foot long. "Chief, there's trouble from the ranchers in Madera County. . . . They're fixin' to drive their stock up into the hills whether you let 'em or no."

It was the driest spring in thirty years in eastern California. The herds lowed, looked up at the green shaded hills, nibbled pitifully at yellow red grass that was too short to nibble.

Mohler sucks at his battered pipe. "But the sickness has broken out in Madera County. We've got cases there. We can't risk letting 'em drive their stock up into the ranges. . . . There's too much of a chance of strays getting away from us up there. . . ."

Mohler rides to Madera, to reason with the ranchers whose poor cattle, still safe from the foot-and-mouth blisters—and death—are turning to bags-of-bones for want of grass. "It is of great importance at such times to spread a feeling of optimism," says Mohler. He shows the frantic ranchmen their duty to cattle-owners all over America, jollies them up. Such, too, is part of his science. And the cattle stay in the valley.

Not the least of his science is the spirit of the men whose beasts he's forced to murder. Part of his science is as simple, as terribly necessary as the back-firing of forest folk threatened by fire. Here is the little Pinole Valley, as dry as the devil—and in this valley a few cattle have been spied, limping, grinding their teeth. With an instinct to flee the drought, cows have busted the fences and made off to join the stock already up in the hills. What to do? What if diseased strays wander into neighboring valleys? Mohler back-

fires. His men ride up to the tops of the hills that border
the little Pinole, drive every last cow, bull, and steer out of
the woods down into the valley—and there kill them all.
. . . From the Pinole the pestilence never spreads.

Like Jack Dempsey, Mohler socks his enemy; like Ace
Hudkins, he sticks to his hopeless fight.

Mohler's is a dizzy science where he has to be everywhere
at once. While his war starts in the hills of Merced, just
before it started, indeed, a lame herd has been driven down a
certain road. "Nothing wrong with 'em!" says the local cow
surgeon, who is himself dreadfully wrong. "Stone-bruised,
that's all, from traveling over gravel." Next day, a second
herd of healthy beasts without ever a limp, two bulls and
fifty-seven cows, are driven *for just one-half mile down the
same road the lame herd traveled yesterday.* A half mile's
enough. It's all this fearful virus needs. The healthy herd
is loaded into cattle trains, bound for Los Angeles. A few
more days, and in three separate packing companies of that
city cattle refuse to eat, slobber, and grind their teeth. And
Mohler has to tear south back to civilization from out of
the wilderness. Here he has to argue, plead, and at last command Portuguese cow-owners who assert the foot-and-mouth
trouble is no worse than a bad cold. From the fatuous
Portuguese he takes their scrub cattle for massacre.

And from the owners of one of the very finest pure-bred
Holstein-Friesian dairy-herds in existence he takes every
last one of their cows too. Before the rifles of his rough
experimenters go these marvelous big-uddered black-and-
white beasts, along with them the celebrated Tilly Alcartra
—world's greatest long-time milk producer. Along with
them the champion, Tilly, dies. It is impossible to have foot-
and-mouth disease unless there is foot-and-mouth disease!

A MAN FOR FUNDAMENTALS

VI.

BY mid-July Mohler's experiment, once more, is over. Hundreds of thousands of cattle are dead, and Mohler and his men, scrambling through the brambles of the hills of even the wild Tuolumne County, looking for the plague with high-powered rifles—find never a case of it. The situation is under control. The red-mouth invisible assassins are under the ground. Not a single case has been reported outside of California—but of course that's not entirely thanks to Mohler's science, for who has forgotten the drastic quarantines and idiotic embargoes put up by the frightened stockmen of surrounding states? Here are thirty-six states, embargoing not only against all livestock from plagued California, but forbidding that state to send them baby chicks, hides and skins, straw, fruits and vegetables. Canned goods, pets, dogs and even bees are forbidden to enter—though how the devil could a bee carry this sickness? Here's a train, loaded with cement and railroad ties, turned back at the point of guns, because its cargo has not been disinfected. Here's a shipment of clay pigeons that Nevada refuses—clay pigeons that have been made in New York, shipped to California, never opened, but re-shipped to Nevada. They're only black and yellow discs for sportsmen to shoot at, but they bear the name "pigeon"—and that's menace enough.

Innocent tourists are turned back, threatened by indignant posses armed with rifles. . . .

On the 12th of July, 1924, a cattleman—name unknown—is riding the Niagra Range in the Stanislaus National Forest, high in the Sierras. He is not a searcher, nothing of scientist, has no veterinarian's degree or titles, is not in the pay of John Mohler. He comes across a dead deer. He gets down off his horse, this unknown man with skin leathered by the weather and eyes wrinkled into slits by the sun. Of course it's nothing new to run across a deer's carcass—here's

125

an old deer maybe, that's died a natural death, or a deer shot by a hunter who afterwards couldn't find him. Mr. Cattleman squints at this deer, pokes at him, then looks into his mouth, and fusses with his feet. Persistently he examines this dead beast stumbled on by chance. At last he pulls out his knife, cuts off the head and the hooves of the forlorn beast, slings them over his horse.

That evening he rides into the camp of John Mohler, where the tired hunger fighter sits, smoking his pipe, along with his fellow fighters, Snyder and Houck. How good to loaf—with the fight won, the work done. . . . Ready to leave, in a few days they'll be back in Washington.

Off his horse come Mr. Cattleman's specimens. "This Doc Mohler? Well, Doc, I b'lieve this critter died of the foot-and-mouth disease. . . ."

Mohler, Snyder, Houck—they all jump up, they all crowd 'round, paw at this booty—there are excited glints in their eyes. That night they sleep, troubled. By the good light of the next morning they absolutely confirm the stockman's hunch. Now the fight is really lost. Now the trouble has really "penetrated to the domain of the wilderness." Now the abominable virus has slipped away into the wild deer to live there forever—a perpetual threat to all the livestock of America. Mohler pulls at his pipe again, thinks of his silly triumphs, his fruitless butcheries, talks to his pals of what this means to American meat. If the foot-and-mouth fastens itself on America as it already has on all of Europe—it means better than a hundred million dollars a year lost to American cattlemen. It means failure for thousands, hunger for some. But Mohler is never dramatic, is always laconic, and of this dreadful morning he only writes:

"This was the most serious situation that ever confronted the United States in foot-and-mouth disease."

Mohler tightens his belt, rides down out of the wilds, wires a petition to examine—and if need be, exterminate—the deer of the Stanislaus National Forest. "And of such other regions as may be necessary." Where's Mohler's wisdom? Where's his sense of humor? His knowledge of American hunters? The news leaks out, the hunters in the California towns and valleys hold meetings, bellow, make indignant speeches—and who can criticize them for it? Here their lovely deer are threatened with massacre—deer it's their God-given right, as hunters, to kill by themselves. Mobs of he-men are actually formed in Sonora, to march into the mountains to drive out the Government searchers, and certain high Authorities of California are on the side of the hunters, properly convinced that Mohler is a maniac, a visionary to think still of driving the plague under ground.

It is Mohler's last stand, and when this strange fighter is dead and gone, let us hope he'll leave memoirs—to tell the secret by what cajolings, by what fantastic diplomacy he won his point. All that can be here recorded is Mohler's permission, granted by the State Fish and Game Commission, to "study the drift and wandering habits of the deer, to decide on proper, efficient, and humane methods of taking specimens, and to ascertain the extent of the disease on the Niagra Range."

Then started Mohler's last obscure science. There go Mohler's men, putting strychnine into the insides of apples to tempt the sad-eyed wild creatures, mixing strychnine with the salt of the salt-logs. "It was no go," said Mohler with a low chuckle. "The bait was no good."

"We'll have to shoot them," says Mohler.

"But that will scatter 'em—and we'll never get all the sick ones!" objects a practical man.

"Well—we'll get rifles with silencers," answers John Mohler.

For one year goes on this strangest of all researches. Twenty-two thousand deer, in that year, meet death that speeds at them from the whispering guns. Two thousand are found infected with the virus of the blisters and the limping feet. But it's three years now since a single diseased deer

127

has been discovered, nor has one solitary cow or calf or bull or steer come down sick from grazing the ranges, licking the salt, or drinking the water of the wild lands into which the terror escaped in the summer of 1924.

By sticking to one fundamental Mohler has brought about the impossible. Now there's not a speck, not an atom, of the living poison above ground in the American land—from the face of our land he has made the foot-and-mouth virus disappear, completely. For one ill he's proved Pasteur and Farmer Brown were right. It's impossible to have foot-and-mouth disease unless there is foot-and-mouth disease. . . . But at what cost—by what murder?

There Mohler has you. He's an American, first and last, a man to figure costs in dollars—not in grief of a cattleman at the loss of his herd, nor in fury of hunters at the loss of their prey. Mohler writes: "Losses under . . . quarantine, slaughter and disinfection, including indemnities, operating, and all other expenses, have not been so great in suppressing all the outbreaks in this country in the last forty years as they would be in one year if the disease became established here."

But that doesn't mean he's hard, or merely efficient. Without the slightest doubt his grand shambles of an experiment has brought the greatest good to the greatest number —and that's at the bottom of all hunger fighting. Mohler sits at his desk now, trying—maybe in vain—to wipe out other threats to American meat by the use of his fundamental. He sits waiting to pounce on the foot-and-mouth terror, waiting like a fireman. . . . And he's always ready to tell of the men who *did* his experiment. Through the land from coast to coast they toil, at a hundred different humble jobs of guarding American meat. Unknown they are, though they've sweat in rubber suits from dawn to dark, week after week, month after month—and that counts in Sundays. Each evening they've had to breathe the poisonous fumes of formaldehyde, to rid themselves of the invisible terror not

dangerous to themselves—but a death they might carry
to some far-off cattle. Their hands are horrid to look at—
cracked into open sores by the eternal chloride of lime. On
improvised beds or no beds at all they've had their rest.
Their energy they've kept up on strange food and not
enough food. They've not fought and killed among hoorahs,
like soldiers—their bloody work they've done to the tune of
ranchmen's tirades and in spite of children's tears. And
when they've won, at last, there's no medal, not even a
parade—and most certainly no bonus.

In such words as this, John Mohler, scarcely better known
himself, remembers his unknown fellow fighters of hunger.

Most forgotten of all is that cattleman—observer of
nature—who first spied the terror in the mouth of the dead
deer that afternoon in the Sierras.

FRANCIS

CHAPTER FIVE. THE AUTOMATIC MAN

FRANCIS

I.

SO FAR, you would say hunger fighting is an outdoor science. But here comes Edward Francis: his peculiar job has kept him for the better part of seven years in a little room with the windows closed, doors shut.

Unlike Carleton, who dreamed wheat under a Kansas sky as endless as all outdoors, Francis toiled with his hands in a dirty little den from six to six every day. And he can scarcely be said to have dreamed at all, as he hum-drummed at his work of making it safe for men to hunt rabbits.

How different from Angus Mackay, the kind of man who'd have felt stuffy after staying for as little as an hour, even in one of your modern palace laboratories. Mackay found his wheat, fought hunger by bending his head with reverence, out of doors, before the grandest facts of nature —only taking care to keep his eyes wide open. Francis, like a kind of free-thinking monk in his cell, bent his head over a microscope, glued his eye to a lens. His job was humble, having to do with a certain danger to housewives who cook for their hunter husbands.

Dorset turned his trick of saving meat to fight hunger on a grand scale, by feeling his way through a fog of wrong science, fixing in his head a couple of simple facts taught him by farmers, then sticking to pigs, never leaving the pig plague as he found it in nature. Now there's no denying that Edward Francis got a couple of most important hints from plain people. But animals? To discover this new disease— he gave it the musical name of Tularemia—he experimented with every kind of beast he could beg, buy, or borrow.

"Don't reason too much—work with your hands!" That was the motto of Francis. "Don't imagine anything—

133

Try everything!" He would bring these words out in jerky jets, squinting, throwing back his head, waving his arms—making strange twisting gestures with his whole body. And Lord—how he worked. Not only with the proper beasts—rabbits and men—did he toil. He was forever putting collars on guinea-pigs, dropping poison on the backs of white rats, sending to Pennsylvania for silver foxes, experimenting with dogs, coming down from dogs to mice. And he has been known—in his toying with death—to fuss for hours with the louse of a mouse, a being that makes up for its utter measliness by bearing the name of *Polyplax serratus.*

How different was Francis from Mohler. Like the notable mixture of butcher, warrior, and engineer that he was, Mohler threw away science, stuck to a single fundamental —maybe scientific—and stamped in the mountains on the worst terror that ever threatened American meat. Hidden away from dawn to dark in a cubicle, paper-littered and no bigger than a bathroom, Francis hoarded every scientific fact like a miser. And for what? Who can call his work epic? But at his modest job Francis tore like a completely inhuman automaton, piling up mountains of facts that were magnificently accurate, that might be fundamental or no —to him it seemed not to matter. But from this jumble and tangle of facts Francis wove a design of truth—very simple. But for this truth, farmers, marketmen, housewives, hunters, from coast to coast of the American land might have gone on losing months of work, some of them dying. Reported they'd have been by their puzzled doctors to have perished from flu, or typhoid, or gall-bladder sickness, or glanders. But Francis, by getting together that mass of fact, spotted this hunger—so unknown, so surprisingly dangerous. There's no one rule for the way men fight hunger.

II.

FOR twenty years before he began his adventures with this dangerous hunger for the meat of wild rabbits, Francis had been a good obscure worker in the boldest band of death fighters that America's ever had the chance to be proud of— but knows nothing about. For better than twenty years his headquarters had been a rambling red brick building on a hill overlooking a great curve of the Potomac in Washington. The basement of this building is a strange labyrinth of rabbit hutches, dog kennels, rat cages—its aroma is not for ladies. The upper floors are inhabited by men whose looks are as peaceful, as ordinarily American, as their jobs are fantastic, and perilous. Such is the Hygienic Laboratory of the United States Public Health Service. And to the Director, George McCoy — bespectacled, thin-faced, pompadour haired—came a letter in 1919, from Health Commissioner Beatty of Salt Lake City, Utah. Somewhat as follows:

"We have a new disease out here—the ranchers call it deer-fly fever. It's knocking out our farmers in the harvest season, it's keeping them from plowing their sugar-beets. Can somebody be sent out to clear this up for us?"

The men on the upper floors of that red brick building put their heads together, talked it all over—for it is one of the most extraordinary facts in these days when science has become somewhat military, that Director McCoy is a director who is too wise to direct.

Yes, Edward Francis would go, so Francis got his orders, and in late July he began packing up a curious assortment of baggage to take out to Utah—to some desert place that used to be called the Pahvant Valley. Where was this Pahvant Valley, anyway, on this largely blank space on the map that is Utah? For better than twenty years Edward Francis had been chased from pillar to post that way, trying to guard American health, trying to put together pieces of the puzzles of strange new deaths. For twenty years luck had

135

been against him. But here was a new job: and he was the kind of man who doesn't grow old, and gayly he packed up his baggage now, which consisted chiefly of thirty mice and thirty rabbits; then there were thirty white rats too, and his menagerie was completed by thirty round bouncing guinea-pigs. He stowed his circus forward in the baggage car, and himself hopped the Pullman behind—for Utah.

What were his thoughts as he rolled west—this man who had spent better than twenty years going on wild-goose chases? Was there such a thing as deer-fly fever? And if there was, what of it? From all he'd heard, it was a miser-able business of a few dozen farmers laid up with pains in their backs, swollen glands, grouching because they hadn't pep enough to go out to the field to cut their alfalfa. From the very time of his graduation from the one-building Miami Medical College in Cincinnati, Francis had tried, tried. He had fairly bootlegged his way into science. He'd become an interne in the General Hospital in Cincinnati —it was in the crude days when that entire hospital had but one little laboratory. The head doctor had had to lock the door of that sacred room to keep the youngsters from messing around, smashing apparatus, but Francis had crawled through the transom at night, worked night after night in secret. . . .

Into the Public Health Service, and stationed at Ellis Island, he'd begun his science by glancing at the ankle of a black man from Senegal or some such benighted African country. Here was a guinea-worm, coming out of that nig-ger's skin! Here was that darky, ingeniously rolling that worm up on a match, day after day, to remove him. The distinction of describing this guinea-worm had brought Francis into the red brick building on the hill over the Potomac, had brought him to twenty years of disappointed hope.

Francis, with his one hundred and twenty assorted ani-mals, rattled across Chicago from the dirty depot that swal-lows up trains coming in from the East to the still more or less clean station that belches them out toward the Far West. Going west, he was—toward what? Already fifty, the little hair he had left was gray. He had cleaned up yellow fever in the steamy pest-hole of Vera Cruz—but that was after Walter Reed and his devil-may-care bozos had made the great discovery. Once before he'd gone west, to the dangerous Bitter Root Valley, to try to find the cause of the Rocky Mountain Spotted Fever—that sickness from which five of the microbe hunters of the Public Health Service have died, while conquering its terror. But Francis had found nothing. To Savannah he'd gone—to try to get the red disease of pellagra, the death of the Southern poor folks, over into monkeys. Seventy-four monkeys and three baboons he'd injected, and found—nothing, only later to watch his pal in the Service, Goldberger the hawk-face, discover that pellagra was a hidden hunger. He had hurried down to the Isthmus of Tehuantepec in South Mexico to fight an epidemic of the Asiatic cholera—but when he got down there he found there was no cholera at all. He had worked, chasing will-o'-the-wisps. Past fifty, his eyes gleamed between the slits of their squinted lids.

In Salt Lake City, Commissioner Beatty told him: "The place they're having trouble with this deer-fly fever is around the town of Delta—about a hundred and fifty miles south of here."

That same day Francis shipped himself with his circus of animals and his very few changes of clothes to this Pahvant Valley, ancient home of Shoshonean red men, now the doubtful paradise of farmers, like the unfortunate fellow, R— S—, who this very day had left his field of alfalfa. This day of the coming of Francis, R— S— had felt a pain shoot from his head to his neck and from his neck down across his right shoulder. He'd crawled down off the seat of his mowing machine, said: "God, but the sun's hot. . . . I'm just too bushed to go on cutting this here hay. . . ." That night the good wife noticed a little sore on the right side of her man's neck. "Looks like maybe you've got the deer-fly fever," she muttered. "Hope not," said the breadwinner. "Got to get in that alfalfa." But the throbbing in his head and neck wouldn't let him sleep, and he tossed. "Feels like I was burning up," he said to his mate, and he shivered. Next morning there was no clatter of the mower.

The very proficient gray-haired country doctor, H. L. Charles, met Francis at Delta depot. "You can store your animals in my garage. There may be some room to work there, too," said Charles.

"Fine!" said Francis, who has an enthusiastic way of saying fine about things whether they're fine or no. To Charles' garage Francis carted his beasts, to find there wasn't quite so much room as he'd hoped, since the garage also did service as a coal shed. "Now show me a case of this deer-fly fever," begged Francis.

An hour later, with Charles who was friend, father-confessor, and sometimes when luck was with him, the healer of those dusty ranchers, Francis was bending over the alfalfa farmer, R— S—. With the good wife and the rest of the family Charles and Francis had held solemn discussion. . . . "Yes, if it's to learn about it, all right, go ahead," the wife—so worried—had told them. And now here lay the husband, tossing, twisting his bed-clothes about him, muttering—holding his arm that showed a tiny red gash at the crook of the elbow. It really hadn't hurt him at all, Francis told the folks, as he shot the dark blood from the arm vein of R— S—, out of his syringe into a clean tube.

Their Ford bumped them back to Delta.

There was nothing heartless about Francis, you understand, but, knowing he was no healer, he knew he could do nothing for that miserable farmer; and he knew that Charles, though a healer, could do nothing in spite of his art. "But that's a case of the deer-fly fever, no doubt of it," said Charles. "Did you see that sore on his neck, and those swollen glands, just below? Well—that's the stuff."

For Francis this was great luck: in the whole Pahvant Valley there was no report of another case of it, and since the poor fellow had the honor to be the single living experimental animal in the known world suffering from deer-fly fever, Francis was enthusiastic. To him, at this moment, the rancher was simply a very valuable part of his hunt. In the doctor's backyard the searcher got out of the Ford, carried that tube of dark blood into his garage-coal-shed laboratory.

It was a Chinaman's chance Francis had to find out anything. For how few of the ills of humans have any effect on guinea-pigs or rabbits or any rodents for that matter? That hot day dragged on into the next one; there were no more cases of deer-fly fever. There seemed nothing to do for poor R— S—, who grew more tired, more tired. Fifty times each day Francis took himself out of Doctor Charles' office, bent his wiry body over a certain two guinea-pigs, a certain two rabbits out there in the coal-shed. The third day came, and was a dreadful bore, and went the way of the second—nothing to do but watch those cursed four animals with the little drop of the blood of R— S— under their skins. Would anything happen? Nothing marvelous had happened, so far, in this searcher's life. Ho hum. . . .

On the fifth day those beasts were dead.

With the easy skill of an old fencer, with a flashing narrow blade that was his little rapier, Francis was at the first guinea-pig. A strong odor of lysol, a splash and a daub of lysol-soaked cotton, a gleam of the scalpel—and the narrowed eyes of the veteran were gazing into the internal mysteries of that guinea-pig. What in the blood of the delirious R— S— had doomed these beasts? Had he something new at last?

But this couldn't be plague! This could never be the bubonic plague these guinea-pigs had—surely not the black death? If Francis hadn't been dabbling with something maybe dangerous he'd have rubbed his eyes—and maybe he did, who knows? Here was the liver of this guinea-pig —normally it should have been the deep red of a well-behaved liver. But here it was dotted all over with little white spots. And here was its spleen, that absurd organ nobody knows the use of, that's usually small, almost hidden away—here was the spleen, enormously swollen and grotesquely peppered with whitish specks. An old hand at handling animals dead of the black death—that most terrible and swift of deaths—Francis, looking at the insides of his beasts, couldn't be sure they hadn't died of it. But he handled his knives with extra care now, washed his hands extra hard, was mighty careful not to let his hand slip—

But it couldn't be bubonic plague. Francis called Charles into the coal-shed and together, excited, they reasoned their riddle up and down and backward and forward. There was no bubonic plague within a thousand miles of this place— no nearer than those ground squirrels in the California wilds. . . . And the sickness of R— S— was nothing like plague. No, of course it couldn't be. . . . But it looked devilishly like it. . . . No, impossible. These beasts had gotten the blood of R— S— under their hides, nothing else. Here was a new disease. . . .

That day a telegram went to Washington to the red brick building on the hill above the Potomac: PLEASE SEND ALL AVAILABLE LITERATURE ON PLAGUE-LIKE DISEASES OF RODENTS. Signed: Francis. Charles was excited now, and like to forget his own practice. "Must keep this thing going in my animals. Got to keep it alive!" Francis kept telling Charles. And together they rubbed up bits of those white-spotted, sick livers in water that was slightly salt, strained this dangerous brew through clean gauze cloth, pumped this death under the skins of healthy guinea-pigs. The days raced now, instead of crawling. And each day they went out to see this enormously important R— S—, who, alas, was making heavy weather of it. From the abscess that the little sore under his ear had grown into, they drew dangerous stuff to shoot into yet other animals. Oh—he was on the trail now. . . .

On the 18th of August R— S— closed his eyes—that from the first day had been so tired, too tired to hold open —for the last time. And the wife told urgent, imploring Francis: "Yes, if it's to find out about it, you may go ahead." Charles and Francis might go in with the undertaker—"provided they took nothing away. . . ." Trust Francis; he got his peep—and more—into the body of the dead rancher. There was the swollen spleen. There were the same strange white spots—no different from the spots on the spleens of the beasts who had perished from the sick man's blood.

III.

FIVE days later Francis felt a little chilly, shivered though the day was hot. His legs didn't seem to be able to make him go where he wanted to, and he was so tired, and cold, and then hot. Doctor Charles looked him over. Nothing to find—only fever: one hundred and two and two-tenths. "Oh, I'll be on my legs tomorrow," said Francis. He *had* to be all right, because in the coal-shed great things were astir. Rabbit after rabbit, guinea-pig after guinea-pig, sickened and died, five days to the dot after a dose of the sickness of their dying brothers—it was like clock-work, no less. He dragged himself into the backyard, could just lift his arm to pin his victims on to the battered dissecting boards pitted with nail holes. . . . He went back to bed.

The next morning he was distinctly not all right. Once more, expert examination by Charles. "Might have been appendix," said Francis, long after. "Would have trusted that man Charles to go into my insides any time. He was a corker, that fellow." Their work made them friends.

141

And now came the scientific bulletins from McCoy, from Washington, from the red brick house on the hill—here were certain thin pamphlets, very dryly written, dreadfully uninteresting, on "plague-like diseases of rodents." That was what Francis had wired for. Now—oh, dammit, how his head ached—he tried to read them.

By George—here it was, this sickness that was so hard to tell, in guinea-pigs, from the bubonic plague! And George McCoy, his friend, his director—who never directed —had discovered it, though not in human beings at all, but in ground squirrels out in California, when he was at his pernickety, very nasty job of working at the bubonic plague that sneaked from Chinatown into the squirrels of that state. Francis' eyes did funny things, the lines of the close-written pages ran together, he was so tired. He read on. Yes, and McCoy had discovered a germ too, clearly different from the microbe of the black death, but very murderous for ground-squirrels. Well, what of it—so long as it wasn't harmful to people. . . . Only a squirrel germ, after all, a mere curiosity. Might stick it in a microbe museum. Oh—if his back weren't only so tired. . . . The name of this germ of the plague-like disease of rodents? It had a nice name: McCoy had called it *Bacillus tularense*, because it came from the ground squirrels of Tulare County, California.

"Must keep this stuff going in my animals. Got to keep it alive!" said Francis. And with Charles trying to hold him back, he got out of bed, and took the long, long journey of a hundred feet to the coal-shed.

"Don't see what's wrong with you," said Charles to Francis.

"Look here," said Francis, "here's something interesting! I believe R— S— may have died from this tularense germ after all, even if McCoy did think it was only a ground-squirrel microbe. Here's a report from Wherry, in Cincinnati. . . ." Sure enough, Wherry, that microbe hunter who would be much more famous if he weren't so completely modest, had fished this squirrel-murdering tularense microbe out of a sick meat-cutter, and a colored cook—out of very badly inflamed eyes they'd complained of. "That shows it'll hit humans too!" said Francis, who forgot his tiredness for a second or so.

"You stay quiet, rest in bed," commanded Charles.

"But I've got to get this stuff back in live animals to Washington. . . . I mustn't lose it. I can't lose it!" shouted Francis. Was he delirious? Probably not. But it is entirely probable that Francis himself will never be able to tell how he got through the next week. Charles be damned! He must keep this stuff going in animals . . . get it back to Washington alive.

He gets himself to his feet long enough to inject four more animals, drops them into cages ready to be shipped, packs up his knives, his instruments, his microscope. In a daze he sees his precious beasts stowed forward, mumbles to the porter to see he gets off at Salt Lake City, changes for the through train east at Salt Lake City, mumbles to this porter to make up his berth, jolts hot dusty days through a thousand-mile blur of successive cattle states, wheat states, corn states. . . . "One thing I do know," said Francis, and he laughed, "I didn't care whether I ever got up again or not."

Into the station, still more or less clean, that swallows up trains rolling into Chicago from the Far West, came Francis. Chicago—change trains for Washington!

"Must keep this deer-fly fever alive in my animals," mumbled Francis, and found himself clattering in a taxi-cab, animals and all, across Chicago—not toward a train for Washington but to the Marine Hospital. Four days ago his guinea-pigs had been infected and that meant they had hardly a day more to live, so clocklike was this death. "Must get it to Washington alive!" muttered Francis and the doctors of the hospital didn't know what to make of this fantastic sick man so eager to keep the flame of sickness alive in his silly animals. The water in the instrument baths boils and Francis totters before the roaring gas flames and lifts out the freshly sterilized syringes and gropes among his beasts and shoots death under the hides of new healthy beasts—in a dream, a nightmare, a blur.

Washington, and here is the searcher, safe home with his booty. The men of the upper floors of the red brick building on the hill crowd around him. "What's wrong? You look like the ghost of yourself!" some one tells him.

"Here are some guineas 'n' some rabbits. . . . Got the virus of that deer-fly fever in 'em . . . will be dead in four days from now—sure." Oh—it was great to sit down, just to sit down for a minute, not to have to think of getting up at all.

"When they die, their livers and spleens look like the bubonic plague . . . funny." Then he turned to Director McCoy: "But I believe they've got the same infection you found in the ground squirrels out in California back in 1911. . . . Bet you'll find your tularense bug in 'em."

Then they took Francis to the hospital, and it was better than two months before he could come back up that hill to work, and it was more than a year before he stopped being tired. "I'd feel okay in the morning, rarin' to go," said Francis. "Start working—and by Jingo, by noon—boy! Was ready to be carried home on a stretcher." The best doctors and diagnosticians in that hospital could make nothing at all of this mysterious tiredness. They looked over their eyeglasses, and said: "Very probably you have malaria. . . ."

IV.

WHILE Francis lay in the hospital not caring whether he saw another guinea-pig, McCoy worked over this ill that his man had so nearly not brought home in those animals. McCoy—who is tall and wears plain spectacles, is thin-faced and might be taken for a superintendent of schools in a Midwest town—had the extreme pleasure of finding that his tularense microbe was no mere murderer of squirrels. Here it was, sure enough, in the blood and the liver and lights of these poor beasts who had come home from Utah, who had inherited the death of the late alfalfa farmer, R— S—. McCoy's face is school-masterish, severe, and surprises you by breaking into a most benevolent smile. Here was his own pet microbe that he'd thought was no more than a curiosity! Strange little finicky germ it was, looking sometimes like a wee stick, but so short that when you adjusted your lens just so, you'd take it for a mere point, a microscopic ball. This tularense bug had an appetite like a spoiled child, refusing to grow on anything—outside of animals—excepting the yolks of eggs. . . . But how it did relish guinea-pigs, rabbits!

Now Francis was better, and you'd think he'd have called this little job of his finished, called it a day, tackled something else. He'd proved the tularense germ was at the bottom of this deer-fly fever—all right, at last after twenty years he'd found something new. But what of it? What did this deer-fly fever amount to anyway? What was the use of plugging any longer at this absurd little plague of the obscure Pahvant Valley—only one rancher out there had died from it in 1919. Only one fellow, so far as he knew, had even had the disease. Why do any more, why go on with it?

"Of course, the deer-flies out there must get this bug of yours out of ground squirrels," said Francis to George McCoy. "That is, if it's the deer-flies that really give it to the farmers. We've got only *their* word for that."

So Francis and McCoy turned over their precious sickness to their friend, Gregory Lake, whose job among other things it now was to keep the death going from guinea-pig to guinea-pig every five days—what could be more simple? And in May of 1920, just before the deer-fly season, Edward Francis was off for Utah again, not quite so tired. Here he is in the Pahvant Valley once more, waving his hands with his eternal enthusiasm, making his plans with that strange, unimaginative coldness that gives the lie to his enthusiasm. Here he is in that dry desert partly reclaimed by men, with four assistants this time. They are helpers it would be disrespectful to science to call scientists.

Do deer-flies really give ranchers this fever? Do they get it from ground squirrels? On the morning of the 28th of May, 1920, he starts out from Delta in a desert-going Ford of a forgotten vintage, a Ford grotesque with a big milk-can lashed to one running board. In this Ford sits Francis, with four double-barreled shotguns, in the hands of Messrs. Jones, Kreiss, Smith, and Roderick Heydenfeldt—who are crack-shot squirrel shooters from California. They rattle out into the greasewood in a cloud of lip-cracking dust, grate to a stop, get ready their artillery, and begin advancing in a line of skirmishers through the thickets of those tough little trees. There is an intermittent popping and booming and banging—and a dying of unfortunate ground squirrels. In the road by the Ford kneels Francis, in the glare of the sunlight under a pale blue sky, slitting and slashing the dead squirrels his hunters bring him. . . .

But they've never a sign of the deer-fly fever. There's never a speck or a spot on their livers. . . .

Now though this searcher was a man who cooped himself up in a two-by-four room for years, there's no doubt that he knew exactly the right time to do his science outdoors. If he'd been like the hundreds of luxurious hunters who search microbes—in vain—today, he'd have put himself up in Delta, comfortable in Dr. Charles's coal-shed, and let Foreman Jones and his three trusty shooters bring him the squirrels. Then he'd have sat in the shade and cut up his booty at his sweet leisure, found nothing, gone back to Washington, reported: "Funny—but the deer-fly fever isn't

146

in Utah squirrels." But here he was, in the hot dust, sniffing about, peering under greasewood, looking foolishly for any chance strange thing. He tramped around after his hunters, wool-gathering absently as Carleton himself might have done, looking at everything as Mackay would have done—just for the sake of looking.

On the first day of June his eye lit on a jack-rabbit, just dead, not shot, but dead naturally. Naturally? Why didn't Francis pass him by? He himself couldn't tell you, he himself felt no hunch, had no premonition that comes to men called geniuses. Rip . . . slash—went his squirrel knife. Wide open to the hot light he pulled this forlorn jack's carcass. . . . Just back and to the left of this dead creature's stomach lay a big spleen, a swollen spleen, a tremendously tell-tale spleen . . . dotted with those fatal white spots.

"Shoot jacks from now on," Francis ordered Jones, Smith, Kreiss—his pals pronounced it "Chris"—and Roderick Heydenfeldt. Believe me they shot them. Ground squirrels? Hell! They're not to be compared with the sport of popping off a bounding jack as he sails twenty-five feet at a jump over sage-brush, through greasewood. From Sugarville in the Northwest over sixty miles to Filmore in the Southeast the four musketeers shot jacks for their boss to cut up and peer into. In twenty days five hundred and fifty-six jack-rabbits were shot running by Jones the economical Scot, by the sawed-off Smith, by the round-faced roughneck, Kreiss, and their good pal Roderick Heydenfeldt. In the cool evenings while Francis pawed over suspicious-looking spleens and livers, the hunters wrangled, Jones the thrifty Scot maintaining it was best to count your shells and not shoot 'til you were sure, Kreiss shouting back that it's best to shoot all over the place, get as many jacks as possible and to the devil with how many shells you use. While his roughnecks quarreled about who shot how many jacks, Francis toiled—rubbing bits of white-dotted spleen on to the shaved skin of the bellies of live, healthy guinea-pigs.

Twenty-three of these beasts were martyrs to that same deadly ill of the year before. As if time-fuses connected to noiseless bombs had been mysteriously put into them, in five days they died. "So it's in rabbits this fever lives, in nature," pondered Francis scratching his chin, throwing back his head, squinting his eyes. And, sure enough, in those very places near the village of Holden, where most of the *sick* jacks had been shot, or found dead—there on the

farms the tired sickness began showing itself among the folks. In the blood of two ranchers, a rancher's wife, and a little girl, aged nine, Francis found the finicky microbe *tularense* of George McCoy.

Well—now to get deer-flies. The ranchers *knew* it was that fly bite that gave them the sickness. Francis asked: "Is it?" He was never a man to imagine anything.

Also, he was no bug or fly expert, claimed to know nothing about the secret tricks and habits of deer-flies, and the Public Health Service had sent him the distinguished and first-class bug-hunter, Doctor Mayne. "Get me some deer-flies," begged Francis. Together they set out for the shores of Blue Lake, an absurd drop of water in the dryness of that dusty land. In the reeds near the shore those black and yellow varmints were supposed to live, buzz, and plot attacks upon ranchers. With them Francis and Mayne took a poor old mare for a kind of a decoy, and getting to the lake, they hitched this mare to a post, and sat down to wait for a swarm of flies to come make a real meal off her. They waited. None lit. They kept on waiting. Not a fly bit that mare—it was disgusting. What to do? Francis had no notion, and you can imagine him turning to Mayne, who was a qualified bug expert, a man who had received his degree of Doctor of Philosophy for knowing so much about bugs —but alas! No matter what you may have learned in books and laboratories about the looks of bugs, about what goes on inside them, about the deepest chemical composition of them—you still might not know how to catch them. . . .

The old mare stood peaceful. Not a fly lit. Then presently a raggedy boy came riding by, bareback on a horse, a settler's son with bare feet and out at the elbows. "Hey, there, son!" yelled Francis. "We're after some live deerflies. How do we get 'em?"

"Easy," said the lad, who switched his pony, loped off through the greasewood, came back with a whole flock of the varmints fastened to his horse's back. He looked at the happy flyless old mare. Then at Francis, and the expert Mayne: "Y' see, they won't bite unless your horse is movin'."

Back to Delta they came with the ice cream freezer strapped to the side of their Ford abuzz with deer-flies. The Government has built Francis an excellent shack, much like Dorset's on the banks of the Skunk, and peeping in there, you see these searchers at a most curious toil. They're holding a lantern globe on the shaved back of a sick rabbit, and inside the globe a fly buzzes, then settles down, bites, sucks blood—before the beast is satisfied they lift the globe off and put it down on to the shaved hide of a healthy rabbit. . . . All day long they stick at this strange job, and

Mayne is to be pitied, working with such an automatic man for work as is Francis. By night twenty flies in twenty globes have bitten back and forth between sick and healthy rabbits three hundred and forty-eight times. . . .

Five days later the healthy beast died. The ranchers were right.

Then Mayne got tired, oh, very tired. No—not a fly had bit him, but he had been fussing around helping Francis make autopsies on sick rabbits—but what of that? He was shivery, and then hot, and felt chilly, and always so abominably bushed he couldn't seem to put one foot ahead of the other. Presently, though it was only seven days after he'd started to work, he became too all in to do anything at all, and took sick leave. . . .

Now this may sound like heresy, but one of the grand points about Edward Francis was that he had no head for putting two and two together. Before he'd set down any kind of a theory on paper he'd be shot. Before he'd even daydream or mull over some bright notion—well, before he'd permit himself such indulgence he'd go back to working with his hands. "Work with your hands! Try everything!" he would always insist. He forgot about Mayne, long ago he'd forgot about his own terrible tiredness: he was too busy getting just one solitary deer-fly to carry death to a healthy rabbit from a sick one by just one bite. The ranchers said it was deer-fly fever. It was.

v.

"WHERE's Lake?" asked Francis, when he got back that fall to the red brick laboratory on the hill in Washington. Lake ought to be about; wasn't it Lake that had the most important job in the whole world—to keep the sickness going, to keep those tularense microbes multiplying to their own delight and to the death of guinea-pig after guinea-pig after guinea-pig? Where was Doctor Lake? Doctor Lake was sick, was laid up with fever, and very tired, in the Naval Hospital next door. He'd been keeping the disease going in those beasts, every five days slitting open a dead guinea-pig, taking out a bit of white-spotted spleen or liver, grinding it up in a mortar, straining it through cloth, shooting a few drops of this stuff into a new guinea-pig. But on the evening of October 23, 1920, he went dizzy, just did manage to drag himself home, got under a big pile of blankets, and was glad to stay there.

The chief medical Rear Admiral of the Navy had looked professionally at poor Lake, given it as his measured opinion that "Doctor Lake has typhoid fever!" Though the tests said no. . . . But what else could Lake have?

Well—why not write up this work now? You'd think Francis would have been satisfied, called it a day, now that he was sure this unimportant little Utah sickness was carried to ranchers by deer-flies, was caused by *Bacillus tularense*, was sucked by deer-flies out of the blood of sick jackrabbits. Here were three good facts, but what more was there to do? After all, in an efficient land like our own, too much Government money and brains should not be wasted on an ill that sickens six ranchers or so in a year—that kills still less of them. But Francis? For some obscure reason that was utterly unreasonable, nothing in the world could have stopped him. Set going on this work—it was no longer a puzzle—he kept at it like some inhuman automaton. Now began his strange years in his funny coop of a laboratory, years in a fog of the smoke of not too good cigars, years without air, years without thought of friendship, or play. . . . "I went over to the hospital next door to see Lake," said Francis. "Never questioned whether or no they were right about his having typhoid fever—even when I knew they'd found no typhoid bacilli in his blood. . . ." He laughed—it is a half-grim, half-hearty laugh—and he al-

151

most never permits himself this guffaw unless it be on the subject of this disease caused by the microbe called tularense. "You see, we look at nature with our *brains*, not with our eyes," he went on.

"I sat there by the bed, watching Lake, went through all the solemn sanitary rigmarole of washing my hands, made all the passes you have to make when you leave the room of a typhoid patient. Why, I never for a moment thought— Why, I was blind, blind as a bat!" In jets came his story.

Luckily there was no efficient Director to call him off his incessant testing and cutting and trying at every angle of this remote little deer-fly fever. George McCoy was absolutely for Francis, was for every one who worked. "I'll try everything!" said that plugging toiler. And together with Lake, now better but still very tired in the afternoons, he began to make blood tests—complicated but accurate, like the Wassermann test for syphilis, they were. He brought out the blood from those ranchers, that housewife, and the nine-year-old girl who'd been sick that summer. All autumn he had hoarded their blood in his ice-box. "We'll try this blood against McCoy's tularense germ," he told Lake. And to be sure that these tests would show only deer-fly fever, and nothing else, he went around getting samples of a lot of the blood of Washington folks who'd never been to Utah and couldn't have had it.

Now if there is anything to criticize about this experimenter Francis, it is that he was too thorough, would always make fifty tests when forty-eight would be plenty. Here in a steamy warm-water bath stood rows of tubes, with the blood of those western folks that had been sick, and with the blood of the good Washington citizens who hadn't. "Look here," said Francis to Lake, "let's try our own blood too!" Was it for fun? Did he suspect something? I don't know, and Francis himself says he isn't sure why he suggested that. Anyway, another of his mottoes has to do with trying as many experiments as possible. Up went the sleeves of these brothers in science.

On the afternoon of January 20, 1921, Edward Francis and Gregory Lake are bending over racks that hold long rows of tubes, regular as a platoon of glass soldiers. They lift them, dripping, out of the water; they hold them up to strong light. Some are red the color of brick. . . . Others have the lovely transparent red of claret. . . . Here are the tubes of the blood of the Utah folks who've been attacked by the tularense microbe last summer—opaque, brick red is the blood in these tubes.

"Four plus! Positive for *Bacterium tularense!*" announces Francis, to Lake, who carefully scrawls after each name, + + + +.

Here is a long row of tubes of the blood of the Washington folks who've never so much as heard the buzz of a deer-fly—claret clear is the blood in these tubes.

"Negative for tularense!" cries Francis and Lake writes down a simple "—."

But here are two sets of little glass cylinders with the blood of Francis—last year the doctors thought he'd had malaria. And here's the blood of Lake—the chief Naval medical Rear Admiral himself had diagnosed him typhoid fever.

"Four plus—for Francis. . . . Four plus—for Lake. The blood of both of them—positive for *Bacterium tularense!*"

But how could they have caught that microbe?

Lake had never been near a Utah deer-fly. . . .

Francis was sure he hadn't been bitten, that summer of 1919, those days he was suddenly taken sick just after the death of R— S—. Could they have caught the ill from their beasts in the laboratory? Nonsense—it is marvelous how hard it is to catch a disease from your animals. . . . It is quaint how folks knowing little about it exaggerate the dangers microbe hunters run. "Why—none of us fellows ever thought anything of autopsying bubonic plague animals with our bare hands," grinned Francis. "There was no danger. . . ."

Francis refused to speculate, theorize about this mystery, and he shut himself up in his cubby-hole, with his microscope, with a magnificent confusion of papers scrawled with plans for experiments. His room was a tangle of livers pickled in alcohol, of the tularense microbes making merry in tubes of slanted egg-yolk, and of papers everywhere. . . . It is reported of Francis that in those days nobody ever saw him come to work or go home at night. But fifty times a day the door of his den would open, out would come the searcher, to stalk through the halls—head down—to have a squint at this or that dying rabbit. Under full blast went his hundreds of experiments on this insignificant little plague of the Pahvant Valley, and George McCoy gave him helpers, laboratory boys to hold rabbits, to shave them, to get rid of them after Francis had set down the last precise record of their death.

Then, one after another, those boys began to go home. They developed pains in their backs, in their necks, in the calves of their legs, shivered, felt tired, shot fevers. It was unheard of, grotesque! Francis looked at Lake who looked back at Francis. They both looked at each other, and grinned. What kind of a germ was this tularense microbe of George McCoy? Could it crawl through glass? Did it hop out at people through the skins of the sick animals? "Seems as if you can't come within a yard of the darn thing without getting bit by it!" laughed Francis. But here was no laughing matter. . . . After all, R— S— had died. . . . It is worth recording, in this place, that such thoughts would never stop the searching of those men in the red brick laboratory on the hill over the Potomac, and while the helpers took sick, one after another, the cages of guinea-pigs and rabbits grew into long rows. What the devil kind of a sickness was this, anyway, and to answer it Francis

made five times as many injections; and in a short while—
in spite of a great swabbing of lysol and every precaution
. . . every single one of six helpers had gone to the hospital. But how—

Francis was happy, and who can blame him? Here was
a new disease. Here was no mere deer-fly fever to bother
a few forlorn folks in a valley with a forgotten name. "I'll
call it Tularemia. . . ." So Francis, who detested all scholarly stickling about words, made a strange marriage of the
name of a county in California hills and the old word of
the Greeks for blood. Why not? Tularemia was certainly
a sickness that consisted in having those tularense beasts
disport themselves in your blood. . . . Tularemia. . . .
Francis was happy.

But how—

"Well, there was one thing we all of us certainly have
done," said Francis to Gregory Lake, "we all had our hands
into those infected rabbits and guinea-pigs. . . ."

But what of that? All of them hadn't had cuts on their
hands, none of them had gashed their hands with blood-
soiled knives. . . . No germ was known that could sneak
through the unbroken skin of a man's hand. "Try everything!" said Francis.

He took a plump healthy guinea-pig, and around the
neck of this beast he fastened a stiff collar, an inch and a
half wide, that divided this beast into two unequal parts
and made him look like some over-sized, wingless, fur-
bearing bee. Gently, on to the hair of this animal's back,
right down on to the unrubbed and unbroken skin of his
back, Francis let fall a single drop of a brew of the spleen
of a creature just dead of tularemia. That was all. The
little beast was held quiet. The collar kept him from turning his head to lick the drop off—not a chance in the world
of any of that dangerous stuff getting into the beast's
mouth. Five days—he was dead. Post mortem: typical for
tularemia.

FRANCIS

Meanwhile a large sign in bold letters was hung in front
of the animal cages:

TULAREMIA!
Keep Away!

VI.

EACH night, after everybody else had gone home, Francis
was to be found before his cages, finishing the notes on the
last of that day's martyrs. Then alone he wandered out
through the halls with their reek of menagerie, with their
silence broken only by a low chuttering, scurrying, munch-
ing, and peeping. Supper, alone, and very simple in the
same Greek restaurant every evening, a walk around the
Potomac Basin, and bed by seven-thirty—such was the life
of Edward Francis, and who could have been happier?
Tularemia, this strange disease, his own disease . . .
"TULAREMIA. Francis, 1921: A New Disease of Man. . . ."
Those words at the head of a little scientific paper
gave him something to smile about, to be satisfied with in
his lone-wolf way on his walks by himself at night. And
now the news of tularemia spread to Europe, and drew a
snicker and a cackle from a famous British medical journal—the very idea of anybody, let alone Francis, let alone
an American, claiming the discovery of an illness never before heard of! The Lister Institute of London sent to Director George McCoy for a culture of the microbe of this
alleged new plague, and off went the tularense germs over
the sea, dormant on their favorite food of yolks of eggs
cooked on a slant in a narrow tube. But they were excellent
sailors, were the microbes of tularense, and down came the
British guinea-pigs of the Lister Institute, turning up their
toes exactly five days after the bugs were shot into them.
. . . And one! . . . two! . . . three! . . . down came
three British expert members of the staff of the Lister In-

156

stitute, with the tiredness in their backs and bones, with the shivers and headaches of tularemia. In less than four months three British scientists were brought to bed with it and one poor female scientist wasn't fit to work for more than a year. . . . A new disease?

"By a brave discretion," said another English medical journal, "the authorities in England have decided to close down all work on tularemia."

Francis piled into his toil at this sickness so strangely confined to the Pahvant Valley, but so extremely catching for anybody that so much as tried to meddle with it in a laboratory. In these days there is no record of his thinking his pet disease was anything more than that: he seemed not to guess for a moment the millions of lurking places it might have in the American land. He stuck to his cubby-hole, and tried everything. It is said of him that he stopped having lunch with his old pals of the laboratory because they insisted on talking, sometimes, about subjects other than tularemia.

Every morning, three hundred and sixty-five days out of the year, this man is up at five. Between shaving and dressing he 'phones to a decidedly low little restaurant near the Army and Navy Building: "I'll be right over." And the man who is waiter and chef puts his cakes on the fire. Seated there in the murk of cigarette smoke amid the mumble of curses, of talk of the crimes of last night in Washington, this fantastic man demolishes his cakes, silent, but with a sharp ear for the talk of this jumble of newspaper reporters, taxicab drivers, and others not so respectable. Does he enjoy the low show? "They're real fellows!" says Francis. He listens, his eyes gleam as he bolts his coffee, now and again he is hugely delighted by the not at all sanitary conduct of the restaurant cat over there in the corner. "Those fellows down there are right down to earth!" says Francis—it is his highest compliment. Such is his society, and such his sardonic amusement, but already his thoughts travel to the

157

strange village of glass aquarium jars, garbage cans and wire cages where his very best friends—those martyrs—live. He walks out into the cold morning, not yet light, and his eyes gleam as he hurries towards the red brick building on the hill.

Long before the janitor comes to try his futile task of cleaning up the litter of frayed cigar ends and crumpled-up papers on his cubby-hole floor, Francis is writing down plans for the day. How does the disease keep alive all winter in those jack-rabbits out in Utah—how does it travel from jack to jack? It's winter out in Utah now, pretty tough hunting—though mind you he's chipper—but who is chipper enough to follow jacks through the greasewood at sixty miles an hour? But here are Belgian hares, plenty of 'em—nothing is stinted up there in the old Hygienic Laboratory, nothing but modern laboratory elegance, and which of those death fighters cares for swell workrooms? Glass doorknobs are not there, nor shining plumbing, nor burnished spittoons—but rabbits? They've plenty. How does the tularense get from rabbit to rabbit? Francis puts a well rabbit in the same cage with a sick one, finds that is enough to send the healthy beast to his doom. Forty-three positive takes of the ill he records from that simple test—out of Lord only knows how many tries. And the nasal discharge of one beast is enough to floor another; and the urine, when injected—though not when fed. Could it be carried by rabbit fleas? "I looked," said Francis, "and I couldn't find a single darned flea on a rabbit. Eight months I kept a watchout for 'em, and would you believe it—I found just three fleas!" But lice? Every rabbit had lice. "We'll try lice," Francis told Lake.

What could be more strange, more *outré*, more perfectly delightful than this plague, tularemia? Here are yellow fever, sleeping sickness, malaria, the bubonic plague—all are carried from victim to victim by just one kind of fly or mosquito or flea. Now tularemia is immensely superior.

Bacterium tularense is much more democratic. To the hilt Francis proved that the rabbit louse can suck the germ up into its body, keep it there alive, deposit it in a healthy rabbit at a new meal of blood. Into the cracks in the wooden cages where guinea-pigs and mice are bred, Francis dug—to find bed bugs. He captured hundreds of them. He tried everything. "Bed bugs were fed first on sick, then on healthy mice," said Francis. "Then I turned the experiment upside down: I had the mouse eat infected bed bugs instead of having the bed bugs bite the mouse!" And he laughed. There you see Francis, helped by the sturdy Lake—oh, he could always depend on Gregory Lake—at the silly job of sticking the tail of a healthy mouse through a hole in the gauze covering a tube that's alive with bed bugs whose healthy bodies are aswarm with devastating microbes of tularense. Two hundred and fifty days a husky bed bug can live in comfort, his body teeming with tularemia, for two hundred and fifty days he is dangerous!

With an energy that's half grim, half gay, Francis tears at hundreds of experiments still more grotesque. He keeps exact tab on every single one of his beasts, compiles enormous, and you'd say useless, tables. "Why, we even checked our bed bugs out in the evening and in, in the morning," said Francis. With a hand-lens he discovers the obscure mite that lives upon mice, and rejoices in the name of *Liponyssus isabellinus*. When *Liponyssus* refuses to transfer the death by biting, Francis grinds some of him up, injects the mess. Yes—*Liponyssus* is dangerous. . . .

There seemed no end to the resourcefulness of this microbe from Tulare, California, and the Pahvant Valley, Utah. There seemed to be no way it would fail to crawl, sneak, ride, or hop around in nature, from one victim to the next. Why then wasn't the American land alive with tularemia? Francis kept on trying everything.

VII.

ONLY a few blocks away from his laboratory, right there in Washington, a simple soul got ready to help Francis solve the most important part of his puzzle. In November of 1921 this man, name E— N—, was taken sick while selling rabbits to his customers in the Washington market. There was a painful lump under his right arm and he felt rocky, feverish. He went to see his physician, Doctor J. Lawn Thompson, complaining, "Doc, there's something wrong here under my arm. An' I feel all in, can't hardly keep going on the job 'til quittin' time."

Lawn Thompson, a highly trained physician, well versed in the book-learning and science of medicine, examined E— N— from top to toe. "You are apparently suffering from a septic infection," something like that Thompson said. Then he wrote out a prescription, that wasn't so very cheap to get filled. "Rub the stuff into your armpit over that lump where it hurts you," he counseled E— N—.

A week later, and back comes E— N—. "I feel worse, Doc. Arm hurts terrible. That stuff didn't do me no good."

Doctor Thompson, having studied in the medical colleges where they teach the latest practical as well as theoretical science, looks serious. He tells his humble patient that his infection is a particularly stubborn one, counsels him to get that prescription filled once again, and to keep rubbing it in over the sore spot. The prescription is not cheap. . . .

"But I don't believe you know what's wrong with me, Doc," protests E— N—. "What I've got is *rabbit fever*. All of us fellows working at the Market know of it. Most of the guys have had it. You've sure heard of rabbit fever? We get it in the fall when we handle those cold storage rabbits that come in from all over. . . ."

"Why—there is no such disease as rabbit fever!" J. Lawn Thompson told E— N—. And there wasn't—in the medical books.

160

But there was one thing that Doctor Lawn Thompson had been educated to believe, and that was the science published in the medical journals, and four months later he opens his new copy of *The Journal of the American Medical Association*. Here's a report by Edward Francis: "TU-LAREMIA. Francis, 1921: A New Disease of Man." In less than half an hour, stuttering, hardly able to get the scientific words out of his mouth, Lawn Thompson has Francis on the telephone. "Doctor Francis, I had a case of tularemia, this new disease of yours, in my office—last fall. Man said he had rabbit fever. . . . I laughed at him."

Thank heaven Doctor Thompson is accurate, keeps a card index of his patients. Yes, the fellow's name is E— N—. He lives right close by. Here's his address. Thanks very much, Doctor—and that very evening Edward Francis is at the home of E— N—, asking him a hundred excited questions, learning the ins and outs of the rabbit fever as only men of E— N—'s closeness to natural things can know it. E— N— is greatly flattered. Of course Doctor Francis can take a blood sample, and up goes the sleeve of the rabbit man, and back to his den hurries Francis. For once even Edward Francis lets himself speculate, dream, lets his imagination wander out to woods and fields from coast to coast of the American land. Why—how silly to think that only the ground squirrels of Tulare County, California, and the jack-rabbits of the Pahvant Valley in Utah were the only beasts to die from McCoy's microbe of tularense! Why, of course—it's all over the country from coast to coast! And Francis sees men in brown hunting-coats leaving their farms in the little snows of November. There are shotguns under their arms; they're accompanied by yelling long-eared hounds. Tularemia? Tularemia's all over!

But is it? He is back in his den alone, fussing with a long narrow tube that has in it the yolk of egg cooked on a slant, and the surface of the slant is covered with gray slime, and that slime consists of nothing but billions of his pets, his bugs, his finicky *Bacterium tularense.* . . . And here he is carefully, through a delicate pipette, sucking the straw-colored serum off the clot of the blood from the arm of E— N—. And before he goes home he sets away, with reverence, a rack of wee test-tubes, each holding a swirling gray cloud of the microbe of tularense in water that's slightly salt, and each holding a little—less and less, down the row of tubes—of the blood serum of E— N—. Next morning—

Early next morning Francis comes to see a strange sorcery. He looks at the shining tubes. The fluid in them is clear as water. What's become of the billions of rabbit-murdering bugs? Francis picks one of the tubes up, taps it a little. Ah—here are the rascals! In clumps, in bunches, in flakes they rise from the bottom of the tube. Mysteriously the serum of E— N— has clumped these microbes, has weighted them down with something unknown, has gathered them together and made them fall to the bottom of the tube like lovely little flakes of snow. From tube to tube down the long row it's the same thing—a thousandth of a drop of E— N—'s blood clumps the tularense germs. It is sorcery. And here in another row, where Francis has dosed his savage pets with the blood of a man that's surely never had rabbit fever—there are the microbes, perfectly afloat, swirling in silky gray clouds as he taps the tubes. It is settled—absolutely. Rabbit fever and tularemia are one and the same.

Next autumn Francis takes on a new co-worker, it is E— N—, the market man, the man who knew there was such a thing as rabbit fever. "Wouldn't have done for me to have appeared at the Washington Market, poking around among those rabbits. Folks might have got scared off from buying them, and butchers might cancel orders for more. . . ." Cagey like some super-crafty old spider in the middle of his web, Edward Francis stays in his den on the hill, and pretty soon the excellent E— N— begins bringing him livers, rabbit livers, from rabbits that have come—in cold storage—from the Cumberlands, from the Mississippi Valley, from the hills of the Ozarks, from a dozen states of the American land. "E— N— was immune now," grinned Francis. "All he had to do was to reach his hand into the carcasses and get out those livers, and bring 'em up the hill."

Nine hundred and fourteen livers E— N— brought, that fall and winter, from Kansas, Kentucky, Tennessee, Missouri. Out of those nine hundred and fourteen were seven that were peppered with those suspicious white specks. . . . Little bits of each of these Francis rubbed up in a mortar, strained through cloth, shot under the skin of a healthy guinea-pig. Five days—

That little test was as simple and sure as the sunrise.

VIII.

THEN it must be in the folks of these states too! But he didn't pick up and go, he stayed in his messed-up room, wrote letters, published papers urging doctors to watch closely for people with very bad sore eyes, swollen glands, fever, and that terrible tiredness—after hunting, skinning, cutting up rabbits. He talked tularemia to everybody, to every doctor he could buttonhole, to visiting microbe hunters, to solemn Japanese and Koreans who came to his laboratory and couldn't understand a word of his rapid jerky sentences that came out in excited spurts of speech.

From sixteen, from eighteen, from twenty-six states of the Union came letters, came livers of rabbits, came little tubes of the blood of hunters, farmers' wives, sheep-herders, forest rangers, locomotive engineers, dentists, meat cutters, chefs, hucksters and housewives. They'd all had their hands in rabbits; they'd all gotten tired. Some had died. From Montana came the blood of folks who'd gone to bed after being bitten by ticks—those ticks had fed on the pretty white snowshoe rabbit. From the same state came the serum of a hunter who'd been bitten by a coyote pup as he'd pulled it from its den—the pup's mother had given it a meal of sick rabbit. . . . From the laboratory at Hamilton, Montana, where Francis' pals of the Public Health Service were working to invent a preventive for the deadly Rocky Mountain spotted fever, and where five of them have died of it—among these obscure desperadoes were six cases of the tired disease.

"Hunters and housewives only come down with tularemia in the fall and winter—but it's open season for laboratory workers the year 'round," laughed Francis.

And then from the hills in the western part of Virginia came bad news: the dog of a farmer in that wild country had brought in some rabbits he'd caught in a field. The good wife had fried them for supper—maybe not quite well done. Two days later the father, and his girl of seven, and his little boy aged two, took sick with sore eyes and swollen glands that hurt terribly. Next day a small sister aged six complained of the same trouble. A few days later the boy of two was buried. On that same day the father and his seven-year-old daughter died.

The country doctors were puzzled. The hill-folks suspected the mother, who'd stayed well, of some foul play. But by a chance a youngster, named Freese, of the Virginia State Health Department, happened into the nearby village, heard the drama of the sudden deaths and the gossip of murder. Only a few months before he'd listened to the story of tularemia from the lips of that fanatic, Francis, himself. Into the hills went Freese, swabbed the throat of the six-year-old girl who still lived, injected the washings from that swab into a guinea-pig. Five, six days and—

Was this a particularly dangerous microbe of tularense, or were those hill people it murdered undernourished, run down? Nobody knows. Francis has no theories about that, nor science to explain it. He has stayed close to his little room, having been away from that dusty hole-in-the-wall six days in all in the last six years—and that counts in all of his Sundays, and Fourth of Julys. He's stuck there, bringing state after state into his net—discovering the dangerous bug from Tulare in the rabbits of nearly all of the states of the Union, New England and New York State so far excepted. And of the folks who have been the victims of the dangerous hunger for the meat of the rabbit, four or five out of every hundred die—quickly sometimes like those Virginia hill folk, or with a queer slow pneumonia. All the rest are simply dreadfully tired, knocked out for a month, two months, or a year. For this tiredness or this death there's no cure—and you may be sure Edward Francis has made vast tests up there with all the known drugs, chemicals, remedies. There's only one thing to do, and that's to rest in bed.

There's no vaccine either; and there's only one way to get immune to it, and that's to handle an infected rabbit, and go through the sickness yourself.

There is certainly no way to stamp this dangerous hunger out of our country, for even a Mohler wouldn't try to exterminate the total jack, snowshoe, and cotton-tail rabbit tribes of the United States.

But Francis has a simple and perfectly certain preventive, for this tularemia, that slips with such fantastic ease from guinea-pigs and rabbits into men, never spreads from one human being to another. In the Pahvant Valley or in the wilds of Montana or Idaho it might be caught from the bites of deer-flies or ticks. But the one sure way to catch it is by getting your hands into the *insides* of a rabbit that is sick with the microbe from Tulare County. Of all the truths the automatic Francis has piled up, here is the little truth that his work boils down into, let him tell it in his own words:

165

"If . . . all cooks, market-men, hunters, housewives and others who dress rabbits, would wear rubber gloves when doing so they would not contract tularemia. It should be remembered that thorough cooking destroys the infection in a rabbit, thus rendering an infected rabbit harmless for food."

BOOK THREE. MAIZE

ANCIENT AND ANONYMOUS

CHAPTER SIX. THE MAIZE FINDERS

ANCIENT AND ANONYMOUS

I.

WHAT FIGHTERS OF HUNGER can compare to the unknown finders of the American maize?

Of all green living things maize is the chief trapper of the energy of the sun's rays. Eaten as corn and bread, and turned into four-legged beasts and their milk, made into two-legged fowl and their eggs, maize is the principal food of the people of the western continents.

What sort of man or woman first found this maize? Wondrous lusty: it shoots from a seed to the size of a tree in less than three months. Tough is this Indian corn: it sends out new leaves after spring frosts and laughs at the cold nights of October. Resourceful: it yields three hundredfold on the soggy lands along the lower Mississippi—and it sends down long tap roots to hunt and find moisture in the southwest lands where there is no rain.

What brown-faced genius with straight black hair first learned to guard the maize? For of all green things this strong helper of man is the weakest: the Indian corn plant is more dependent on man than the most absurd poodle. A thousand times more domestic is the maize than the most helpless goldfish: without endless storing, hoeing, reaping, saving, and sowing by men, this plant would die out—utterly. Unlike wheat, unlike any food giving life to men, there is no wild maize: none has ever been known to escape the hands of men to grow free. It can't grow free. With heavy kernels tight on a cob and enclosed by enormous husks, no wind that blows can scatter the seed of it broadcast; untended by man, the young plants—though so vigorous—are killed off by grass in a jiffy.

But who first knew all that? What kind of prophet with what strange insight was this first aboriginal American with

169

high cheek-bones who first *felt* the absolute need to save the maize, to store it, always to hoe it, knowing he must sow it again—knowing it would never rise by itself again through some kind quirk of God or trick of nature? . . .

From what wild plant could this Indian corn have come? Today there are fifty colleges where savants with their heads full of big-named facts about maize study the chemistry of its life-stuff, the mathematics of its breeding. But never a one of them can breed corn from any wild plant—not even from the tasseled Mexican grass, teosinte. "To be wild," smiles Guy Collins, corn historian, slouched in his chair and sucking at his pipe, "any parent of the maize would have to be very unlike the maize itself!" So it's silly to search for the wild parent now. And it's foolish to guess the time of the birth and the finding of the maize—in Peru there exist fossilized ears of corn untold thousands of years old; from Iowa there are stories of ears of maize that have left their record in slate deposits deep underground. Yet, in some misty month when the world was young, a wild green plant changed suddenly into this delicate food plant that would surely have died out—left to itself. Or, for some months, or years, or hundreds of years, two unknown wild green tasseled grasses married and begat and conceived fantastic children that themselves were enormously fertile— but as helpless to survive as so many abandoned human babies. . . . In those mysterious days a man—or was it a woman?—happened by, a clod of a man, with a dirty face. It was an epic accident.

Who will ever know the language of that man's scientific report of the finding of the maize? Was it written? Or did he tell it in a mumble of low-pitched growls and a jumble of high-pitched grunts to a college of his mates held in the warmth of that new invention—fire? Or is maize older than tame fire?

THE MAIZE FINDERS

II.

HEAVEN knows how many thousands of years afterwards —after straight-haired Americans had nursed the flame of the seed of it all those thousands of years—new immigrant Americans, civilized white men, scrambled out of their boats on to the coast of eastern America—and took the maize. There was nothing scientific about their discovery but it was only a matter of their empty stomachs turning somersaults. It was the first bleak Massachusetts autumn for those Puritan white men: the going was hard. Then Miles Standish and his scouts, in despair how to fill their bellies, came upon fields of an outlandish new kind of grass tall as a tree. They stumbled over mounds, dug into them; looking over their shoulders in fear of possible owners, they pulled out of the ground a little old basket filled with Indian corn. "We dug further," wrote their scribe, "and found a fine great new basket of very fair corn of that year—six and thirty goodly ears of corn, some yellow, some red, others mixed with blue, a very goodly sight."

Guarded by their flintlocks, they filled an old kettle with it, stuffed their wide pockets full of it, put it in their great hats, and Miles Standish and his God-fearing men scampered off with it believing it better to ask the Indians whether or no they might have it—afterwards. They were hungry. "And surely it was God's providence that we found this corn," wrote the recorder of the deeds of those pious Pilgrims, "for else we know not how we should have done. . . ."

The civilized white men took the maize, and their ignorant friend, Squanto the Indian, taught them the science they needed to know, to fight their hunger with it. To make the thin Massachusetts soil rich to feed the greedy corn, Squanto gave them the trick of catching shad that swam up the streams into the ponds to spawn. "An acre set with these shads . . . raises as much corn as three acres without," wrote the Pilgrim setting down the first written report of Indian science. And the Pilgrims? As today, they were lawmakers. To be sure of their great yields they passed a severe law requiring that all dogs be tied by the leg while fish were in the cornhills. Then the power of the maize pushed wave after wave of white men west. Driving the givers of the maize before them, the sons of those first white men pushed west from the stony lands of the East across the red clay of the Piedmont up over the Alleghenies to the black loam of Kentucky, Ohio, Illinois—their man-power stoked by the energy sleeping in the seed of the maize.

Energy, guts to push onward, shoulders to fall trees, hands toughened to the sang hoe, sharp eyes to shoot the maize-givers: all these they needed—not science. For ten thousand years and more their enemies, the Indians, had bred an amazing variety of strengths and virtues into their maize—by a sing-song science made up of chants, legends, ceremonies. They'd bred corn for cruel weathers and impossible soils. And now these white grabbers came, and what prospecting for metals could compare to this happy finding of bonanzas by the white men going west—for in every valley, on each plain, in every oak opening, was a new variety of Indian corn adjusted to rain and the richness of black lands, adapted to drought and the lightness of sandy soil. Here's the white man's maize science: A dash in the dawn toward sleeping tepees, brave Daniel Boone at the head of it. Then shouts, the thud of body against body, the popping of muskets, the last wail of a child. Now the enemies, the maize givers, are gone, killed, drunk, or chased west. And here for the redoubtable Boone and the hard-boiled Clarke is just the right sort of maize on the right kind of land—maize that even in those days yielded fifty, seventy-five, a hundred bushels to the acre. With no modern agricultural machinery either, mind you; but only with an ax, a crooked stick, a bent piece of iron. . . .

G. N. Collins sits slumped behind his gurgling pipe, his

172

face tanned and lean with a hint in it of the look of those anonymous breeders of the maize now gone west forever. Tireless experimenter is Guy Collins, tracer of the mysterious blood lines of this yellow grain, and he smiles at the claims of modern searchers to have done anything much at all for the good of this Indian corn. "Flint, pop, soft, sweet —why, it was all here when we got here!" laughs Collins. "During the four hundred and twenty-five years we've been fooling with it we've put nothing into it, almost, that you can't duplicate in the maize of the red men."

So corn came to be the overwhelming American fact not by the brains of the pioneers but by their tired legs, their aching arms. Collins tells the song of the spread of the maize written by the savage old Thomas Carlyle: "How beautiful to think of tough lean Yankee settlers, tough as gutta-percha, with a most unsubduable fire in their belly, steering over the Western Mountains, to annihilate the jungle, and to bring bacon and corn out of it for the posterity of Adam."

III.

OBSCURELY, amid the din and the sweat of the white man's spreading of maize to make modern America, began the white man's maize science. What searcher in the harsh days of the middle eighteen hundreds, what unknown college professor, what gentle botanizing teacher of young ladies, first traced the grotesque sexual monstrosity of the Indian corn? Let his bones rest, let his name be forgotten—it is enough that he found this fact: that every maize plant is husband to many wives and is itself wife to an unknown number of husbands. This white searcher dug out what the Indians couldn't know: that in nature a maize plant rarely marries itself to beget seed of its corn children of the following year. The plants of the maize—fundamentally—are as strikingly individual, as various, as so many human beings are different from each other. This obscure impractical botanizer probed out this fundamental fact: that like wheat, every corn plant is both male and female, but its male and female parts are not shut up in the same flower. Unlike wheat, unlike any other grain, the man and the woman parts of the Indian corn are on widely different parts of the plant. . . .

At a time when you'd swear that the toil of raising more hundreds of thousands of bushels of corn to turn out more thousands of fatter pigs and better cattle *for sale* was the one thought in the whole Midwest land—in these hectic days a few silly dreamers didn't work.

They gaze at the tassel proud like a plume at the top of the maize plant, pull bits of this tassel off, put it under their little hand lenses, take a little step ahead of the science of the red men.

Here's a row of spikelets that make up that tassel—and each little spike has two tiny flowers—the observers carefully, idiotically count them: roughly there are twenty-five hundred flowers to every maize plume. Male flowers they are. . . .

Through corn fields these dreamers go. In the corn fields you'll find them at the appointed mysterious time in high summer when those flowers open, thrust forth their anthers mad for mating, and from these anthers scattered by the wind go millions of grains of gold-colored pollen—the plant sperm. The warm winds blow: the air of corn fields is alive with eager pollen.

"Well—what of that?" sneer the practical corn and hog men.

But the professors keep peering at the maize plant, and far below the male plume, down the cornstalk they spy the strands of sticky green silk pushing their way out of husks that enfold the young cob on the ear shoot. Waiting for the pollen as maids wait for their men are these green strands of silk. The searchers open the husks of the ear shoot, trace the

174

strands of silk to their source: to the female flowers set in exact rows on the cob. Around them the air is alive with pollen: through the air from tens and hundreds of neighboring corn plants come myriads of grains of pollen to marry the silk of one single plant. From the tassels of that same plant goes pollen to mate with the silks of dozens of its neighbors.

Such is the fantastic sexuality of maize: every ear of corn may have a hundred fathers; each tassel may be part father to a hundred ears.

IV.

BUT what of it? What was the use of such science? Without the help of any dreaming botanists at all, as if there were no science of maize except to plant it, reap it, hoe it—the black land of middle America poured its strength into millions of bushels of corn. If we only bend our backs enough, if our hands are tough enough: such was the science of the American men, and the forests of Ohio shrank into woodlots and the oak openings expanded into new forests—of maize. Having given the maize, the last Indian was gone and the muskets hung on the walls of the farm-houses—mementoes of grandpa.

Now arose a new kind of corn-dreamer, a farmer corn-breeder who would hardly know a pistil from a stamen and who would blink at you if you asked him what an anther was. But he had a shrewd love of corn and a wordless awe of it that had in it something of the Indian—though straightaway this white man, being a true American, began to try to standardize corn in a way completely un-Indian. First and among the most famous of these corn-dreamers was Jake Leaming of Ohio. Jake had got the start of his corn from his father, Settler Chris Leaming, who began with the old reddish-black kind of corn the Indians knew was good for that particular part of southern Ohio. For

175

sixty years Jake Leaming walked through his maize fields, with two or three simple notions in his head of just what an ear of corn ought to look like. For just those points, each year of those sixty years, he kept selecting seed ears—never thinking of the pollen fathers of those ears.

The result? It was amazing, grotesque! Old Leaming made a miracle with those no-account black kerneled corn-ears swiped from the Indians. But it was perfectly natural, for in this the seed of maize is no whit different from the seed of men and women: that asleep in the seed there are traits, characters, that come from millions of ancestors. From the looks of a father and mother you'd better not try to predict the looks of their children: from a no-account drunken father and a servant-girl mother comes Beethoven, the colossus. And now, from his runty red-brown ears of Indian corn that carried in them an endless variety of traits of the first maize from Peru, the tough maize of the Zuñi of the dry Southwest, the strange corn of Quezaltenango— Jake Leaming began selecting, selecting, selecting. . . .

Never having seen the inside of an agricultural college, this man had his own notions of what good corn ought to be like. To realize these ideas he raised a family of seven husky sons, who with hoes in their hands by the time they were half as tall as a hoe handle took the place of the culti-vator not yet invented.

"All the weeds you can find in Jake's cornfield you can carry 'round in your hat," said the farmers roundabout.

"We had to start stirring the ground as soon as the corn-plants appeared, and pa kept us at it 'til long after we boys could see no use for it," said George Leaming, Jake's son.

"Weeds? They're deadly poison to corn," said old Jake himself.

Then he would walk into his fields as marvelously free of any weed as his good-wife's kitchen floor was free of a speck of dust; the magnificent rows of straight green trees

would swallow him up; between these rows he walked—
looking, and forming his wordless notions.

"Ah! There's one of them red-headed woodpeckers . . .
flyin' from one plant to another. Wait—there! He's took
a toe-holt on that stalk there, peckin' into the husk—eatin'
at it. He knows better'n I do what ears ripen earliest. . . .
That's what I want," mulls Leaming. And out of his over-
all pocket he fishes colored bits of string—ties a bit of
string to this early-ripening maize plant. When the mystic
time comes, just as the shucks begin to turn a brownish
yellow, Jake will come back and pick that ear to save it for
seed. "It's early-ripening corn we need," mutters the
breeder.

He compared what his own eyes could see with what he
saw was the instinct of the woodpeckers. "It's long tapering ears that are the ones they go for," said Leaming. "Long
tapering ears on plants that've got thick tapering stalks—
they're the early ones." Leaming's brain held nothing but
lore of corn, became an animated library of facts about
corn; from nobody knows how many disastrous years of no
rain, of rains that lasted forty days threatening a return
of biblical flood, of frosts that came when the corn grains
were still in the milk—from these years Jake remembered
the sterling behavior of certain strange corn plants that
bore two ears to a stalk. "It's the two-eared sorts that're
tough," said Jake. And he selected, picked out, kept selecting from the two-eared plants. And he used to say: "What
I want is ears sticking out from the stalk—reaching out to
shake hands." No bit different from the exactest laboratory
searcher, there was no end to his care or the trouble he took.
In the spring from corn stored all winter he selects all over
again!

There he sits, on the end of a log, encircled by tubs and
neatly corded piles of extra-selected seed ears. There's a big
butcher knife driven into the end of the log. Jake pulls it
out, twists a fine gold ear away from him against the edge

of the knife—so he shells every grain of the seed for the sowing of that spring, and every spring. And Leaming corn? Year after year Jake gets yields running better than a hundred bushels to the acre. First man on record in all of Ohio is Jacob Leaming to get this enormous yield of six hundredfold. Leaming corn—those words run from stove to stove of one country store to another, where the wiseacres sit by the cracker-barrels and convenient to the sawdust-box spittoons. And in 'seventy-eight this formerly obscure Jake Leaming's corn wins the Grand Prix—in Ohio it's "Pricks"—at the Paris World's Fair Exposition. One hundred ears of Jake's corn are solemnly adjudged superior to all other varieties of corn in the world, on a basis of highest feeding value as determined by chemical analysis—however anybody would determine that; and on a basis of the beautiful tapering ears of it, on a basis of heavy weight of corn per ear, on a basis of the slender cob. "Gosh!" say the judges, "Jake's corn is nearly all *grain!*"

And in Leaming's front parlor, where the shades are drawn on all days excepting Christmas, days of weddings, funerals, and certain particular Sundays, there is a diploma of the Grand Prix, and here lies in state a silver medal. . . .

There is no record that Jacob Leaming himself wanted to go against the old wisdom of the Indians, who had the hunch, the superstition, that certain kinds of maize should grow in certain places, who had the belief there ought to be a thousand different sorts of maize. There is no evidence that Jake wanted to spread his particular sort of tapering, deep yellow colored ears over the whole state of Ohio, over the whole corn belt. But in fifty thousand farmers 'round him there already stirred this strange American spirit: This guy's got something good—I'll get the same thing. So, all over Ohio, across the magnificent black belt of western Ohio and over into Indiana among those strange poetic Hoosiers, spread the golden seed of the Leaming yielding four, five hundredfold—according to the land it was sown in, depending upon the kind of man who put the seed of it under the soil of that land. Would the famous Leaming keep on yielding that way? What matter in those good days? The folks of the new corn belt were comfortably off—in pork, beef, chickens, butter and eggs, and with a good roof over their heads. The early days of the famous Leaming corn were days when folks didn't have to watch, with worry for their mortgages, their exact yields per acre. There were no installments coming due on that new Atwater Kent; it was not necessary to find cash for the boy who must go to college. . . . Those were the horse and buggy days when the most important sounds in the sleepy farm villages were the rattle of harness as the horses stamped their feet before the general store, and the drone of the flies buzzing in and out of infrequently opened screen doors. Who needed a record yield? Farming wasn't a business.

But the corn of Jake Leaming—how could it stay Leaming? Faithfully Jake had picked out, selected for the early-ripening, tapering, high-yielding, two-eared sort—but after all he was selecting against a dormant heredity that was as complicated, as various as the manifold characters that go to make up the human race. And after all, he'd only been selecting *mothers*, the seed ears, the seed that ripened from the rows of the female flowers on the ear-shoots. The pollen, from the fathers of that seed? The pollen had come from the plants all over the field, from fathers good and bad— every plant bearing tassels shedding pollen had an equal chance to be part father to Jake's finest ears. What genius could fix for keeps the blood lines of this enormously complicated maize—that would stay uniform only so long as old Leaming himself, with his particular notions, selected the ears of it? In the Leaming seed slept the characters of a thousand varieties of maize from prehistoric days in the high valleys of Peru and the jungles of Tehuantepec on down. Was there really such a thing at all as a fixed variety of maize? Could there be such a thing any more than there can be a fixed type of human being?

The corn-belt farmers didn't worry about that; here was a guy had something good—they'd get the same thing. And here was a new kind of corn to beat even the Leaming, bred by the long-bearded esthete, James Reid of the Delavan prairie in central Illinois. Accidental was the beginning of Reid's beautiful corn, as chancy as the start of the Marquis wheat in Canada. Old Robert Reid, sire of the poetic James, had trekked west from the Red Oak settlement in southern Ohio by prairie schooner in 'forty-six; and after the custom of pioneers he took with him his own special Ohio corn, the Gordon Hopkins. The very first spring, Settler Robert put the seed of his pet Gordon Hopkins under the new Illinois ground. And that spring the robins shivered and looked forlorn and the puddles of water stood too long on the black land, and the green shoots of the maize struggled up, slow and irregular, in this new country where it didn't belong. "Got to get some kind of a crop—" muttered Robert. He fished around, got a few pecks of the native corn of the country, the Indian corn called "Little Yellow." With a hoe he went through the fields putting the seed of the Little Yellow in the hills where his Gordon Hopkins hadn't come up. . . .

That year the pollen and the eggs of the Gordon Hopkins and the Little Yellow were married by the prairie wind: such was the birth of the Reid Yellow Dent. . . .

James Reid, son of Robert, was born for an artist, but his father was poorly, and Jim had to start out throwing the harness over the team's backs while he was still in knee pants and before he was tall enough or strong enough he was guiding the plow. "I had a fool idea I might be a picture painter," Jim confessed through his beard in his old age. But corn was the one way to put food in the mouths of his father, now doddering, of his good wife, of his daughter Olive. So Jim took out his hankering for loveliness on

JAMES REID

gazing at marvelously cylindrical yellow ears of maize,
pretty bastard children of the Little Yellow and the Gordon
Hopkins.

In the autumn he sat, caressing those ears, reveling silently in the feel of them, picking them out for seed with an
uncanny eye for the form and look of them. And here
around Delavan ran rumors of another hundred-bushel-to-
the-acre corn. Was it in the nature of these ears to yield
so heavy? Or was it just James Reid's good black land? Or

was it because he was a good farmer keeping strength in his soil by the manure from his herd of cattle, by his shrewd rotation of crops? Who knew? Who then had the science to *compare* the yield of this Reid Yellow Dent? Surely not James Reid, who shuffled without ever a word down the arched avenues made by the rows of his maize, a sack slung over his shoulder, picking out ears that pleased him!

"How did you pick out your seed, Mr. Reid?"

"The Lord knoweth; I am his pupil," answered that sage after the manner of a pious Middle Western oracle.

While his corn became the rage of the prairie, Reid was a failure in business, having only certain private and sniffish dreams of beauty. But business can use dreamers, and the able seedsman, Gene Funk, when he started selling seed corn from his flat black thousands of acres around Bloomington in the early nineteen hundreds, sent the enthusiastic corn professor P. G. Holden down to get the "very finest Yellow Dent from James Reid for breeding."

Reid had no patent. There were no royalties.

Holden was a lean bespectacled and bearded corn crank, and he found the venerable James sitting in his corncrib, looking solemnly down his long white beard at one of those perfect ears, better than nine inches long, each kernel slightly and smoothly dented, every kernel a unit in a row straight as if God had drawn a ruler along it.

Said Reid to Holden: "Here's a very nice ear," which was a great deal for that close-mouthed sage to say.

"Why do you select that one?" asked Holden.

An insufferable silence. . . .

A drawl, a murmur: "Oh . . . I don't know, exactly . . . I guess—because I *like* it!"

But botheration! Here was Holden, the corn authority, sent down by his boss, Gene Funk, to learn *why* James Reid liked his pet ears—that also happened to yield so heavy. Holden kept at it:

"Is it because the ear is rounded, well filled at the butt?

182

Or do you consider the kernels to be just the proper depth? Or is the color of it just right?"

The sphinx took his time. . . . "Yes, you're right . . . I guess it's because of all of those things . . . and more too. . . ."

It was exactly as if some enterprising boy just out of college should go to Carl Sandburg to ask him how he wrote his poems. How the deuce could the most eminent professor —and Holden was an acknowledged corn shark—learn how to pick out the best yielding ears of corn from such a mum and enigmatical man as this patriarch, James Reid? There was absolutely nothing of the conscious comparer, the Angus Mackay about him; and if he had a subtle way of knowing a heavy-yielding ear of corn, his system was as secret and mysterious as the instinct by which Leaming's red-headed woodpeckers pounced on early-ripening ones. Such too is science.

Reid was a terrible business man; he had no tongue for ballyhoo nor any impresario; but he was a showman all the same. His corn was lovely; to all the fairs roundabout he sent it, and he himself didn't go with it, but he didn't have to: those tremendous golden cylinders made up of close-packed, keystone-shaped kernels spoke for themselves. They had to be champions, those ears of Reid's! Mysterious is the spread of grain over the surface of the American land, for reasons, sometimes, as finicky as a fashion, as a rage for short dresses and no hips among women. Not because they were sure the Reid Yellow Dent corn was the best yielder did the common men of the corn belt begin to bellow for it, not because it was tough against a plague, as Mark Carleton's durum wheat was resistant to the black stem rust, did they howl for it. They clamored for this Reid corn because it won the Grand Sweepstakes ribbon, fifty dollars in cash, and a Parlin and Orendorff breaking plow at the State Fair at Peoria; because it stood the judges on their heads at Chicago and was dubbed "World's Fair Corn."

183

Here you had dirt-farmers, clods of men not knowing one note of music from another, unable to tell a real painting from a chromo: but they'd turn their pockets inside out for a bushel of Reid's original seed, they paid such silly prices as one hundred and fifty dollars for a bushel of it. They turned six states green in the summer and gold in the autumn with it until seven hundred and fifty thousand out of every million acres of corn land in the corn states were growing corn whose ancestors stemmed from a certain little corncrib in central Illinois. The Reid corn was beautiful.

It cannot be proved that this Yellow Dent maize, grown by James Reid himself, *selected* by him, would not grow a record crop on just the right rich black land. . . . But there was the rub: every Tom, Dick, and Harry didn't have Reid's knack. And with the thousand characters sleeping in the blood of those fair ears how long would that corn stay strictly *Reid?*

v.

NOW started one of the most silly sciences in the comedy that is the history of science, certainly the most outlandish nonsense in the long history of maize: it is amazing that farmers who are supposed to be hard-boiled, from Missouri, skeptical, would fall for it. Now started a way of breeding corn that was far as possible away from Nature, away from the Lord's way. . . . "I never argue with the Lord," was old James Reid's formula for breeding corn. In the last of the buggy days, the easy days for the corn-belt men—just before the coming of the grim days of the present when they need real money and haven't got it, arose the quaint custom to breed maize according to rules drawn up by a committee!

That fantastical old gentleman, Mr. E. S. Fursman of El Paso, Illinois, became chief cook and bottle-washer of the

Illinois Corn-Breeders' Association, and he was helped by the famous Orange Judd. Fursman wasn't a corn breeder himself, was hardly a farmer, but he was a tremendous corn-belt patriot, knew corn to be the very root of Illinois life, and in a confused way he was mad about the drama of this ubiquitous life-giving maize. He was tickled to death when anybody called him a "corn crank," and he was known to orate on the subject of maize in a murky smoking car all the way from Bloomington to Chicago. There stood the fanatic Fursman, at the end of one of those old rickety wooden coaches that reeked horribly and invincibly of dead cigar butts, shouting at the top of his voice above the clank and rattle of the train about the marvels of maize. How he held his strange audience! Farmers, drummers, small businessmen, and all that flotsam and jetsam of life you'll find in a middle American smoking car, listened with their mouths open, like a jury impressed with a witness, whispered their understanding to each other. "We *Must* Breed Better Corn!" Fursman would roar at the end.

Fursman got eighteen farmer-breeders together, among them President Coolidge's good old Illinois uncle, in solemn assembly to accomplish his one purpose. Alas—every man jack of them had his own idea of what the ideal and ultimately proper ear of heavy-yielding corn should look like, and every idea was different. As in all science done by committees the final aim became peace and concord through compromise, instead of a search for truth. And at last these eighteen gentlemen got together and with the utmost solemnity invented a scorecard for a perfect ear of Yellow Dent corn. Never an experiment nor a yield test did they make. By arithmetic out of their eighteen heads and with entire disregard of experience they set up a mark of perfect corn for breeders to shoot at. They didn't try out how much this corn would yield—just figured it out. Such was the beginning of the lovely, ten-inch long, rough-dented ear that for a score of years won millions of dollars in prizes, and set the maize yield of the corn belt back by millions of bushels during the next twenty years.

James Reid himself was one of the founders of this association and didn't believe for a moment in this nonsense of trying to outdo the Lord by mathematics. The new corn stemmed, most of it, from his own beloved ears, but he knew these fancy, rough-dented ears—so far as yield went— weren't a patch on his original smooth ones. But Reid, who was an exceedingly queer fish, let old Fursman rave, let those absurd corn mathematicians cook up their philosophical ideal ear of corn for the corn judges. . . . He shut his mouth. He even won a few medals with this chaffy new rough corn himself—nothing easier than for that sharp-eyed man to find such trash in his own corn fields: a corn field's like humanity—you can find bums and saints and geniuses anywhere, in any family. James Reid died in 1910, and if his own marvelous Yellow Dent Corn didn't die with him, at least it's safe to say that particular kind of maize went to sleep, was lost. . . . The corn judges judged an ear of maize by their score-cards; thousands of farmers picking their own seed of the Reid corn had their own private wishes and notions of what it should be like: hundreds of little quirks and traits that had slept behind James Reid's smooth yellow ears now came to the surface to make hundreds of new maize varieties—good, bad, and hopeless. Oh—who would ever really govern the tangled inheritance dormant in the kernels of the maize—tangled as the mysterious blood lines in the loins of men and women?

So Reid passed, and with him his maize—which really had been a wonderful yielder, had been marvelously tough in new counties and prairies where it didn't belong, had put dollars into the pockets of corn-belt men. "He left but little of this world's goods for the support of his wife and daughter who are now residents of Delavan, Illinois," wrote the good Oscar Sommer who tried to raise a pitiful ten thousand dollars to care for the folks of that mum old white-beard.

Oscar failed to raise it. Seventy-five percent of those piles of gold that lie every year in the autumn between the tawny corn shocks all over the corn belt had come f. n ancestors picked by the Delavan corn-sage. But Sommer wrote: "Mrs. Reid is practically destitute and in feeble health without any other means of support than that contributed by the County Board of Supervisors, the Red Cross, and fri ds of the family. . . ." Mrs. Reid died a public charge. And who knows the fate of daughter Olive—in her last years James Reid's right-hand man at his job of picking strong seed for the middle American land? But let that pass. Who knows the reward of the first maize finders in the early days of fire?

Who among hunger fighters is so foolish as to hope that he, or his deeds, or his own seed, will last? Like one strong individual tree of the maize is each hunger fighter. It is silly to try to make either one of them permanent. It is right that the seed of both of them—the man and the maize plant—should merge with the great river of the life of its own species, should disappear in the living matrix of its own kind.

VI.

IN the early nineteen hundreds this same Prof. P. G. Holden, who had worked to make money for shrewd men with the corn of Reid who couldn't make money, went from Illinois to Iowa—to the real corn state, to the one corn land laid down by God and the glacier for the particular purpose of growing maize to turn into meat on four legs. Holden pumped up the men of that dark-earthed state into a fury of corn improvement. Slim, bespectacled, not too practical, a believer in the goodness of God, an adorer of the intangible science of the sad-faced James L. Reid, this corn-evangelist P. G. Holden set fire to the Iowa corn men's shirts. It was Holden started the corn shows of Iowa. Even young boys were worked up by this preacher Holden into a passion for better maize. He did an immense amount of good, did this lyrical Holden. Because of him farmers all over sweat to keep up the fertility of their land; that would make their corn ears bigger, more beautiful. Through Holden careless men began to have a care to select their seed corn earlier in the autumn, to dry it better, to coddle it, pamper it: that would give them a chance to win the sweepstakes at the corn show. By their kitchen stoves they sorted and mumbled over their corn ears while their lush land lay under its white blanket: this work would give them a finer stand of more uniform Reid Yellow Dent with which to take a shot at the Gold Medal next year. So the little scrubby eight-rowed Indian corn of the country was buried under a wave of millions of bushels of the bright yellow seed from Delavan—a wave started by Holden.

In these early nineteen hundreds things were jake for the Iowa men: the vigor of the maize sent the value of their soil up and up and if selling maize and pigs and cattle wasn't enormously profitable, selling the land that grew them certainly was excellent business. . . . It brought cash for the trip to the Coast, for the boys and girls to take that two years' course at Ames, for one of those new-fangled autos, for all of the dozens of new things dirt-farmers now began to believe were necessities of life. In those days a thin boy whose face was too earnest for his age met the enthusiastic Holden. The boy was Henry A. Wallace, grandson of the famous Uncle Henry beloved of the prairie men. Henry was a town-boy, just out of knee-pants. He had grown up in Des Moines, the city that sits in a bowl surrounded in the summer by limitless gold-plumed armies of maize plants dressed in green. Since he'd first come to understand spoken words, this excessively serious boy—though no farmer—had watched the forests of maize give up their heavy ears out of land whose price went up and up, that brought more gold, brought prosperity. Corn could hardly help being the life of Henry Wallace, as it was of his land and his people.

In the office of the Wallace farm paper a boy's corn show was held that year: the distinguished Holden came across thirty flat miles from Ames College by the Skunk River to judge and pick out the very finest, heavy-yielding ears, to award the prizes. The boys crowded 'round the corn professor as he stalked judicially up and down between the beautifully arranged piles of ears of the Yellow Dent. Henry Wallace hung on every word of this learned Holden, believed him, adored him, only, there was this about young Wallace: out of his thin face too old for his age there glowered a pair of doubting gray eyes. . . . Those eyes were out of place in a boy of seventeen. But Wallace listened to Holden.

Gravely, for the instruction of youth, that good man held up a great cylindrical ear that was not so good to his learned eye. "This ear, boys, shows a marked lack of constitution!" cried Holden. "And look at this one, for contrast," said he. "Observe its remarkably strong middle!" And such is the folly of teaching—that every boy, hypnotized, could do none other than see what Holden wanted him to see. Solemnly the professor judged and awarded the medal to the very finest ear of all those hundreds of ears of maize, pronounced it champion.

A mob of disappointed and happy farm boys straggled out of the room. Henry stayed. The professor unbent. "Now, young man, if you really want proof that I'm right, why don't you take thirty or so of the finest of these prize ears? Then next spring plant them! Plant them, one ear to a row of corn. Then harvest them next fall—and measure the yield of them." In words like these Holden stoked up young Wallace.

Now there's no question that nine hundred and ninety-nine out of every thousand boys would have said: "Thank you, sir, I'll try to do that,"—and would have then gone off and forgotten all about it when the sounds of bats against baseballs were heard that next spring. What the devil was the use, anyway, of proving that Professor Holden was right? Of course the finest looking ears must be the heaviest yielders! And there's no doubt whatever about the sincerity of Holden himself in his science of corn-judging. But the next spring Henry Wallace took those thirty-three fine ears, shelled them into separate piles, stuck them under the soil, four kernels to a hill, in thirty-three rows, one ear to a row, on a little piece of land his father gave him.

That summer he didn't forget to hoe this little insignificant corn patch. That autumn this too-solemn boy husked those thirty-three rows separately, never forgetting the labels on them. His tongue sticking intently out of the corner of his mouth, he shelled the ears, determined their dry weight as if he were some precocious analytical chemist. And here he sits, at night, covering sheet after sheet of ruled paper with figures that look like eighth-grade arithmetic: he is calculating the bushel-per-acre yield of the rows from those thirty-three ears.

Alas!

The very finest ear of all, judged champion by Holden, gives a row that is one of the ten lowest yielders of all of those thirty-three. Wrinkles bunch up over Henry's glowering eyes.

And the rest? There he sits, puzzled among his sums. There's absolutely no rime or reason to the result of them. Professor Holden, bless him, might as well have gone around blindfolded at his judging exhibition, picking ears at random and calling them highest yielders by the feel of them! Alas—these ears with a sublime foolish topsy-turviness yielded all over the chart without any relation at all to the sage judgments of Holden.

It was insanity. It was wrong by all the rules. It was blasphemy and heresy for this believing boy. But it was the beginning of his strange life which, as you will see, was a

HENRY A. WALLACE

mixture of farm-paper editing, figuring of statistics to prove
that Iowa farmers get the dirty end of the rope, savage
fighting for the rights of Iowa corn-belt men, theosophy and
astrology, and backyard science. But here was the beginning
of his backyard science. Seventeen-year-old Henry Wallace
sits in his room, gray eyes glowering at his cold figures,
chewing his pencil to wet, distracted slivers. . . .

Here were these thirty-three ears of corn, graded by
Holden, the highest authority, in an exact order of finer and
finer ears, heavier and heavier yielders. But here they were:
reducing that judgment to complete absurdity and buffoonery. They yielded all over Henry's chart, from thirty-
three bushels to the acre for the worst to seventy-nine
bushels to the acre for the finest. And some of the worst
lookers were the best yielders!

Here was no school or college lesson in science for this

high school boy. Here was real experience in science burning itself into the brain of Wallace; and from that day forward he stuck up his nose at mere beauty in an ear of corn, understood the truth of the salty saying: "You can't tell by the looks of a frog how far he can jump."

This yield test of the thirty-three ears seared a fundamental hunch into him: that this old saying holds for the yielding power of maize no less than for the acrobatics of frogs.

At the moment of this obscure experiment by a boy so young he had no business to be dabbling in science, the Iowa folks didn't yet have to feel bothered about just how much their corn would yield. Wallace, an experimenter ahead of the proper age, was also an experimenter ahead of his time. The value of the corn land went up and up: the boys could sell for two hundred dollars an acre what their fathers had bought for a song. Any old maize would do. Times were fat: the land was lush—with money: curve-dashed Oldsmobiles steered by a stick began to appear, and get themselves stuck in the Iowa gumbo.

But these days were nearing an end. Pretty soon tough times would be here, when the bushel-per-acre yield of the maize would be fundamental, when the up and up value of the black land would come to a peak and then fall down with a bang, when the vigor of the maize would be the one hope against debt, against the foreclosure of mortgages, against the loss of the land won by the fathers. In the old days the saying went: "The strength of a people is measured by their ability to overcome geographic barriers." That was past, accomplished by Daniel Boone and by Jake Leaming's father, by James Reid's grandfather and the great-grandfather of Henry Wallace—all of them had crossed the Alleghenies. The new saying would go:

"The new strength of a people must be measured by their ability to overcome *economic* barriers."

Here is Henry Wallace—never realizing it—going

towards this new frontier, the barrier of hard times.

Here stand the delicate, vigorous, finicky trees of the maize, ready to help the corn-belt men. The value of this maize in a single year is far ahead of the value of wheat in several years. But even so how will the maize help the corn-belt men to trick hard times? By growing bigger and bigger yields of it on smaller fields? By lowering the cost of growing the maize that now has to be sold at such a pitifully small price because of its very abundance? Bigger yields on smaller fields—is that an out for the corn-belt men who are proud, and want to help themselves? Room they must have on their black land for other things besides corn: but as much corn they must grow as ever. Corn is basic, fundamental.

But who will *fix* the power of maize to yield high, this maize whose yield Henry Wallace found to be so shifting, so subtle, so out of all relation to the fine looks of it?

Who will pick one, or two, or three blood lines out of the thousands of traits of maize, and breed them to give always, surely, a record crop?

George Harrison Shull will try to do it, and Henry Wallace—in his backyard—will help him. To look at Shull you'd say there could be no more impractical man: he's only one of those dreaming botanizers. But here he comes, enormously practical in spite of his absent-minded mulling over theories. He arises—thousands of years after certain anonymous red men—as the first white *breeder* of maize.

193

SHULL

CHAPTER SEVEN. THE MAIZE BREEDER

SHULL

I.

OF HOW THE FIRST ABORIGINAL RED MAN—or woman—stumbled on to the first green accidental tree of maize there can only be a poetic guess. But there is written record of the curious and fundamental maize exploit of the civilized white man, George Harrison Shull.

Shull married a maize plant to itself. By the dwarfish and ill-begotten children of that incestuous marriage this little professor was surprised. Through the runtish off-spring of this unnatural union, consummated by his pottering with certain paper bags, he began for the first time of all men to trace down, to uncover pure blood lines of maize that had been mysteriously hidden and hopelessly mixed for nobody knows how many thousands of years. For maize Shull discovered the silliness of the superstition that like produces like. To the breeding of the Indian corn he brought sureness—where everything before had been as full of whims and chances as the issue from the passion of any human boy and girl. For maize this obscure Shull was certainly a new fantastic sort of pioneer.

It would be wrong to say George Shull was the first to try the utterly impractical, you'd almost say impossible, stunt of fixing the fathers an ear of maize should have. Thirty years before Shull made his highbrow paper-bag marriages of corn at Cold Spring Harbor on Long Island, the botanist Beal in Michigan was castrating maize plants, depriving them of their manhood by pulling off their tassels.

Beal—who was a learned Quaker—was urging practical Michigan men to try new complicated tricks of breeding maize. Tall, loathing tobacco, proud of his austere teetotality, Beal traveled north to the Farmers' Institute at Traverse City. The dirt men from miles around trooped into

Campbell's hall, having come in from their new-cleared land in bob-sleighs, stamping the snow from their socks and rubbers around the red-hot big-bellied wood stove. Professor Kedzie was going to talk to them about kerosene lamps and illuminating oil; Professor Beal was about to instruct them in "Horticultural Experiments and How Discoveries Are Made." But principally these plain men were lured to this intellectual feast of 1876 by excellent music, rendered by the Traverse City Silver Cornet Band. Little did they know they would listen to landmark science in the breeding of maize.

Beal rose to his great height and peered at his smelly meeting. "What do we think of a man," he asked earnestly, "who selects the best calves, pigs, lambs, only from the best mothers, paying no attention whatever to the selection of a good male parent?"

These Michigan men—though not polished—weren't given to butting in on speeches or even answering these professors, their obvious betters. And anyway they wouldn't say out loud with the women around what they'd think of such a fool as that—and what they thought privately wouldn't be fit to print. What would a good farmer think of a fellow who bred livestock just from the mothers? . . .

With something of the owl in him, waiting like the schoolmaster he was for his thought to sink home, Beal squinted at his grown-up pupils dramatically. "But that," he said, "is just what our farmers are doing now, selecting from the largest, fairest ears of corn!"

There's no record how many of his moustached listeners, with the blended aroma of pine trees, tobacco juice, and barns in their beards, understood the polygamous, promiscuous way of a maize plant's marrying and begetting. Surely not many of them knew the bizarre physiology of a maize plant being husband to a hundred wives and at the same time wife to half a hundred husbands. Carefully Beal got all that through their heads.

198

"But it's only the ears—those are from the mother plants —that you pick for seed. Yet those ears have been formed from silks that have got pollen from every conceivable kind of father. There are lots of slender, unthrifty stalks in your field—yet they shed pollen which blows by the chance of the wind on to the silks of the very best plants. There are plenty of barren stalks, that don't shoot ears at all—but they've tassels, from which pollen goes all over the field. . . ."

Well—what about it?

"What I suggest," offered this dreaming professor, "is that you go through your fields, spotting those poor plants, and jerk off their tassels before they shed pollen. That'll keep them from mixing their blood with the rest of the corn."

Here was the first fanatic for corn eugenics—nearly as foolish as modern folks who without humor advocate picking out human fathers by science instead of letting nature do it with a sidelong look in the eye or a pink rush of color to the face of a maid. The farmers listened—with more or less respect. But what was this tall loon of a prof raving about, anyway? What man had the time to go through his whole field of corn every day during the whole two weeks or more of tasseling time—pulling off tassels from bum stalks? How'd you know a stalk was barren? Sometimes the ears shot out very late! And if a plant was barren— did this prof know whether or not barrenness ran in families, whether it went down to the children? Let this feller come out and be their hired man for a while and see how much time he'd have to be mooching 'round in a cornfield two weeks in July—with the wheat ready to cut!

No—the skeptical farmers had a lot of sense on their side. And even Jake Leaming, or James Reid, who in these very days were founding the varieties of their magnificent Yellow Dent corn by the old Indian way of picking out the finest fairest ears, couldn't have made head or tail to Wil-

199

liam James Beal's theoretical proposals. How control the
fatherhood of an ear of maize? Here's the best corn crank,
here's Jake Leaming himself, standing in the middle of his
field in high summer, standing in an invisible rain, a golden
rain of pollen that makes the air sneezy, that settles on his
hands, in his eyebrows, on the sleeves of his shirt—and on
the silks of a thousand maize trees all around him. . . .
Who'd say what pollen should go where? Who—but some
professor? Botany? All right—but Beal ought to be learnin'
it to city boys in white collars and town girls that went
to college because they aimed to teach school. Botany!

Of course it was outlandish that William Beal had ever
become a professor—it was as strange as the trick of a fine
ear of corn yielding nothing but runts and nubbin ears every
now and again. Look at Beal's father: he was one of those
pioneers whose faces had the mark common to all of the
stump-grubbers and tree-fallers of those grim Michigan
days—a thin-lipped mouth drawn down at the corners.
. . . No highfalutin monkey business in the head of old
Beal. He helped carve Michigan out of the woods. But his
boy, William James? When he should have been sweating,
this lad had gazed at the Pottawattamie Indians, hilling
up their maize, planting it year after year in the same old
hills in Lenawee County, southern Michigan. Young Beal
had watched bear pounce on the back of his father's scream-
ing pigs and make meals off those critters before they were
dead. He'd seen myriads of cotton-tails, skunks, squirrels,
busy bothering his father's corn standing in shocks in clearings still too rooty to plow. The boy didn't seem to care
for his dad's thin-lipped life.

So, out of this now lost lovely country, where the gray
geese trampled down the wheat near the little lakes, where
the burning log-heaps in the autumn evenings threw giant
shadows on the tree rims of the clearings, Beal bumped.
He jounced away, over corduroy roads—to the University
of Michigan. Next he went east—to Harvard College, and

here he had the nerve to brace the famous Swiss-American, Louis Agassiz. "I have the ambition to be a botanist and zoölogist," William told that formidable man.

"But why do you want to study zoölogy?" roared Agassiz. "There's no money in it! You must make up your mind to be poor all your life!"

II.

NOW here is Beal, crammed full of the lore of sea-urchins and the intimate parts of fossil fishes by this completely professorial Agassiz. Here is Beal—a professor in the little one-building Michigan Agricultural College at Lansing that did very well to have three professors in all. Here you have Doctor of Philosophy William James Beal, an impractical jack of all the sciences of horticulture, a fanatic for cross-breeding like the old druggist of Marquis wheat fame, William Saunders, only with his feet much farther off the ground than Saunders. This Beal will improve the Michigan corn crop!

"To infuse new vigor into varieties, I propose in the case of corn and other seeds to get seeds from remote parts where they have grown for some years and to plant these different seeds near each other and so mix them," wrote the dreamer Beal.

In the not too fertile fields close by his absurd new college, Beal started an experiment Jake Leaming would have snorted at. From Farmer Jacob Walton of the town of Raisin he got a White Dent corn—Walton had kept that corn "pure" on his own farm for ten years. Farmer Hathaway, from way off at Little Prairie Ronde, sent Beal some ears of his pet Yellow Dent—fifteen years he'd nursed it, selected it, grown nothing but his own maize without mixture from foreign parts.

"Too much care is needed for experiments, to trust them to others," said Beal. So he tucked a row of white grains of the Walton corn under the ground with his own hands—he was at least that much of a gardener. And in the row next to the Walton he planted the yellow seed from Hathaway, and beyond that again a row of the Walton. So, strangely, in alternate rows he planted these two sorts of corn, saw they were well hoed, watched them shoot up with that fantastic vigor of maize in May and June. Then came July—and what an experiment! Here is Beal, pottering up and down between these rows of the Dent and the Walton, just as tasseling time comes on, at the very beginning of the maize honeymoon. The intent and serious Beal walks with dignified deliberation through his small green forest, just as the tassels begin to send out their plumes to crown the trees of it. He starts a brutal operation:

He jerks the tassels off the tops of the Walton corn plants. With a hawk's eye, with a scientist's ruthlessness, with an experimenter's care, every morning he goes, yanking the hopeful fecund tassels off the Walton corn before they've ever a chance to shed their pollen. So he castrates the corn of Jacob Walton.

Now the silks of this completely female Walton will have to be fertilized by the pollen from the Hathaway of the rows on either side of it. So Beal cross-breeds the Walton maize with the Hathaway. Now he can be absolutely sure of both the fathers and the mothers of the Walton corn. That autumn he husks the Walton ears, labels them. For the next spring's sowing he stows away these cross-bred mother ears whose fathers have come all the way from Little Prairie Ronde. Patient and long as the years is his toil.

"It is easy enough to observe isolated facts; any one can soon learn to do that, but when you *compare* two or more objects, then you take a step forward in philosophy,"—so old Louis Agassiz had counseled young Beal, had dinned at his pupil Beal—who didn't need to be dinned at. A comparer born, like Angus Mackay, was Beal. And next spring amid the hopeful songs of the just-arrived meadow larks,

Beal puts his newfangled hybrid seed under the ground. Four rows of it he plants—through the middle of a field of the prize Yellow Dent corn, called the best in Michigan by the authorities of the Agricultural College.

The result is superb. That fall Beal is happy, as he shells the ears of this new Walton-Hathaway hybrid maize, weighs the seed from these ears, measures their yield in bushels per acre, compares the yield of this new cross-bred seed with the yield per acre of the standard Yellow Dent corn of the college, the champion corn of Michigan, grown close by in the same field. The comparison knocks his eye out: the result is immense: from the same amount of space in the field that yields one hundred pounds of the college corn, the tall professor reaps one hundred and fifty-three pounds of his hybrid—"Walton x Hathaway." And the hybrid plants, marvelously tall, heavy-stalked, are far and away better yielders than the average of their own parents, or than the better of their parents!

If Beal hadn't been dignified and given to an extraordinarily solemn peering at nature, he would have danced up and down, given an oyster supper in honor of this event to his fellow professors. For here was a moment in his life: here was a prophecy—based on reasoning—come true. That's the moment in the life of any pure scientist, and Beal certainly belonged to that breed of men. And he must be absolutely right about this strange vigor of the hybrid children, because here came a scientific report from across the ocean, from England, from the foremost biologist in the universe, from Charles Darwin himself. That bearded saint of science had brought together the seed of petunias from remote places and married them—and the issue was much bigger and better petunias. "Ah—check!" Beal could whisper. But here's what was finest—Beal had thought the maize stunt up all by himself, and read about Darwin's petunias afterwards. All by himself he'd discovered this principle of the increased vigor of these bastard maize children—it was new. . . . Only was it really new?

How long before the unscientific days of Moses had the first experimenter bred a mare to an ass, to be amazed at the birth of the mule—more vigorous, stronger, far huskier than either its mare mother or its jackass father?

Well, granted—but here Beal had done the trick with plants, not animals; here was a new way to breed maize for a record yield. But was that new? For how many thousands of years had the Indians, by rituals, by curious idiotic-seeming ceremonies, charged certain lone wolves of their tribes with the growing of the pure seed of one definite sort or color of maize, far apart from each other, far away from the villages? For how many thousand springs, at each planting time, hadn't they then taken three or four of these sorts of seed and put them under the ground together in one cornhill? How was that different from the scientific experiment of William James Beal—excepting that the professor had pulled off the tassels of one sort, confined the fathers to one variety. . . .

The Indians knew nothing of the physiology of tassels and silks: they only had some dim notion that sexual doings occurred between their mixed seeds, had a superstition that mixing breeds of maize pepped up the growth of its trees— caused those trees to yield them more corn bread and hasty pudding. . . .

III.

"A MAN must not hesitate to throw three or four years of experiments in the waste-basket before he appears in public" —this was a saying of Beal. But this strange business of the vigor of cross-bred maize children was nothing to throw into the waste-basket. "It seems to me the greatest chance ever offered, to make a good experiment in this country for the benefit of the farmers!" So Beal told a hard-boiled meeting of stump-grubbers in 'seventy-seven under the elms and willows close by the lovely ribbon of the Grand River at Ionia.

He harangued them—as became a savant—on this mysterious lustiness that appears in the first generation of the offspring begot by the pollen of a corn from one place and conceived by the silks of a maize from another place far distant.

Those farmers chewed at wisps of hay, thoughtfully spat their extracts of Peerless tobacco, as Beal explained that this vigor of the cross-bred corn *didn't last*, that you'd only find it in the first year of the seed, that next year the seed from these high-yielding children would just be ordinary corn seed again—or maybe even worse than ordinary. . . .

"Of course the two varieties, from each place, will have to be crossed every year to give this high-yielding seed," lectured Beal. "But it will be money in your pockets to plant cross-bred seed every year . . ." he finished.

His audience broke up, went off muttering to itself under its big straw hats—what busy farmer is going to plant two kinds of corn, *every year*, for seed? What the hell? Who's going to take the time to jerk the tassels off one sort, every day, several times a day, for weeks during tasseling time—just to get seed this here college professor claims will yield half again as much as regular corn? And would it yield half again as much—every year?

Even Beal couldn't swear to that. It was one of his sage sayings that "what happens one year in an experiment may be reversed the next . . . and experiments should be continued ten years or more."

And why should Beal's result have been anything more than a chance? How many different traits of fatherhood were dormant in those yellow grains of the Hathaway Yellow Dent corn? How could he be sure that the very same fathers, which after all were distributed here and there, helter-skelter, among millions of pollen grains—would marry the same mothers who were here and there in hundreds of thousands of silks? Let's be kind to old Beal, tinkering experimenter ahead of his time! He had no notion of the enormous individuality of maize. He just had luck—the right pollen happened to nick with the right silks the first two or three years. . . .

Was the Walton maize pure? The Walton maize was as mixed up as a nation of humans—a mob of ten million individual people. You might take a broad-beamed husk of a Danish girl, marry her to a brown-eyed, heavy-shouldered stevedore from way down south in Italy: the kids from this hybrid marriage might turn out themselves to be heavy yielders—to have ten children apiece. . . . Or again some of the girl-children might be barren, and the men might turn out to sire one or two runty children, no more. So with maize. Good old Beal had made a grope and a stumbling step ahead: he'd wanted to give maize the right sort of fathers —but the fathers from a variety? The grains of pollen from any variety of maize are as numerous as the grains of white, dazzling sand on the shore of Lake Michigan; they're as different as the sperm in the loins of the men of America.

If William James Beal had stuck to just this one kind of experiment he might have sensed this mixed-upness of the heredity of corn, might have turned the trick that George Harrison Shull thought of, thirty years later. Alas, in the years of 'seventy-nine and 'eighty, the yields of his crossbred seed weren't nearly so phenomenally heavy. Other professors, Henry of Wisconsin, Georgeson of Texas, Gulley of Mississippi, men he'd induced in his first enthusiasm to try crossing corn from different parts of their own states, didn't report good results or any results to him. And he himself had a thousand things to do, among others he had to teach history—which he detested. And besides, his random curiosity set him pottering at a hundred experiments: burying seeds in the grounds in bottles "to be taken out of the ground at a remote date to determine whether they would sprout." For years with religious regularity Beal pruned the limbs of apple trees the twenty-fifth day of each month of the year to see which pruning would make them thrive best. He planted the pits of peaches diseased with the yellows. . . . He crossed the flowers of yellow and Danvers onions. . . . He toiled at an enormous collection and description of North American grasses—

But to breed pure the blood lines of maize, to untangle those tangled mysterious lines—that was not a job for such a universally curious man. There was a job for a single-minded fanatic, eating, dreaming, sleeping, experimenting, thinking maize alone. So old Beal scratched the surface of this strange business of the vigor of hybrids—and then his find went to sleep, his little fact of the heavy-yielding cross-bred corn was lost. . . . But the old gentleman botanized to the last, remained wrapped in the study and worship of nature to the very end of his eighty-some years. To the end he stayed poor, proud, and stern. In his last year, when he couldn't walk any more, he still tottered outside, seated himself on a box, and sawed a definite number of sticks of wood every morning. . . . Strange as the mixed-up traits of the maize are the quirks of men. What if Beal had put all that persistent Quaker severity of his into the one job of mapping out the blood lines of maize? . . . But then in Beal's heyday in Michigan the folks didn't need record yields—and discoveries have a trick of rising from the needs of men.

IV.

BUT not always—for nobody would claim that George Shull took his jump ahead of the red men, made his discovery of the one way to make always a record crop, because the corn-belt men needed such a crop or demanded it. In 1904, when this intensely academic little man began pottering with maize plants a thousand miles away from the corn belt, he had no notion whatever that the prosperous heart of the American land would ever need anything but the energy of its sweating men. Shull had other fish to fry, wasn't thinking of such a prosaic business as the national corn yield per acre. He was a scientist purely, with his head in theoretical clouds, mooning over such abstruse problems as the Galtonian Regression in Pure Lines—whatever that means. . . . This innocent Shull never dreamed that in twenty short years the American dirt farmers would be dragged into the terrible American need to be efficient, would have to raise bigger yields of maize on smaller fields, would be forced to cut the cost of raising their maize—or go under.

So, Shull's adventures with maize go contrary to what you might so far think is the whole point of the story of hunger fighters. From Mohler, from Carleton, from Angus Mackay and the earthy rest of them you'd say Truth was secondary—you'd swear Truth came as a by-product of their toil for tougher wheat, of their sweating to fight pestilence threatening meat on four legs, of men's need to grow more bushels of this or that to the acre. Are Shull's fantastic experiences the exceptions that prove this rule? Who knows? Who can recount all the whys, the wherefores, of men tricking Nature, fighting hunger?

Like Beal, George Shull was born on a farm and grew up there refusing to be charmed by the delights of rural life. A remarkable family were these Shulls. Five brothers had George—and three of them became university professors with their names in *Who's Who*, another an excellent painter of scientific subjects, and the fifth a superintendent of a flock of high schools in Indiana. Who will say that like produces like? Surprising as the tricks of the maize were the various destinies of these brothers Shull—who so strangely did not breed true to what you'd think was the farmer blood of their father and mother.

Of course the times were ready for George Harrison Shull's academic experiments and difficult theorizings. With

208

a degree of Doctor of Philosophy from the University of Chicago, where knowledge grew out of oil, Shull got a job at the Carnegie Institution Station for Experimental Evolution on Long Island, where theoretical probings into the mystery of the origin of life were supported by iron and steel. Charles Darwin, aided by the noble ballyhoo of Thomas Huxley and Ernst Haeckel, had convinced a great part of the civilized world that Eve had not come out of Adam's rib, and that old Adam himself was, if not a grandson, then surely a blood cousin to some remote baboon. Living things—evolved. All life was in flux. But how, exactly, did one species arise from another? That was what this Station for Experimental Evolution at Cold Spring Harbor had been founded to find out, and here was George Shull, an obscure experimental philosopher, digging at this gigantic fact that may forever remain a mystery.

Like every biologist of his day, George Shull had been brought up on *The Origin of Species*, just as Tennessee boys are brought up on the Bible. From this sacred book he had learned that it is in the nature of species of living things to vary, maybe ever so little from their parents, but just the same to vary. This holy book taught him that these variations in the millions of individuals of magpies or monkeys or men *pile up*. And if these piled-up differences help magpies or monkeys or men in their fight for existence, then they're inherited by the offspring. And so species change. So it was that all life was supposed to have developed, beginning with a mysterious stir in a formless slime, changing up and up through insignificant amebas to lovely zebras and intelligent men. It was an inspiring and majestic story—but was it so? Surely life has changed— but how? Huxley had burned a faith in this yarn of evolution into the hearts of men of science, but here was Shull, one of a thousand obscure little men, who said: "All right —we believe in Evolution, but how have Sequoias arisen after the time when there were no trees, only ferns, and how have camels come to be after the remote time when there was life, but never a single beast on four legs?" Gallantly Shull—and a thousand others—began gnawing at this terrific, this hopeless riddle.

Shull belonged to a pioneering breed of observers of Nature, who weren't content to excavate, reconstruct skeletons of little five-toed horses, and concoct stories of how these five-toed beasts turned into great brewery horses with one hoof to each leg. He was one of a brainy gang who did more than describe the looks and the habits of plants and animals. Like the pious Dutchman, Hugo de Vries, like the wizened Dane, Johannsen, he had an immense curiosity about hidden properties of plants and animals, traits tucked away in their sperm and their eggs, mysterious chemical quirks in them that might be at the bottom of how any plant or animal differed from its father and mother. To dig at such puzzles these fellows had to do more than write essays, they had to experiment, they had to breed. And Shull from the first was a relentless, incorrigible breeder.

There's no doubt he got his start at the breeding of maize from Johannsen, the Dane, who began toppling over some of the most sacred tenets of the Darwinian faith—by weighing beans. This theoretical fusser in Denmark took a whole lot of beans that came out of the same field, were supposed to belong to one and the same species of beans. With a silly patience this Johannsen weighed endless individual beans, set down the exact number of centigrams each one weighed, got a headache looking down long rows of figures to find these strange beans varied a good deal in their weight—in a word, a bean wasn't just a bean!

Then he took a single one of those beans, planted it, with a fantastic patience garnered its offspring. He did this with a lot of heavyweight, welterweight, and lightweight beans —and roughly the heavyweights raised heavy children and the lightweights lighter ones, but—

But—very roughly: When this pernickety Johannsen

took a heavy child bean that had come from one parent, and his lighter brother bean who was the child of that same parent, and planted those two—and weighed *their* children—

These children didn't turn out heavyweights and lightweights at all: they went back to the weight of the original grandfather bean Johannsen had started out with! "When I start out with one bean—I am founding a pure line," murmured Johannsen. "Inside such a pure line, the children may differ in weight—but that difference isn't inherited. . . . It isn't by a piling up of little differences in weight that you finally get a definitely bigger bean, a different species. . . . No—every species of beans has within it a lot of pure lines, of little species that breed true each one to itself. . . ."

It was from these revolutionary—and utterly useless?—bean measurings of old Johannsen that George Shull in America began fussing with maize.

v.

"so," muttered George Shull, "within a pure line, grown from one seed, you can select 'til you're black in the face, you will never get anything different."

All right—all right for beans. But beans were different from many other living things. A bean plant fertilizes itself—one plant is its own wife and husband. But here are other living things, and it's a different kettle of fish: these others cross-breed, as stallions mate with mares, and men mate with women. Do such unchangeable, such definite, such strangely fixed blood lines run through the seed of humans —of men and women? Maybe such blood lines are there, only masked by the enormous outward difference of each human body from another. . . . So Johannsen's beans made George Shull ponder such impossible questions.

But how the devil breed men and women to find out?

SHULL

Here now comes Shull's horse sense to help him. Here is Indian corn: every plant of it is naturally just as cross-bred as any human child. . . . Then in a flash, while he's at God knows what trivial duty, a hunch comes to George Shull.

Indian corn is cross-bred in nature, yes. But Indian corn is a kind of plant you can absolutely easily *breed to itself!* It carries its sperm on its tassels, high up; its eggs are concealed in the flowers on the young cob inside the ear shoot, far down the stalk. Marry maize to itself—just as beans naturally marry themselves, and then—

What will come out of the cross-bred maize when he inbreeds it? What lies masked by the enormous natural cross-bredness of maize? So George Shull picks out maize for his experimental animal.

Into the gravelly soil of Cold Spring Harbor, at the Evolution Laboratory, Shull tucks the seed of maize—not for a minute dreaming of the fantastic practical consequences of what he's doing. Does this gardening theorist have a single notion he's hatching a revolution in the breeding of the billions of bushels of the crop of the American maize? Not a bit of it. Comes May, and the green shoots of his absurd little cornfield poke their tips towards the sun. Comes July—and with it the puberty of the maize, the mystic time of tasseling and silking. The small, bearded theorist trudges out to his field with a handful of labels, strings, paper bags—his simple apparatus. Over the lovely plumes of a just-emerged tassel he ties a paper bag—not a grain of pollen shall escape.

Over the ear shoot of this same plant—the gentle green silks, sticky and hungry for pollen, haven't forced their way out yet—the precise Shull ties another paper bag. No chance pollen shall marry these silks—so eager for mating.

Days pass. Shull comes. Shull shakes the bags 'round the tassels, cocks his ear. Yes, golden powder is dropping from the hidden tassels. Carefully he takes off this little paper

212

sack, shakes the yellow, life-giving dust in it on to the silks of this very same plant—young silks from which he's just removed their paper covering. Then he ties the paper bag back over the silks so that no chance pollen from maize roundabout may mate with them adulterously. The ceremony of the marriage of the maize plant to itself is finished.

Alas—Shull's maize plants don't fancy marrying themselves. The seed from these inbred ears? What seed! The next spring these inbred plants are slow to come up. The ears on the stalks are fewer. They're much smaller than the ears of maize ought to be—but then, that was natural. Every practical cow-breeder and horse-breeder knows that the young beasts lack vigor, are in general what you might call a mess—when you inbreed their parents too closely. And such too is the superstition about the offspring of first cousins among humans, and the belief about the children from the immoral matings of brothers and sisters, or of the incestuous loves of fathers for their daughters. But what animal in God's creation could inbreed so closely as the maize plant—that Shull married to itself?

The first generation plants that came from the inbred ears were a sad sight, would have absolutely disgusted any good corn farmer or corn breeder like Jake Leaming—but here's Shull again, at tasseling time the next year, going at his runty plants once more with his paper bags and labels. Once more he marries them to themselves. Here's the lucky thing about George Shull—he's never been a practical corn breeder, has never picked for fine fair ears, he's only the slave of a highbrow notion. Once more he collects the ears of his inbreds. Again the next spring he plants them. And alas—

They are worse. They are fearful excuses for what corn ought to be. The plants of the second inbred generation are more runty, spindly, late-ripening, more nearly barren, more generally worthless—and you'd say absolutely good-for-nothing. Imagine the snorts of an Iowa dirt-farmer, chanc-

ing to walk among these sad inbred plants of George Shull
in the summer of 1906, at this silly little scientific farm at
Cold Spring Harbor. But there were no farmers around to
make fun of Shull's nonsense. Again Shull bagged the tassels and the silks of these feeble excuses for the noble plant
of the Indian corn. He inbred them once more—though
you'd swear by now they'd got too feeble to marry at all.
Some of them were too hopelessly sickly, their tassels im-
potent, their ear-shoots barren, and they died out, passed
away. But others—

Ah—here is something surprising! From the first inbred
generation he's noticed it. Shull peers up and down his
garden. Here's something to notice besides the mere badness of his inbred maize. Here are a lot of plants, that have
each one of them grown from the seed on his first inbred
ear—from that first plant he had married to itself. Shull
walks up and down along this pitiful row of weak-kneed
maize plants—mere shadows they are of their lusty parent.
He walks, wool-gathering.

He looks at these wrecks of corn-plants, brooding, hardly
seeing them. Then his eyes light up, the flash of a thought,
the beginning of a hunch flashes through his head. Here are
all these plants, coming from one parent—but look at them!

Here's an inbred child hardly three feet high—a dwarf
you'd call it.

Next it is a brother that's tall, spindly—a gawky seven-
footer.

Close by is a thickish corn plant—bushy, with a lot of
suckers growing out from the bottom of it: beside it is a
brother with just one stalk, no more.

Here's a plant with its poor ear sticking out—reaching
out to shake hands, as old Jake Leaming used to say. There's
one next with its ear sticking up straight, on a short
shank. . . .

But they've all come from one plant married to itself—
it is extraordinary! Does George Shull think for a moment

214

of the mere miserableness of these inbred children, of their poor yield, of their wretchedness that would make any corn-man turn up his nose at them? Not a bit of it. Each one of these he marries to itself, that summer, bags the tassels and the silks as before. And next summer comes, and by the sacred name of the old priest, Mendel, each one of these different inbred sorts breeds true—to its dwarfness or its spindleshanks, or its starchiness, or flintiness, to whatever trait made it look different from its inbred brothers. And next year the same again—here are *pure lines* of maize coming out of that first old inbred parent of 1903—that looked like any old ordinary corn plant, that was an ordinary cross-bred corn plant . . . but that hid in its seed all these marvelously distinct blood lines—now breeding pure, each true to its kind! It was extraordinary! What matter whether these inbreds were miserable yielders, giving pounds where cross-bred corn, pollinated by the wind, gave bushels? What matter the scorn of any corn crank? In his mind, at least, he has the right to dance a fandango. He has uncovered the composition of a field of maize.

George Shull has taken maize—apart.

It was as if this unknown, botanizing little gardener had reached his hands through the mists of ten thousand years and more to pick out the unknown, the primitive life stuff that had so mysteriously married, intermingled, to found the noble plant of the American maize.

But what use to the corn belt, or to the teeming millions of America and the lands across the sea who are fed from this middle of the American land? As yielders, all these pure-line inbreds are washouts. But Shull never thinks of it, would never listen to derisive giggles or contemptuous snorts, but instead wool-gathers once more, gets himself a new lot of paper bags and cuts himself another bundle of ends of string. . . .

Now he'll try crossing these inbred lines. He'll marry different ones of these feeble strains—if their seed'll only

last, if they won't perish from general good-for-nothingness.
. . . Here's the seed of one of those dwarfs—and that isn't
the worst you can say for that plant. Here's the grain off
one that has bred true for tallness—which is all anybody
could advance in favor of it.

In the summer of 1906, bagging their tassels and ear-
shoots once more, he crosses them. The pollen of tall-stalk
—the father—he shakes on to the silks of dwarf—the
mother.

What'll happen to their cross-bred seed? It's a purely
scientific question, you understand. It's the kind of test the
old Abbé Gregor Mendel had done with tall peas and short,
forty years before—to found the whole science of heredity,
and die absolutely unknown. That summer George Shull
makes dozens of such marriages of his different, miserable
inbreds. It is 1906.

Spring of 1907. The seed from the matings of these pairs
of ill-begotten inbred parents is sown. Summer heat, good
rains on this silly corn garden. Growth of these cross-bred
children—and what growth! What in the name of the great
mathematical bean-weigher, Johannsen, can this mean? Incredibly tall, full of vigor, heavy eared are these new cross-
breds—surely as lusty as their original parents bred by the
chance of the wind. All over Shull's garden are astounding
rows of tall maize trees giving the lie to the old saying that
like breeds like.

"To my astonishment," wrote George Shull, very dryly,
"I obtained extraordinarily powerful plants without exception more vigorous and productive than the best of my inbred races."

And here's what's most amazing: certain wretched
dwarfs and spindleshanks have bred to produce yields—
Wait, Shull wets his pencil, scrawls down columns of
weights in pounds from one magnificent row, calculates
them into bushels per acre, compares them with the yields
from the very best of his original stock, that he has never

inbred, that he's kept carefully fertilized with mixed pollens from fifty plants. Yes, here are an inbred father and mother that have bred to produce an amazing yield—ten bushels to the acre better than the best of the original naturally cross-bred plants. Ninety-eight bushels to the acre they yield. At last here's the sure way to grow—always—the record corn crop.

In the heat of his totally unlooked-for discovery Shull forgets his science of the mathematics of breeding. In the next years Shull hybridizes dozens of his sick-looking inbred strains of corn. All of the hybrids, or certainly most of them, shoot up amazingly in yield over their poor fathers and mothers. But certain ones of them—and here's the trick of it, the nub of it—breed, year after year, nick together just right to produce bonanza yields, completely unlooked-for yields. And here's the funniest part of it—to look at any given pair of inbreds he's about to marry, Shull can't tell at all what the prize-winning marriage will be. But once he's found a pair, by crossing them, growing their seed, measuring its yield, in short, by *experiment*—once he's found such a pair, they do their high-yielding stuff year after year. It's sure!

Shull has taken the maize apart. In unexpected abominable, ill-favored pure lines—he's put his finger on the function of yield.

He's no different from a horse breeder who might by chance get, by inbreeding, a scrub-looking stallion that would mate with an inbred mare to give, each year, a phenomenal colt that would go the mile in one minute, forty seconds.

He's no different from some mythical, fiendish Doctor Moreau, who on his island might inbreed human beings, sons to mothers, fathers to daughters, brothers to sisters. And who then for his own sinister delight might cross these frail inbred folks with others to produce at will saints, mathematical geniuses or horribly skillful masters of crime.

217

VI.

THAT winter of 1907, George Shull told his revolutionary story at the meeting of the American Breeders' Association at Washington. To a mixed audience of pig, cow, horse, corn, wheat, and gooseberry breeders he told his strange story, showed them the miserably scraggly moth-eaten little ears of his inbreds, demonstrated with an innocent gusto the magnificently uniform, heavy-yielding children that were born of their union. . . .

He made a ripple, but a very quiet ripple, not a splash— this was before the present piping days when scientists report their experiments hot off the griddle by wire through their press-agents. But anyway, Shull, who was as sniffishly aloof as some old-fashioned European professor, would have had none of such nonsense. What was most important was to get expert corn breeders to begin taking the American maize apart, finding thousands of inbred strains, marrying the hundreds of thousands of possible combinations of these pure lines to find the few that would nick just right—for the record crop.

Himself, he knew very little that was practical about applying his trick to the breeding of the billions of bushels of the American maize, and he was the first to admit that, insist upon it, and urge energetic men, like the famous Professor East, to start this revolution. Eight years Shull toiled at this work, then called it a day, and turned to primroses! To the highly scientific breeding of lovely *Oenothera*, to the evening primrose he turned. "Of course," said the modest Shull, long after, "it was far better for Dr. East to push ahead with the development of this new way of breeding corn. He'd worked with corn a long time at the University of Illinois, and had a far better corn background than I," and his brown eyes beamed amiably over his little half-moon spectacles. . . . As if this strangely inventive, patient, dreaming, sharp-seeing little man would

218

need a background to turn this trick. Did the first red men, who found the maize, have a corn background?

But no matter. Shull had done his stuff, made his discovery, had got nothing for it except the measly scientist's pay that gave him three squares a day for himself, his wife, and his two, four, six young Shulls, and a roof over the heads of all of them. But he'd done it anyway for the sheer fun of doing it, and—hats off to him!—he wanted nothing more than that, excepting maybe a good word from some hard-boiled old breeder who understood the vast new world he'd opened up. Praise this unknown opener of new roads did get, from no less a man than the formidable N. E. Hansen, the famed plant explorer, the celebrated breeder of hardy fruits for the northwest American lands. At the Breeders' Association meeting in Omaha in 1909, old Hansen made saucer eyes at the sight of the beautiful cross-bred child ears, as they lay side by side with their runty inbred parent ears in George Shull's exhibit. Hansen saw the point of it: saw that here was the first man of all men, red or white, who could breed such heavy-yielding ears of maize—*at will*. The enormously experienced Hansen leaned down, gave George Shull a pat on the back, said:

"You have all the other corn-breeders skinned a mile!"

Such was Shull's pay. And so he called it a day, went back to his theoretical researches, back to the peace of his garden at Cold Spring Harbor, and then—here was an honor!—to be Professor of Botany in the un-American peace and privacy of old-fashioned Princeton University. There he went back to his peculiar, intimate joy of mulling incomprehensible theories, to the beauty of his primroses whose flowers opened their colored petals to the cool of evenings of hot days of high summer.

VII.

GREAT truths—only let them be sound enough—need no ballyhoo. Corn-breeders, botanists, experts in heredity all over the American land in a score of experiment stations and universities, rushed at the checking-up, the repeating, the expanding of Shull's grotesque fact of the marvelous yield of hybrid children of a certain few inbred pure lines of maize. Edward East of the experiment station in Connecticut, now a professor of Harvard University and famous for writing a book warning mankind that pretty soon the world will be so chock-full of us we're all going to go hungry— East had seen Shull's marvels at Cold Spring Harbor in 1907, opened his eyes at the Washington Breeders' meeting. East had been marrying corn plants to themselves, too, and now East too discovered inbreds who cross-bred to give a tremendous kick upward in corn-yield. . . . But of course the whole business didn't look practical: in the first place, who was going to keep the seed of the inbreds pure, keep on marrying the inbreds to themselves, get *enough* seed from these pure lines that were so feeble, that so strangely hated to produce seed from themselves alone? And here was another serious rub: Shull had proved, there was no doubt of it, that to get the record crop these inbreds would have to be crossed each year—it was only the first seed of these marriages that yielded so heavily. . . . Plant these hybrids the second year, and their yield went down—even below the yield of ordinary corn, cross-pollinated by the chance of the wind. So East for a while went away from the one solid fact of Shull, tried crossing varieties of maize, even as old Beal had done thirty years before, and sometimes he got heavy-yielding seed, but next year it was no go.

And why should it have been? Here is just where old Beal had missed out—by not *knowing* that any variety of maize is a complicated mess of natural hybrids of the endless pure lines that make it up. When you cross two varieties, what guarantee have you that you'll marry just these pure lines that nick to give the record yield?

But Edward East had the energy of a dynamo, a fanaticism for corn, was obsessed with that strange fear—probably nonsensical—of the approaching starvation of human kind, and his fiery personality stoked up his young men to keep at this job of trying to get the heaviest possible yield of corn per acre. How his young men slaved at it! And presently—there was no way to get 'round Shull's fundamental truth—they were back at the job of accumulating hundreds of strains of pure-line inbreds, and crossing infinite endless combinations of them to try to find the record yielders.

There was the extremely modest, serious, red-faced transplanted Kansan, Donald Jones, pupil of East, working in East's old maize fields near New Haven—why any man from the free plains of Kansas should want to breed corn in cozy little Connecticut is something I can't answer. But here was Jones, inbreeding and crossing maize in this state that raises country gentlemen much better than maize, and it was Jones who invented the double-cross. How to get enough seed, for a big corn-farm, from these detestable, feeble inbreds? Jones inbred many pure lines out of old Jake Leaming's corn. He cross-bred two of them that nicked just right. He inbred pure lines from a variety of maize called the Burr. He married two of these. The vigorous children of these two sets of inbred parents gave him plenty of seed with a strong kick in it. Next he cross-bred these two hybrid children, made a double-cross. And the grandchildren that he got from those original down-at-the-heel inbreds, gave plenty of bushels of seed with that mysterious wallop of the freshly made hybrid in them.

For five years Jones tested his double-crossed Burr-Leaming—made every year—against the five best kinds of Connecticut corn. Knock-out: Burr-Leaming hybrids yielded eighteen bushels to the acre better than the old varieties, as an average for those five years. West to the corn belt went this news. West to the formerly prosperous black lands where the times were now nothing if not hard-scrabble, went the rumor of this sure chance for bigger yields on smaller fields. Such results, and the need for them, were the best advertisement for Shull's truth. There certainly was no whooping nor any hoorahs for George Shull himself. And few of the dozens of searchers who now, all over the dark corn lands, began bagging tassels and stalks, could tell you which of those six Shull brothers had done this trick. Many of the experimenters who began searching for that will-o'-the-wisp of yield in their thousands of inbred pure lines could not have told you whether it was Shull or East that had started their excitement. . . . Shull remained hidden by the blooms of his primroses, while his truth spread, multiplied, brought hope. . . .

VIII.

BUT now Shull brought hope to Henry Wallace, that farm-paper boy who when just out of knee-pants had got his first hard lesson from his backyard science with Evangelist Holden's thirty-three pretty ears of Yellow Dent. For years Henry had been going around, making himself unpopular at corn shows by muttering, not very distinctly but still plainly enough for everybody to hear—especially the dignified old corn judges—that "looks mean nothing to a hog." His face had grown a hundred times more serious than his superserious face when he was a boy of eighteen, scrawling the idiotic and confusing results of his tests of the yield of the thirty-three pretty ears. When he smiled, which was rare, there was a twist to his smile, and from a rebel look in his eyes, whenever anybody talked about American prosperity, it came to be muttered about that this Henry—though a bright enough boy—was not up to his father, the late Secretary of Agriculture, and was certainly not the forward-looking constructive force his granddad, the beloved "Uncle Henry," had been in Iowa. No, this young Henry A. Wallace, sneering at corn-shows, getting a reputation as a profound juggler of economic statistics, fussing darkly in his backyard with corn, holding long talks in his dusty editorial sanctum with that wise old bald-headed Norwegian farmer, Frank Faltonson, was something of a Bolshevik.

These were years of foreclosures of mortgages around Des Moines and all over the Iowa land, the loss of land won by the toughening of muscles, the stiffening of joints, and the salt sweat of seventy years. "Looks mean nothing to a hog," repeated Wallace, and he kept pounding it into his Iowa folks that their one hope to lick this new frontier of hard times was the raising of the greatest possible number of pounds of livestock off the least acres of land by the smallest amount of human labor. And that meant raising the greatest possible number of bushels of corn per acre. Of course, that wasn't Bolshevism, that was just Henry Ford common sense, but Wallace didn't stop there. He was, besides, one of the original hounds for McNary-Haugenism, and there were plenty of bankers and rich men who would tell you that this Wallace fellow was ready to ruin the rest of the country by robbing industry to save his good-for-nothing stick-in-the-mud Iowa farmers. I haven't a doubt Henry would do that, too, if he had a chance. He was first and last a fanatical patriot for his Iowa soil and its men.

But yield, yield, yield of corn per acre—bigger yields on smaller fields: he was always dreaming that above everything else. And when he said that looks meant nothing to a hog he was only using a trick for telling the farmers looks meant nothing to yield of maize per acre. How Wallace grinned at the result of that first farmers' yield test in Woodford County, Illinois! From this test, the first big smash at the old beautiful but idiotic corn shows, had risen the fame of the plain farmer George Krug, of Minonk— who still has not the slightest notion, believe me, why anybody should think he is a bit different from any other one-hundred-acre dirt-farmer. M. L. Mosher, friend of Wallace and like him an exact comparer, weigher, measurer, had told the Woodford men:

"There's only one way for you fellows to find out who has the best yielding corn in the county. That's to try all your seed out, side by side, on the same field, under exactly the same conditions of fertility, planting, cultivation. . . ."

These plain Woodford men saw the point of it, the common sense of it, saw what the great majority of highly educated college graduates have never gotten through their heads from four years of boning in expensive granite colleges. One hundred and eighteen of these men with their overalls held up by nails and the smell of barns on their feet stuck by Mosher's experiment for three years before they'd an inkling of where their corn stood in this test. Then, in the winter of 1922, that serious farm adviser called his loutish co-experimenters together, and hundreds more were there, and among them Henry Wallace.

George Krug is champion. First of the lot stands the not at all handsome corn of this red-faced slab of a man—beating all comers with a yield of seventy-eight and one-tenth bushels to the acre, as an average for three years.

Is this barge of a man a corn-breeder? Not so you could notice it. Corn's nice, corn's all right, admits the weather-beaten George. . . . "But wouldn't y' like t' see my chickens?" he asks—and Krug's smile of intense pleasure at the thought of his high-laying chickens makes a hundred wrinkles around his slits of blue eyes.

At what corn-shows has Mr. Krug's corn won prizes, sweepstakes?

"But I've never taken my corn to any show or fair!" protests George.

By what science or system does he breed his heavy-yielding maize? The widely known Mr. Bill, agricultural editor of the *Bloomington Pantagraph*, writes to ask Krug that.

KRUG

With a pencil on little slips of ruled paper Krug answers: "I use my own judgment in picking, selecting a heavy, solid ear. . . ." And he adds at the end: "If you use this letter, please write it your own way."

And, in short, Krug discovered his high-yielding corn—just by hefting the ears of it!

If Henry Wallace ever laughed out loud at all—which is doubtful, since I have only heard him permit himself a sort of indistinct chuckle—he would have roared now at this fantastic result of the Woodford yield test. But he went back to Des Moines, and wrote in *Wallaces' Farmer*: "If Krug corn had been raised all over Iowa in place of the strains of Reid's Yellow Dent now raised, the corn of Iowa could have been produced on a million acres less of land."

Now, with the calm, genial H. D. Hughes of the State College at Ames—about Hughes there is nothing at all Bolshevistical—Henry Wallace plotted a revolution. He got

225

ready to turn Iowa corn-culture bottom-side up, by back-room conferences with important members of the Iowa Corn and Small Grain Growers' Association, by cajolings of old farmers who had always believed in corn shows, by speeches, by letters, by editorials, by nobody knows what tricks. Wallace, and Hughes, and certain anonymous allies induced the Iowa dirt-farmers to join in a gigantic scientific experiment, to start a sort of vast communal science.

All over the state, in twelve appointed districts, the corn of any farmer who had any pride whatever in his crop, who had enthusiasm, and the will to improve himself, and a few dollars in cash—and there were not too many dollars kicking around in Iowa, those days—every such man's seed corn might be entered to be grown, and tested: for yield.

And in this science, in which you didn't have to have a degree of Doctor of Philosophy to dabble, Henry Wallace was one of the most furious dabblers. Nobody had a higher regard for the heavy-eared corn of that unconscious scientist, George Krug, than had Henry Wallace. But Wallace had this fundamental clear in his head: that a variety of corn is not a variety, that Krug corn is not just Krug corn, that when this famous maize got into the hands of a farmer who hadn't Krug's mysterious knack of hefting it for heaviness —the shifting blood lines of it would change, and other, less valuable, even low-yielding blood lines would come to the surface. . . .

Wallace had got Shull's basic facts into his head. He became absent-minded and rather neglectful of his wife, his children, or of the way his clothes were buttoned, mulling this one thought: "Only pure lines of corn, only inbred lines of corn are fixed, don't vary. . . ." So, in a little plot of ground in his back yard, on Saturday afternoons and Sundays, he began bagging the tassels and silks of corn plants to inbreed them. He was the very opposite of Shull, who had inbred maize for the love of his scientific theories. In Wallace's head raged one idea: to breed corn for yield. He wrote letters, begging the seed of inbred strains of maize, from Donald Jones in Connecticut, from the bald-headed Hoffer in Indiana who had inbred strains that were immune to root-rot; from the religious Rotarian, Holbert, in Illinois, who had stumbled on a strong-stalked inbred strain called "A"; from the critical Kiesselbach in Nebraska who had inbreds that nicked to give heavy-yielding seed; from Frederick Richey of the Government in Washington who had married to itself the Bloody Butcher corn from China.

Every minute he could steal from the editing of his farm-paper, from his duty as a father of a family, Wallace hunted inbred strains, begged them, bred them himself, and hung great rows of the miserable-looking ears of them on wire racks in his basement garage. He had no pride in his own, cared not a snap of his fingers where corn came from; he was obsessed by one notion: to stick the best possible corn blood into his hybrids, to cross pure-bloods that would give the best, the surest yield.

All the practical objections to this new wrinkle in corn breeding bounced off him 'til old seedsmen, and young professors, could only think that this Wallace was stupid, or slightly crazy, or both. Who in the world would ever get farmers to *buy* this inbred hybrid seed, every year? Who was going to be put in control of the serious job of keeping alive the feeble flame of the low-yielding seed of the pure lines? Who was going to see to it that there would be plenty of this newfangled hybrid seed, every year, for the sowing of the immense corn-belt crop? And if a hybrid was good for northern Iowa—would it do for the black lands in the southeast down near the Mississippi? To all these valid objections Henry Wallace stuffed his ears, closed his eyes, and if he'd ever permitted himself profanity—which he doesn't—he would simply have said: "Oh, hell!"

In his back yard and on a little patch of bad land down by the river he toiled—at marrying inbreds, at testing their yield. This gnawed at him: that his people were face to face

with hard times, that they must have seed that would produce the greatest possible amount of dry, shelled corn per
acre, that to drag themselves out of their slough they had
got to raise their stuff at lower cost. Well—he would give
them high-yielding maize. It was hopeless work, lonesome
work, thankless work: for the brown-faced growers of food
for the American land, the very tanned men whose complaints of hard times poured on to his farm-paper desk—
these men he was out to help, sniffed at his efforts.

One man stuck by him, helped him over the hardest
bumps, the disappointments of his amateur science. This
was H. D. Hughes, at the college at Ames. Hughes smiled
at Wallace's hundreds of failures, at the miserable yields of
the seed of hundreds of mismarriages of his inbred strains.
On the accurately sown flat black fields at the college at
Ames, Hughes tested the yield of the ears of Henry's
hybrids—no matter how ill-begotten and abominable those
ears might look. Hughes smiled his good smile, looked at
Wallace with eyes that twinkled from between their
wrinkles, said:

"Stick to it, Henry."

Never for a moment did Henry allow himself to become
tangled up in the mathematics, in the attractive and mystical science of heredity—full of big words, of abstract ideas
understood by a couple of dozen highbrows of American
universities. It is remarkable enough that Wallace didn't
get bogged in this pure and useless science, for his brain's
of the kind that'll spin theories for you all night long, without the aid of blessed alcohol, or tobacco, or even coffee.
But no—like a puppy to a root Henry stuck to the simple
fact of Shull: Inbreed, from every possible variety of corn,
as many pure lines as you can, 'til your arms hang tired at
your sides from bagging tassels and silks. Then marry them
—'til you find the pair that nick for the record yield.

The looks of his maize ears only made him smile—and
never was there a more outlandish museum of runty ears,

crooked ears, ears looking moth-eaten and only half covered with kernels, never were there more thoroughly disreputable ears, than this collection before which Wallace mulled, made notes, in his basement garage in Des Moines. The seasons didn't come often enough to suit the corn passion of Wallace, and he turned winters into summers and raised two generations of his abominable corn a year—by begging the use of other fellows' greenhouses. The mass of his work became too much for him, and he wheedled his good friend, the wistful and genial Simon Casady, Jr., who'd had no experience at all with corn, to jerk the tassels off inbred mother strains on his little estate on the hill southwest of Des Moines. Now came news, from Hughes at Ames, and from Henry's own back yard, of unheard-of fantastic yields, and here at Wallace's side stood another ally, a practical man, a hard-boiled, energetic, ambitious dirt-farmer—Newlin. Built for a prize-fighter was Newlin, and he might have been one if he hadn't been prevented by his Quaker religion. But Newlin knew heavy-yielding, bonanza maize when he saw it, was a shark at devising quick ways to dry thousands of bushels of its seed, was one of those sinewy workers of the breed that had made America, who believed—for all his religion—that God helps those that help themselves. Newlin and Casady helped the harassed Wallace towards his day of days.

IX.

NOW George Shull's little fact began to be true—for what little laboratory or garden fact is true, or amounts to anything at all for men, until it tries its mettle in the stern field of practice? In those very years when the spirits of the Iowa men were at lowest ebb, in the early nineteen-twenties, mysterious strains of maize began to make their appearance in the twelve districts of the Iowa State Yield Test—in that new kind of community science started by the Iowa men to see what their corn would do, under average conditions of wind, of drought, of soil, of weather, in twelve different parts of the state. Mysterious seed of maize—called "Hibred"—began to win banners, medals, prizes, sweepstakes, 'til the old corn-breeders, proud for thirty years of their own varieties of the Yellow Dent, began to protest, to howl, to demand that this new kind of corn be put in a contest all by itself. . . .

Came the year of 1926, and it was a walkaway for the powerful hybrid children, born from the deplorable ears in Wallace's basement-garage museum.

Grown side by side, under conditions for strict comparison, the crosses of Henry's inbreds yielded three bushels more to the acre in southern Iowa than the best of the old varieties.

In the north-central districts the hybrids averaged four bushels more to the acre.

In south-central Iowa they were six bushels better in average yield, than the cream of the Yellow Dent varieties, selected by the old corn-breeders from their fairest ears.

In northern Iowa, the children of the inbreds romp home with an average of ten bushels more to the acre than the best of the local varieties. . . .

So it has happened in the three years before 1926, and so it happens again in 1927—and more and more farmers turn their backs on the long tables with their beautifully piled ears of show corn in the Armory at the State College at Ames. More and more of them, especially the young ones, squint their eyes at the comparative figures, the dull, dry figures of the yield tests. There they stand, asking eager questions of Henry whose hybrids have this strange trick of standing at the top of every yield column. . . . So Shull's fact begins seeping into the heads of the new generation of hard-time pioneers.

And so Henry Wallace takes the entirely highbrow fact,

found by George Shull in his evolution garden, out into the hot sun, beating rains, stalk-breaking winds, early frosts of rolling Iowa prairie. So he proves Shull's little fact's rightness.

But is this amazing high-yielding hybrid corn right in practice? Who'll know until every man jack of the Iowa men—or until half of those men surely, at least, is sowing every year the hybrid seed?

This is Henry's last experiment, his own particular test, impossible for the dreamer Shull, not dignified enough for the hundreds of experiment-station searchers and college professors who are inbreeding and marrying the inbreds of maize all over the American land. This is an experiment not too vulgar for the farm-paper editor Henry Wallace. Worshiper of maize in a most mystical way, bitter patriot for Iowa, hater of capitalists, Wallace now becomes a capitalist himself, forms a little company with Casady and Newlin, to sell this magic seed every year to the corn-belt men. But will they buy it every year? Will they break through the ancient custom, old as the maize itself, of picking out the fairest ears? "Developed—Not Discovered. Made to Fit —Not Found By Chance." Such is the slogan for Henry's Hibred seed. He sells his seed, so far at a loss, to men who'll grow record crops of corn from it to their own great profit. Like some good disease the news of the hybrid corn spreads from farm to farm. And Henry drives about in a funny, asthmatic old Winton auto, asking, asking: "How were your yields with the new corn this year?" Such too is science.

But beneath this strange, twisted jack-of-all-sciences' experiments, there is faith. For even if the hard-pressed men of the Midwest *see* the millions they'll save by growing the magic seed to raise more corn on less land, who'll keep alive the spark of the inbreds, grow them pure, cross them every year from now on for the next year's seed? Who'll keep the torch of this mysterious incestuous life, after Henry is gone, worn out by his appalling work—or killed by one of those

231

fantastic experiments on diet that he's perpetually trying on himself? Will such men arise?

Sure they'll come. That's a matter of faith in the heart of Wallace. There he sits at his desk in the dingy office of that grand farm paper, *Wallaces' Farmer;* the faces of his father, his grandfather, the famous "Uncle Henry," corn-belt gentlemen they were, look down through dusty glass on this blood of theirs who has inherited their spirit of *noblesse oblige.* Henry sits mumbling a sing-song into the glass mouthpiece of his dictaphone. Letters he's writing, telling Farmer Baker of Beaconsfield, Farmer Bear of Decatur, Farmer Hartman of Waukee, to be sure to do well their job of detasseling to cross the inbred seed he's sent them. Already his subdued undramatic enthusiasm—it's a sort of intense smolder—has fired dozens of young dirt farmers to become his unpaid co-workers in this delicate science.

Plenty of red men were found through the thousands of years of the days before history to keep the candle of the seed of maize alight—despite wars, during droughts, through floods, among migrations innumerable.

"Oh, sure—there are more than enough intelligent young fellows in this state to keep the hybrids going," says Henry. His dour eyes beam for a moment with a gleam of pride for the humble and anonymous hunger fighters of his Midwest land.

HOFFER

CHAPTER EIGHT. NEW SOIL FROM OLD

HOFFER

I.

WEST OF THE MISSISSIPPI you'd say the most powerful plants of maize, yielding five hundredfold, would never be able to weaken the land. That deep black soil seems to hold life, strength, for as long as there'll be white men— or red—to till it for maize. So Henry Wallace and his men are right to think mainly of the blood lines of their maize.

But east of the Mississippi many patches and in some places whole stretches of the American land are tired. Drive along the new hard roads of middle Ohio, of the Hoosier State, of Illinois, over beautiful highways that shine in the rain, over high-priced highways the corn men are taxed to death for, and you'll drive past fields where the maize yield has gone down and down. Sad and pessimistic scientists have plotted dots, splotches, areas there where the corn yield has fallen twenty-five percent; with their mouths down at the corners these savants prophesy it'll soon be cut in half as compared to the yields of the days of Abe Lincoln, Jake Leaming, James Reid. In our young country this land is already old.

Listen to the corn professors, pathologists, agronomists, other ists, who are prophets of doom, and they'll tell you of fields planted with powerful seed of maize, fields that yield rows of pitiful dwarfed plants, land where maybe half the corn plants bear no ears at all. Go with them on to these sad farms, watch them pull up this and that discouraged-looking maize tree by its roots—and they'll point out to you the root-rot that sucks the life out of corn. You'll see with your own eyes the seven separate diseases corn may have. You'll hear the names of horrid parasites, the *Gibberella* and the life-destroying *Rhizopus*, that gnaw at the roots, take the green from the leaves, keep the plump kernels from the ears of our poor American maize. Their story is true, their science is accurate. Their prophecies of disaster might be right—if it weren't for men like George Hoffer.

Hoffer, who is magnificently bald-headed though still young, who is taciturn, untalkative, has founded a science that makes the maize plant itself talk to the farmers. The sick corn can tell the corn-belt men its hunger, explain what food the land fails to give, ask for the right chemical stuff to make it laugh at the attacks of those parasite molds—the *Rhizopus, Gibberella*, the *Fusarium*. The maize plant itself can help its guardians make their old soil new.

II.

HOFFER came West to Lafayette, Indiana, in the county of Tippecanoe, as a botanist, enormously ignorant about corn. "In fact," mumbled Hoffer, "when I began teaching at Purdue I didn't know an ear of Reid corn from an ear of Leaming—I wouldn't have been able to tell a Flint from a Dent." What he knew about the diseases of maize that worried Hoosier farmers was zero; what he knew about fertilizer plots and the complicated chemistry of soil was less. He was a town boy, with no appreciation at all of the basic need of the American land for high-yielding corn, and you wouldn't have to talk to him two minutes to understand he came from that peculiar and stubborn sort of American known as Pennsylvania Dutch. His folks are descended from that famous Swiss inn-keeper, Andreas Hofer, who stubbornly didn't know enough to know that it was impossible to lick Napoleon, and who gave up his life to put one of the principal crimps in that conqueror's ambitions.

He had come to Indiana, where you might see five down-at-the-heel farms to one good one, from Lebanon County in Pennsylvania where every farm seems a little bit better than the one before it. He was a boy from among those strange

stick-in-the-mud Teutonic people who sit contented in their
long valleys not seeming to realize there are much better
parts of America, so far as soil goes. But, in spite of this ignorance and conservatism they've made the most prosperous
part of the American nation out of their fair-to-middling
land. Travel down the ribbons of roads running from east to
west through these Pennsylvania Dutch valleys, and you
pass a panorama of fields tilled with marvelous care, of
barns bursting with plenty. And the towns that draw life
from this land? Here you'll find fanatically neat and buxom
women sweeping their sidewalks every afternoon as the sun
slants shadows down the long village streets, you'll find
thrifty folk who own Cadillac cars, driving them twenty-
five miles an hour on Sundays and the rest of the week keeping them up on jacks. In these towns are God-fearing folk
who believe the Good Book literally, are convinced the Lord
turned water into wine and not grape-juice. They still drink
beer whose silky foam brings tears of joy to your eyes—the
only good beer, alas, left in the American land—and these
folks put God before the Constitution and obey His natural
law that yeast must ferment malt, in spite of the interdic-
tions of prohibition agents. From this old-fashioned country
George Hoffer came.

From such a town, where genial red-faced motor cops
will still direct you to the best saloon, George Hoffer went
to the little Lebanon Valley College. "I sort of specialized
in chemistry there," stammered Hoffer, in a low offhand
voice that makes you strain your ears to get his drift, that
always gives you a feeling he's bored to talk about his own
unimportant history. And like so many American boys,
Hoffer had a random and haphazard history. His father
was well-off—as whose father wasn't in those parts?—and,
not having to work in the summer, George went on a scientific expedition to Bermuda to dredge up strange fish. Another summer he rambled along Chesapeake Bay, gathering,

classifying, mooning over still stranger fossils. Some more time he spent at Columbia University in New York, and here he had the luck to sit at the feet of the wiry, bristly-moustachioed Prof. Carlton Curtis, who is a great bug on botany, but who puts the art of fishing above the science of plants and trees, and who, in his eagerness to pursue this greatest of arts, has been known to jump out of his canoe before beaching it, leaving its management in swift white water to his poor wife. . . . So eager is Curtis to throw his fly at salmon who are maybe there—who can tell? "It was Professor Curtis who gave me my very first inspiration to devote my life to *experimenting*," muttered Hoffer. "I feel I owe what little I've done to Curtis."

Such was Hoffer's training to probe into the riddle of the miseries of the American maize crop.

So Hoffer came as a biologist to the Hoosier State, a state with tired land that had grown corn from the days of the eighteen-twenties and 'thirties, when Abe Lincoln had first muddied his feet in its yellow clay soil. Nothing like his fat Lebanon County was this Hoosier land. Here was a prosperous farm whose good land gave eighty bushels to the acre of prize-winning Boone County White Dent corn. Close by, Hoffer saw a string of wretched little farms with fields of dilapidated maize—in short here was a state that grew pleasant and smiling folk, hospitable people that break into a laugh as they point out the best gravel road to the town you want—poets and dreaming folk this state grew. . . . A little better than it grew maize.

Hoffer was at his job of teaching botany, when one day, after class, a sturdy, very tanned, invincibly farmerish-looking boy came up to him. This boy was Jimmy Holbert. "What ails this corn, Professor?" asked Holbert, and he narrowed his eyes at Hoffer. . . . What could Hoffer say? What could he tell this James Holbert, who was almost, you might say, born a corn crank? Already Holbert had raised blisters on his hands and callouses under the seat of his trousers riding Gene Funk's corn plows over the flat enormous prairie farm of the Funks in MacLean County, Illinois. Holbert had taken his medicine along with the hardest-bitten hired men, never said booh about the blisters on his bottom, kept his eyes, his ears, the very pores of his skin open to take in corn lore from Funk—and from the maize plants themselves.

"I found Holbert to be way above the average young fellow," said Funk the corn baron, "made him one of the family—just as much of a son as one of my own boys. . . ."

Hoffer didn't tell Holbert what was wrong with his ear of corn, couldn't possibly tell him, because he at that time hardly knew that anything at all could ever be wrong with the lusty trees of maize. But Hoffer remembered his old teacher, the fisherman, Carlton Curtis, and he answered Jimmy Holbert:

"Let's find out what's the matter with it!"

That was the start of a strange research. Holbert was chock-full already of practical corn lore, and full of that energetic sort of enthusiasm for the deep stuff of science you'll find in young Midwestern Americans before they harden into—Americans. Holbert proceeded to teach his teacher, Hoffer, and together they began asking clumsy questions. Together Holbert and Hoffer pulled ears of maize from stalks that had grown up straight and strong only to tumble down, broken at the joints of them at the height of their maize careers. Here were plants with broken ear shanks, others with leaves that were fired and had strangely lost their green. They took kernels from the ears of such plants, peered at them, found molds growing on them. Molds were parasites on the maize seed. Were the molds the cause of the maize sicknesses? Such notions were in the air of corn science then—borrowed from the microbe hunting of the diseases of beasts and men.

They put moldy kernels from the ears from plants of broken-stalked corn side by side with clean kernels from the

239

ears of straight-stalked plants on big sawdust and lime-stone germinators. Carefully they kept the heat of the germinator rooms at just the right temperature to sprout the seed. Faithfully they moistened the cloths on which lay the sick and healthy kernels. Four, five, six days they waited—watching the tiny shoots grow out from the tops of the seed, delighted at the delicate hairy roots that writhed out of the bottoms of both the sick and healthy kernels.

The sick and healthy seeds, both of them sprouted—but the roots of the sick ones became tangled up in matted thready masses of molds—like infinitesimal snakes. Next spring, at the Funk Farms at Bloomington, Illinois, where there's all the land in the world for experiments—Holbert planted the seed of the sick ears that had shown molds on the germinators.

By the side of them he stuck in the seed from the perfectly healthy, bright-looking, horny-kerneled ears. That autumn the pupil who taught his teacher and the teacher who was very secretly busy learning from his pupil—in a most determined Pennsylvania Dutch manner—saw and recorded a picture, fantastic and pretty.

Here were two rows of maize plants, straight and bronzed, with fine ears ready for husking: these came from the bright-colored seed. Between these rows of splendid brown soldiers there stood, or, rather, drooped, or better still *lay*, a miserable rank of sick, dilapidated, broken-down, utterly useless stalks . . . with few ears—and those few chaffy.

That sad row came from seed off a moldy ear.

III.

IN the cornfields as well as in the laboratory Hoffer made up for lost time, gulped down a thousand facts about maize. Together with his dynamo of a student, Holbert, he did hundreds of experiments, set down in neat tables big dif-

240

ferences—sometimes thirty percent or more—between the yields from sick and healthy seed. Together this pair of men got red-rimmed eyes bending over the corn germinators in warm, dank rooms, learning to spot, getting to know how to tell this mold parasite apart from that one. . . . From fat bound volumes of botanical journals they learned to pronounce the jaw-cracker names of these molds. Day after day they bent over the miniature forests of sprouting corn seedlings that lay in regular rows in warm boxes: they knew the life-sapping mold, *Fusarium*, by its pretty pink color. They showed each other the blackish specks and patches of the dreadful *Diplodia* that sucked the strength out of corn roots. They pierced down into the inside of corn kernels: they picked out seedlings, healthy enough looking on the outside, but, cutting into them, brought to light the ghastly mold, *Rhizopus*—from its lurking-place inside the seed.

Together they published a scientific report, not for farmers but in the highbrow journal, named *Science*. That made Government authorities at Washington notice them. And for the discouraged Indiana men they put out a cheerful bulletin, that wound up:

"For permanent corn improvement, only ears from disease-free stalks should be used."

Here was hope for farmers whose corn was sick. "Here's the way to get rid of sick, root-rotted corn," said Hoffer and Holbert: "Test out all of your seed for the next year on germinators. Use only seed that doesn't show molds. That's the way to boost your yields." And it did look as if this husky pupil and his shiny-domed teacher were going to make this whole sickening business of broken-down maize, barren-stalked maize, maize whose green leaves were fired with streaks of red and brown, a thing of the past. The Cereal Office of the Bureau of Plant Industry at Washington—from the headship of which Mark Alfred Carleton had just been fired—took notice. From then on part of the pay of Hoffer and Holbert, and their scientific expenses, were

HOFFER

given by the Government. Farmers pointed to them as Government corn experts and they were by way of becoming great shakes, big guns in the Indiana and Illinois corn land.

Then the ways of these two men parted: Jimmy Holbert went to work in the long two-story brick seed company of Gene Funk at Bloomington. There he buried himself in the study of the parasite molds of the roots of corn, discovered new corn diseases—so many diseases that for a while he was actually behind in naming them, couldn't think up enough long names for all of them. In front of Holbert's desk was a proud framed cog-wheel of Rotary; at this desk he conducted himself like an earnest Christian, wrote exact scientific reports on these discouraging corn plagues—and there's not the slightest doubt Holbert is the last word on parasites of maize. Hoffer is different. Almost from the start of his dreaming about the chaffy ears and broken-down stalks of it, he begins to have heretic, original, impossible ideas about these sicknesses. He begins to think of the health corn might draw from good fields, rather than the sickness that might attack maize roots in poor land. And here he is way ahead of the doctors of human ills—who were hardly yet dreaming of resistance to microbes that human beings might draw from the right food. . . .

Hoffer walks through corn fields, cuts corn stalks open lengthwise—peers into the pithy tissue of healthy ones, and broken-down sick ones. For some reason unknown to us his brown eyes keep taking in certain earmarks of the joints of these cut corn stalks, but here's something new, something not in the scientific magazines or books:

In every last root-rotted corn plant, from every poor field, Hoffer spies a band of brown unnatural color—just below the joints of the stalks . . . especially in the lower joints.

Thousands of healthy plants, from good soil, he cuts into as well. Their joints are a nice healthy greenish-white.

242

They're sappy, look sound. But the sick plants? Brown joints—nearly always.

Hoffer still had conventional ideas—in spite of his dreams. "The brown color at the joints of the sick corn plants must be caused by the working of the molds, the parasites," he told one of his student helpers. It's no wonder at all that he thought that—for weren't the greatest fighters of human death still obsessed with germs, harping on microbes as the main and principal causes of most ills? Microbes get into living beings and so cause disease—that was still the simple picture scientists had in their heads. And Hoffer proceeded to put one of his student assistants at the job of fishing in the brownish, discolored joints of root-rotted corn to find just what gibberellas or rhizopuses were raising the devil there. Those molds must be there, since the joints were sick.

The student probed, squinted, made cultures of a thousand brown-jointed cornstalks. He sweat. He found—nothing.

"Mr. Hoffer—there aren't any molds there," said the assistant.

"But they've *got* to be!" insisted Hoffer. The boy went back at the job, tried again, failed. He was an excellent boy, with the true makings of a searcher in him, who refused to say he saw what he couldn't see, and didn't see anything simply because he ought to see it. "They're not there, Mr. Hoffer!" reported that boy.

Hoffer fired him.

He put another assistant on the same job—instructing him in all the delicate inside stuff of mold-fishing, microbe hunting. The second boy sweat likewise. "There aren't any molds in the brown joints of these stalks!" reported this second boy.

"But there must be!" said Hoffer.

"All right—you just try to find them yourself!" came back his assistant.

243

Every kind of kink of his three years of root-rot experience Hoffer tried—and not a mold did he find in the discolored joints.

"We were certainly sick about that . . ." muttered Hoffer, who strangely never refers to himself as "I"—not even to his own most solitary ideas, experiences, hunches. It was a bad day for the theory he'd cooked up with Jimmy Holbert about these terrible molds. . . . Here these cornstalks were unquestionably sick—but showed never a parasite. . . .

Grief piled on grief, to mix Hoffer up, to discourage him. He went down to Shelbyville, southeast of Indianapolis. He took seed corn from sick plants and healthy ones down there with him. Here was a bag of moldy kernels—by its side a sack of nice bright horny ones. He planted rows of each kind, side by side, in soil that was acid—and planted more rows of each kind in soil he'd made sweet with lime. The corn grew, and alas!

On plants from nine perfectly healthy ears, the yield on the sweet soil was thirty-seven percent better than the yield on the sour. . . .

But wait: he planted corn from the sick moldy ears, too—and the sweet soil boosted the yield from these sick ears sixty-two percent. . . .

"Hrmph!" growled Hoffer. "The kind of soil makes much more difference than the kind of seed I plant. . . ." Where now was his science? Where now his confident advice to the Hoosier farmers?

Hoffer should have quit his science now, should have called it a day, should have forgotten his interest in the supposedly terrible *Fusarium* and *Gibberella*. But it was not for nothing he was born of those central Pennsylvania folks who keep on drinking beer when the weight of the laws and the high authorities of the land are against them. His science was wrecked; his theory lay in ruins; the facts didn't fit his ideas. But that was when he worked best.

244

And he proceeded to send moldy and healthy sweet-corn seed to experiment stations in Iowa, Illinois, Ohio. Check: his facts, right for Indiana, were right all over. The Iowa, Illinois, Ohio experts planted his sick and healthy seed side by side, in rich soil and poor soil. Sure enough: the results were the same. Everywhere the mold-free, healthy seed gave the highest yield of corn—but the good soil made much more difference in yield than did the business of whether or no the seed was moldy. . . .

IV.

WHAT poison is it that a maize plant sucks out of certain soils, that makes it fall before the gnawings of molds? Or do corn plants stay strong, resistant to sickness, because of good food they get out of some land? Does the *Gibberella* eat at them because the right food lacks in certain other soils? There were impossible questions for you—questions too complicated for corn experts and soil doctors, a thousand times more learned and experienced than Hoffer. Then by chance on a train the Pennsylvania German met a sweet-corn canner, and this manufacturer sobbed to Hoffer about his tribulations. "We're having all kinds of trouble with the black in our canned corn," complained that canner. "We pack our corn and it looks all right. Then the customers kick and the housewives howl about it; our stuff comes back, full of black specks. We've spent a lot of money, hiring expert chemists. . . . These fellows tell us the black specks are *iron*. . . . Say it comes out of bad tin cans. . . . But we buy the best cans! What're we goin' to do about it?"

This had nothing whatever to do with the sickness of corn, naturally. But Hoffer got his bread and butter from a job where he was supposed to help Hoosier farmers, and the sweet-corn farmers got their bread and butter from what they sold to sweet-corn canners. "So what," asked Hoffer, "could I do but promise that guy I'd do my best

245

to try to find out where those black specks in the corn cans came from?"

He was by way of being a detective—as every searcher worth his salt must be. He patted his shining dome of a head, sucked at his pipe in which the fire had long ago died, mulled to himself:

"Do these specks of iron come out of the cans? . . . Or are they hidden in the sweet corn before it's put into the cans?"

Here stood a row of cans the corn-canner had sent him. And here too were some ears of uncanned corn that came from the same place. Hoffer relights his pipe for the half-dozenth time: "Iron in the corn itself?" There is a tinkle of bottles of the simple test for iron—any high-school boy chemist knows it. On to the grains of corn go a few drops of the thiocyanate of potash. Then a few drops of strong acid. A deep red flush spreads over the kernels. No doubt of it— there's iron. Slowly the red color fades from the grains—but it's sure: the ears have iron, before they're put in the cans. But then, anybody knows there's always iron in maize— but how much? Maybe here there's too much. But how much would be too much? So goes Hoffer's woolgathering—a thousand miles away from any thought of the root-rots that are knocking down the Hoosier corn yields.

But might the sweet-corn *stalks* show the blood red of the iron test too? Had iron for some reason piled up in the kernels, maybe? The canner sent Hoffer stalks that had borne these iron-laden ears. Here he is, his pipe's on his bench, and he's chewing at a match now—Hoffer is eternally chewing at something. He cuts the stalks down lengthwise with a stainless steel knife. He peers at their joints. . . . Hello! What's this? Sick joints, brown joints—exactly like the joints he'd seen a thousand times in root-rotted maize from all over Indiana. Again there's a clink of bottles. On to these brown joints drop a few drops of the chemicals that'll tell you yes or no for iron: and the

246

brown changes magically into a flame of red—into splashes and splotches of blood red. . . .

With the irresponsibility of some sniffing puppy, Hoffer forgets the distresses of the corn-canner, goes back to his old puzzle of the brown-banded joints of the sick corn. Now he's got it, solved it. It's iron, it can be nothing else but iron that's at the bottom of the mystery of these brown hands. It's a poisoning with iron that makes maize the prey of the *Gibberella*, of all those other root-rot molds! But what a fool hunch this is. Where in the whole science of the sicknesses of plants, or animals, or men—is there one single example of iron being bad for living things, of weakening them to let in nefarious microbes? There's no such thing. Iron is good for living things. Since the beginning of time doctors have fed iron to anemic folks—iron means strength. But Hoffer never for a moment thought of the science of others. His hunch was Bible truth for him; in his head he cooked up an entirely improbable explanation that gave him pleasure—as a child will find pleasure at cooking up a yarn about pirates and bogey-men.

In certain fields corn plants suck up iron—too much of it—from the soil. The iron piles up in the lower parts of the joints of the stalks, causes that brown color, plugs up the sap tubes that run through those joints—why, it was just as if you blocked off the blood-supply that carries life, food, to the members of a living human body. . . . When the sap can't flow up from the roots to the leaves—why shouldn't they fire, turn yellow, brown? When the sap can't get down from the leaves to the corn roots—why shouldn't the roots go moldy, go rotten before the attacks of the molds that are everywhere in the soil? And if the corn ears get no sap—why shouldn't the grains of them turn chaffy. . . . Why shouldn't the yields go down?

Was this only a child's story? Into the fields went Hoffer, pulled up pitiful, broken-stalked corn plants by the roots; into his laboratory he brought them, and cut off those stalks near their bottoms. Then he dipped the lower ends of them in water that he'd colored with the dye called methylene blue, that strange dye which spreads so quickly through any living thing. This is the dye Midwestern boys used to feed each other pills of—and then guffaw at the frightened faces of their victims as they came out of the vine-covered little houses with half-moons cut in their doors. . . . Mysteriously the methylene blue penetrates to every corner of the tissues of a living thing, coloring its tears, its every excretion. And now Hoffer looked, and sure enough, he was right: above the brown-banded joints—those iron-loaded joints—the sap tubes of the cornstalks showed no streaks of blue. Those joints were blocked—by iron.

The summer of 1919 found Hoffer sweating calmly between rustling dusty rows of maize, under a hammering sun, in a hundred Hoosier corn-fields. He was on the trail. He was right. Wherever there were plants with fine ears, heavy-kerneled, stiff-stalked—never a splotch or a dot of red did the iron tests show at the joints of these stalks. Wherever the fields were sad with plants that were wilted, broken—there was that flaming, telltale red. So Hoffer dug out a truth about maize that the wisest physicians have yet to find about men. For who can tell the secret of the precise chemical stuff that may lurk in the body of one child—to make it fall before the microbe of pneumonia, while that child's brother or sister remains immune to the malignity of the same germ? But the root-rot of corn plants? It was iron at the joints that let the *Gibberella* start its gnawing.

But how keep this iron out of the joints of sick corn? And why was it that in some fields this iron crept up into the joints of the maize stalks—while in others it didn't? Hoffer had no idea—and how to find out? And was it iron alone that was dangerous? Here were a couple of fellows in Rhode Island who were making out that aluminum—chemical cousin of iron—was bad for plants too. And sure enough, from fields near LaFayette, Hoffer brought in

248

stunted corn, dwarfish plants, with leaves that looked as
if they were dying between the veins of them. From Bat-
tleground, Hoffer brought such leaves to the gray-haired,
pleasant-faced chemist, Carr, who was helping him—and
the ash of those plants held five percent of aluminum: that
was more than twice as much as the ash of big healthy corn
plants close by. . . .

Every searcher gets lost in fogs, in masses of mixed-up
facts where nothing seems clear or connected. The days of
all inquisitive men born of women are long and full of
trouble. How to keep aluminum from piling up in maize?
How to guard it from iron? Never a notion had Hoffer,
so, like the indomitable Francis, he worked with his hands,
fussed at experiments that proved what he already felt
sure of. Here he is, planting a field of corn on rich, virgin
soil—where it'll show never a sign of sickness. The plants
shoot up strong and straight. Here's Hoffer, on his knees
between the rows of them, and into the bottom of one after
another of those good, living cornstalks, just above their
first joints, this strange man bores little holes with a sharp
cork-borer. Into each of these holes he pokes—it's a nice
tight fit—a little glass tube, swelled out into a bulb at its
free end, and each one of these tubes he ties carefully to its
own corn-plant. He crouches, intent, in the shade of these
maize trees, pouring solutions of the salts of iron, of aluminum, of a dozen other chemicals into those bulbs—so his
maize trees may gradually drink them. . . . From one
plant to another he crawls, sweat standing in beads on his
bald head, his pipe dangling from the corner of his mouth—
'til each plant is drinking its particular poison.

Poison? As the days go by, George Hoffer walks between those rows, muttering, stooping, examining, lighting
his eternal pipe only to let it go out after a puff or two.
Oh, yes—he's right, but especially those Rhode Island fellows, Hartwell and Pember, are right. . . . Less than one
three-thousandth of an ounce of aluminum fires the leaves of

249

these strong plants—just as they'd discolor in bad acid soils, kills the leaves between the veins, massacres the plants themselves. . . . But he's right about his iron too: small bits of it, sucked in from those little glass tubes, turn the corn joints brown, wreck the joints exactly as they're wrecked before the molds of the root-rot start their devilish work at them. . . .

But what's he going to do about it? How does this pretty experiment help Hoosier farmers, worried with low yields, and then lower yields still? The Government, the state of Indiana, had been paying him to knock out root-rot disease, to boost the corn yield, and at the very beginning he'd promised them a lot—but here he was in a muddle. . . . Yes, it had helped some that he and Holbert had taught farmers to use only the seed that showed healthy on the germinators. "But what's the good," and Hoffer took his everlasting pipe out of his mouth and waved it, "of putting mold-free corn into the ground, *when that ground itself is swarming with molds?*" As well bring children completely free from tubercle microbes into the world—and expect them to go through their lives never swallowing one of those nasty germs or never inhaling one. . . . No—the molds didn't matter, the ground could be full of them—so long as there wasn't this confounded poisoning with aluminum, and iron. But how get rid of it?

And through these years, in that Hoosier State, in the muck lands of southern Michigan, on the brown lands of Ohio, and southern Illinois, and down through Kentucky and into Tennessee and toward the Gulf of Mexico—in certain fields in all these places the invisible particles of iron and aluminum, silently, mysteriously, seeped up into promising maize trees through their hairy roots. And the corn yields went down. . . .

Hoffer kept fumbling, stewing, chewing matches, trying. He had the slender, nervous John Trost to help him, who had china-blue eyes, read immensely in science, trying his best to ruin those eyes, and took his work altogether too seriously. Hoffer might stew, yes, but he stewed in a kind of offhand way, his excitement was leisurely and under his breath: the best thing that you might say for him was that he never overworked himself but always kept on working. Trost turned up facts out of books, and here were those two Rhode Island sharks, Hartwell and Pember, once more: they'd hit on a way to keep different sorts of plants from sucking up too much aluminum—by adding lime and phosphates to the solutions in which they grew their tiny seedlings. When a solution was acid—the seedlings sucked up aluminum. When these Rhode Islanders limed it and phosphated it—the aluminum stayed out.

"That might be a way to keep our corn from dwarfing, from dying between the veins of its leaves, from leaf-firing, too," guessed Hoffer, and that winter the two of them moiled in their dank greenhouse at LaFayette.

They went out and searched up and dug pailfuls of poor soils, bankrupting, mortgage-foreclosing kinds of soil, from Pike and Daviess counties to the south, from Bartholomew, Hancock, Shelby counties southeast of Tippecanoe. . . . Into pots they packed these hard-time soils; tucked in good healthy seeds of maize; treated some of the pots with lime, others with phosphates and into other pots they put a little of the chloride of aluminum. Trost nursed and tended the seedlings that struggled up to peep over the edges of those pots in the steamy greenhouse, at the end of ten weeks he harvested every last one of these young maize plants, weighed the dry weight of each plant from every pot. . . . Together Trost and Hoffer got out their lenses to look for the root-rotting molds.

Again, yes. There was no doubt the phosphate was fine —in the phosphate pots the young plants stood up green and sturdy. Rot was at the roots of the seedlings in the check-pots—that held poor soil without phosphates. And the aluminum soil? The seedlings hardly poked their shoots out of the ground before they blighted, died, shot to pieces under the ground by the mold, *Fusarium*, that tangled its deadly tentacles 'round the root hairs.

Every man around Hoffer's workshop now began to throw his hat up in the air for phosphates. Trost made a bold experiment, soaking the seed of corn in the savage mold, *Gibberella saubinetii*—but so long as phosphate was there in plenty in the soil, the roots of the young maize plants laughed at those molds.

The dark-haired able Garrard—who makes fine experiments in an offhand way without seeming to have spirit or enthusiasm for them—comes to Hoffer, shows how more and more phosphate makes corn grow better and better—'til it grows so fast at last it gets hungry for nitrogen!

Well—if phosphates guard against aluminum, why shouldn't they keep the still more dangerous iron out of maize? Aren't iron and aluminum chemical cousins? Hoffer jumped at this hunch, never stopping to think of the eternal complicatedness of Nature, forgetting that one experiment is worth a thousand reasons, analogies. Now to help out the farmers, to make the Hoosier men's old land new. He set out to show them new facts about the old fertilizer, phosphate—how it would make maize tough against all kinds of root-rots. With Trost he went south from LaFayette to Linden in Montgomery County, to a poor sort of farm, famous for its bad yields, down corn, chaffy ears. In that soil, while the redbirds whistled their love-calls and the orioles built their nests, Hoffer and Trost planted healthy seed of maize. On to one plat of that soil they put lime; next it they strewed phosphate; other plats they left as checks. Then one hot day of high summer, they sent out invitations, calling folks to see the miracle of the defeat of the root-rot, and the new high yield of that field.

It was a flop.

Farmers came, hard-boiled, ready to be convinced not by scientific explanations—but by the looks of Hoffer's corn.

Experts were there too—fellows who considered Hoffer a corn upstart; even one of the dignitaries of the Bureau of Plant Industry from Washington was on the ground—with an eye cocked maybe to give Hoffer a mark in the black book. And Hoffer stood around among them all, wishing the ground would open and swallow him up, blushing at the supercilious smiles of the corn sharks, wondering what could have happened to this corn that started out so lustily two months before. . . . Here were ears, hanging down desolately on broken shanks; here was a horrid, a shameful spot, right in the middle of a well-phosphated plat, where the farmers chuckled over nothing but broken-down stalks, and chaffy ears hardly fit to feed to a scrub hog. One of the experts bent over, pulled up a big corn plant that stood supported by nice big brace roots—all right, but where were the rest of its roots—the ones that would feed the ears from the soil? No roots to speak of—all rot. . . .

"Oh—we were sick that day, you bet," muttered Hoffer. And he smiled at the salty memory of it. "That day certainly knocked our phosphate theory in the head. . . . Funny, too, that was—because in some fields phosphate knocked out the stunting, the root-rot, okay. . . . Gosh, I didn't know what that bird from Washington was going to do to me!" And Hoffer laughed.

That day he pulled from the limed, the phosphated fields at Linden, stalks of rotted maize whose broken joints were brown with iron, stalks that turned a terrible telltale bright red under the drops of the thiocyanate and acid. It was a flop.

v.

YOU'VE all seen or heard tell of certain fighters who are most dangerous just after they've staggered to their feet with eyes glazed after taking a count of nine: such a one was this Dutchman, Hoffer.

Why hadn't phosphating the soil kept the iron out of

those corn plants? Hoffer's boys, Trost, the dark-haired Garrard, Weaver, the exact analytical chemist—all of them pawed and fumbled for explanations. Hoffer waited, sucked at his pipe, chewed up endless matches, while his head cleared from the disaster at Linden, he watched for an opening, but never foamed at the mouth with impatience, never cursed his luck, never took his troubles to bed with him. There is something undramatic, profoundly unexcitable about Hoffer. "Of course I didn't work nights about it, go back to the laboratory in the evenings over this trouble," said Hoffer. "That time I devote to my family—that's the only time I have with my wife and my boys."

Drive through the rich Lebanon Valley or through any of that Pennsylvania Dutch country and you'll see dozens of Hoffers—placid, eating three very square meals a day, shutting up their businesses at six. A regiment of prohibition agents wouldn't worry them. And so Hoffer plugged along —and then one day, with no warning, like a thief in the night, came a little offhand fact, in the shape of a letter— from Terra Ceia, North Carolina. Where the deuce was Terra Ceia? The letter was from Mr. R. W. Howell, farm manager of the Nissen Farms—what were they? Mr. Howell had never heard of Hoffer; Hoffer had never dreamed of this obscure Howell; Howell had sent his tale of woe to his Congressman, who'd sent it on to the Cereal Office of the Bureau of Plant Industry at Washington, who'd sent it on to Hoffer—who was supposed to be the last word in America on corn root-rots. Though privately, at this moment, Hoffer was convinced he was not so hot— as the street boys say.

Mr. Howell was nobody in the *Who's Who* or *American Men of Science*, but he was a straightforward and sensible farmer with a degree from the North Carolina College of Agricultural and Mechanic Arts, and Mr. Howell very distinctly knew what he wanted—which was to know why

the devil the corn of the Nissen Farm—seventy-five bushels
to the acre a few years before—was now shot to pieces, was
now grown at a loss, was now barren, was now rotted at
its roots. Why?

Howell had cut the timber off this land at Terra Ceia,
rotted it, planted the first corn by making holes with sticks
in the porous, peaty soil—almost pure organic matter that
land was. He'd "stuck" his corn among the fallen trees
while there was still too much wood about to use the plow.
Amid the glow of the smoky, acrid fires of that well-rotted
wood the corn grew, gigantic and yielding astoundingly.
Folks came to buy this grand new land. Howell sweat pro-
digiously, getting off the stumps, draining the water-soaked
peat by a system of canals and lateral ditches, cutting down
the maize trees after the corn had been husked and turning them every fall into a great blaze like a prairie fire.
Howell was diligent; looked after every detail; drained this
land well—and then, alas! the strange dark soil began to
settle. The very bottom seemed to drop out of this rich
ground, one, two feet, down it sank. The wood was gone
now; the ground was plowed, cultivated. . . . But instead
of the hundred bushels to the acre yields that had grown
when the corn was put into holes made with a stick and
covered up with your foot—the plants shot up, and then
suddenly broke off at their lower joints, bore ears that hung
down ominously limp, and strange bare spots appeared on
these fields where no corn came up at all!

Corn couldn't be raised at a profit. Howell wouldn't tell
any prospective farmer it could be if it couldn't. Who'd now
buy the land?

Howell must certainly have been no ordinary student at
college—he actually remembered many things he'd been
taught in his class-rooms and had the knack of doping out
things he'd never been taught. He pulled up some of his disgusting corn plants, saw that their roots were rotted,

squinted closer, and so he wrote to his Congressman, "I observed something on those rotted roots in the way of a *Fusarium*."

And he ended his letter: "Our yields are next to nothing in many parts of our fields."

What to do?

"Please send me a quart sample of your soil," wrote Hoffer to Howell of Terra Ceia, "and some of your diseased cornstalks." And then George Hoffer—who never had claimed to be a shark on fertilizers—added certain recommendations more or less at random, with no experiments on Howell's soil to back them: "In certain soils potash deficiency counts; in others, phosphate." He advised Howell to try the effects of these elements as fertilizers. After all— he had to recommend *something!*

The soil came to LaFayette, and thoroughly, like a conscientious Government servant, Hoffer tested it; his men found that this black peat was acid, that there was no soluble aluminum in it, that it had great amounts of iron. "Your soil lacks lime," Hoffer wrote to the worried and embattled Howell. "I would suggest you set aside small areas of your land, a tenth, a fortieth of an acre to each acre, and give those plats heavy doses of limestone, at increasing rates, of two—four—six tons to the acre. Plow that into your soil."

Not a word did Hoffer mention again about potash; he forgot about Howell, turned back to his calm worries about iron and root rots and what in the world would keep iron out of living trees of maize.

But Howell? Howell remembered Hoffer had told him to try potash, and, anyway, Howell remembered everything, read everything. . . . By George! he had to make that land yield corn so his employers could get rid of it to new farmers. . . . Howell read every possible soil book. "All information I was able to gain from every point of the world dealing with muck and peat soils indicated that

256

in practically every case potash was the one essential fertilizing element . . ." wrote Howell.

But Hoffer had said lime, had advised lime particularly!

Howell was of the line of Angus Mackay, a farmer comparer. In the spring of 1922, while the downy green of spring masked the discouragement of those Terra Ceia lands, Howell laid out his test plats: some with no tons of limestone; some with two tons to the acre; others with four; yet others with six—exactly as Hoffer had said. But he did more, did this Farmer Howell. Other little plats he laid out, with all the different amounts of limestone—from no tons to six tons per acre. But to each of *these* plats he added phosphate.

And to another set of little oblongs of ground, exactly like the first two, with more and more limestone, Howell added potash, crude sulphate of potash. . . .

Into all of them he sowed good seed of maize.

"I am testing the relative value of different fertilizer elements, both individually and collectively, in connection with lime and no lime," wrote Howell to Hoffer. Both individually and collectively—there he was at the very guts of science. . . .

Carefully Howell plowed each of these dozens of little plats of corn, the right number of times he cultivated them like the efficient farmer that he was; then he laid them by, and waited.

By late July he had the answer to his needs, the cure of the troubles of the tired Terra Ceia land. On the phosphate plats, and on the plats that had got phosphate and limestone, and on the land that had got limestone alone—even six tons to the acre of it!—there was sadness, there were broken-stalked, droop-shanked plants of maize with ears hanging down, chaffy, dejected.

But on every little plat where he'd put the potash, the corn trees shot up straight and strong. It was wonderful. Nearly as good these plants grew as if they were on the

257

best black Iowa loam. It was potash that turned the trick—
oh, no doubt of it. That stuck out like a sore thumb. "It has
increased our yield from two hundred to three hundred
percent," wrote Howell to Hoffer, in jubilation. "In fact,
there were spots where nothing would grow . . . but now,
with potash, we're going to get forty to fifty bushels to the
acre. . . . And there's no root-rot. The roots are thrifty
and well developed!"

Quietly, naturally, the pieces of Hoffer's mixed-up puzzle now fell together, solved by this fantastic accident.
Hoffer knew all about the poisonous work of iron, that
weakens maize at the joints and lets the molds get in their
deadly work. He'd thought nothing much at all of potash.
Howell was obsessed with potash; he thought nothing
whatever of iron. . . . Six hundred miles apart these two
men had been working, never having seen each other. . . .

"Please send me two corn plants from each of your
plats," Hoffer wrote Howell—urgently. "Be careful to get
no dirt on them; tie them up if possible in heavy paper."

Dozens of corn plants come on their strange errand from
Terra Ceia to Tippecanoe. With Trost—who was tense—
with Weaver and the rest of them, the matter-of-fact
Hoffer unwraps Howell's precisely labeled maize trees.
There is a tinkle of the little bottles of thiocyanate, of
muriatic acid, for the old iron test. There is silence, save
for the rasp of the stainless steel knives as Hoffer's boys
slit open the maize plants lengthwise, lay bare their joints.

Hoffer's teeth take a grip on his pipe, and the drops of
thiocyanate, followed by the drops of acid, fall on to joint
after joint of stalk after stalk.

They've got it.

On every last stalk that grew on Howell's plats with
no limestone, with every amount of limestone, with phosphate and limestone—the joints of the corn flame the bright
blood red. The telltale red surges over the brown joints and
says: "Yes: iron is here."

From the potash plats? Hoffer writes simply: "In plants from any of the plats that received potash, the amount of iron in the joints was slight." And no root-rot, and no poisonous *Fusarium* mold. . . .

Howell had found a way to hold his job, to make that North Carolina land pay. Hoffer had found a new truth—as a by-product of Howell's need.

VI.

so George Hoffer took a long step ahead of the Indian, Squanto, who taught the Pilgrims to boost their corn yields on the thin New England soil—by putting fish in the corn-hills. Fish are good for maize, but where in Indiana, Ohio, Tennessee, Kentucky would the white men find the fish—for the billions of cornhills on their millions of acres of tired land? So George Hoffer took a step ahead of the grand handsome old German, Baron Liebig, who had given the white men their substitutes for Squanto's crude fish—who'd shown them how to renew their soil, with lime, with phosphate, with potash. But Liebig had never taught any farmer to tell exactly how to put which chemical on what land. Did this man's muck land need potash? Did the next fellow's yellow clay need nitrogen? Did the neighbor's acid ground need phosphate?

Who could tell? In every state the agronomists of the experiment stations had tried to tell—from years of careful plot tests of this and that chemical mixture of fertilizers for a particular kind of soil at his own experiment station, one scientist might say: "Phosphate boosts the maize yield ten bushels to the acre." But how could this scientist tell that a certain troubled farmer's land—*that looked just the same* as the land of his experiment plot—needed phosphate? There are mysterious differences lurking in two samples of yellow clay, or of black loam—differences not dreamt of in the best soil scientist's philosophy.

From the looks of a soil, from the deepest chemical taking apart of a soil, there's no telling what the maize sucks up from that soil, either in food or poison. And so it came about that every American state had its own particular science for the chemical feeding of tired land—for tired lands the keenest man couldn't tell apart. It was a strange idiocy.

Now came Hoffer, with a simple trick to make the corn plant talk, tell its needs, make new land from old, boost the yield of the American maize crop on nobody can tell how many millions of acres of land no longer new.

Quietly he went at his enormous job, with the simplicity of the anonymous ancestors of Squanto he tackled it; with the sweep of Mark Alfred Carleton himself, he imagined his work. Hoffer knew the dirt-farmers themselves weren't expert chemists; with horse sense he cooked up chemical tests that would make the living corn tell—in colors—its hunger to the plainest farmer. Down corn, rotted roots, broken ear shanks and chaffy ears? A couple of drops of thiocyanate, of acid, out of each of two little bottles, poured onto the joints of a just tasseled corn plant, freshly cut lengthwise to bare its joints—does the red flame come? If it does, then there's iron plugging the joints—and the field needs potash.

Here's a field with no root-rot, but the yield is low, and the leaves of the maize are pale green, or yellow. A couple of drops out of another little bottle, poured on to the pith of the cut stalk, *between* the joints. Does a blue color come? If no—then it's nitrogen for which the maize plant hungers.

But there's a field where the maize is stunted, where the leaves are fired, where they have that strange yellow dying-between-the-veins. And the soil? A little blue litmus paper shows it is acid. It's phosphate that field needs—to guard the maize from the poison of aluminum. . . . So Hoffer made the maize plants talk to their masters.

With an American sweep. with none of that strange conservatism of his Dutch folks who'll stick forever in their

Pennsylvania valleys, Hoffer now sent men, in 1925 and 1926, armed with stainless steel knives and the little kits of bottles for the stalk tests, up and down America, and back and forth across it. Early 'til late they covered the maize fields, from hot July 'til the frost caught the maize in October. Through the black prairies of Kansas, Nebraska, Iowa, went Hoffer's men: sure—the test showed it: little or no red in those corn joints—plenty of potash in these western fields. But through southern Illinois, and Ohio, and Michigan, and heaven knows where else east of the Mississippi? Here were rotted roots, gnawed by the *Fusarium, Diplodia, Gibberella;* and here were the red joints of this less than thirty-bushels-to-the-acre corn, crying for potash. So Hoffer mapped and plotted the hunger of American soil.

Now at last he could really help the Hoosier men. Here were the Rauth brothers who farmed it on the heavy clay of Warrick County, down by the great curve of the Ohio River. For years they'd been harvesting less corn, and less. Hoffer came, peering at their maize out of innocent-looking brown eyes, wiping the sweat that glistened on that outstanding round head of his. A slash of the stellite knife, drops from the bottles. "Yes, potash," murmured Hoffer to those despairing brothers Rauth, whose soil had done well to give twenty bushels of corn to the acre.

Up went their yield, next year, to sixty.

The men of Cass County, northeast of Tippecanoe, came to Hoffer, and his stalk test showed red, showed iron in the joints of Elmer Elliott's corn on his light clay land. Potash —and that half of the field yielded nine bushels to the acre more than the half that Elmer left untreated. Potash —and up went Claude Pavey's maize yield on his black sand soil, twenty bushels to the acre did Claude's yield increase. And so with half a dozen more Cass County men who took part in this practical science: six, eight, ten bushels more of good maize to the acre they got—and no rot at the roots of their cornstalks. And here was a neat proof: in the joints of the stalks of the maize of E. J. Zeck and Carl Miller there was no red flame of the iron test. But they used potash just the same. And their maize yield didn't go up at all!

To Europe spread George Hoffer's fame, and to Europe he went to show the foreign soil-scientists his little kink that makes the corn plants give an accurate answer to their masters who ask them: "What are you hungry for?"

But Hoffer's head is not turned by his fame. He slumps down in his chair, keeps lighting his pipe and letting it go out, chews at his matches when his teeth get tired of gnawing at his pipe bit, and better than any one he knows what he still doesn't know about the mysterious needs of the soil. "Of course we haven't solved the riddles, all the riddles, of starved corn, sick corn. . . . We've only scratched the surface yet. These little stalk tests aren't a cure-all. There's soil erosion to take care of—and how much do we know about drainage, and what exactly should we do about changing the level of the water tables? . . . And then there's weeds—think of the thousands of fellows who just don't fight weeds!"

But Hoffer has taught the American dirt-farmers, who now have to cross the frontier of hard times, a trick that will help thousands of them to boost their yields on their fields that once were tired—to grow larger yields on smaller fields. Shull—the botanist—put his finger on the heavy yielding blood lines. Hoffer has found a little trick to uncover the hidden hunger of maize—the hunger that's at the bottom of its sickness.

Hoffer keeps on with his experimenting, his chemical tinkering, and he's reasonably happy. "There's no money in all this for me," says Hoffer. And deep down in him he knows there's millions for the potash and phosphate folks in it, and in the end millions for the dirt men whose land used to be old. Then he steps on the starter of his 1920

Dodge touring car. "But I get a lot of fun out of it," adds Hoffer.

And in his poverty he's not unique. Henry Wallace still drives that ancient Winton, that I've helped to push up hill, and I doubt whether George Harrison Shull—what with six children—has any car at all, and it's these men, and a hundred others as poor or poorer, who turn the basic tricks that raise the level of American life, who are doing the job of giving a fair shake to the dirt men who guard us from hunger.

But these searchers are not in a class by themselves, either. How are they different from the miserably paid engineers who bring water a hundred miles for New York City to drink, or the shipmasters who make it safer to cross the ocean than to walk across a crowded street? And will the designers of the new craft that'll take us safe through the air be millionaires?

Who knows, maybe it's not only in the cards, maybe it's for the best that this breed of men stay poor. I knew a doctor, who had the brains of a searcher, and showed great promise to turn new tricks to fight death—on pay of five thousand or so dollars a year. Then he up and married a rich girl, and went to live in a house fit for a grand duke, with a fountain in its yard, and under the water of the fountain's basin played lights colored red and blue and green. There's a nurse for each of his three children. And now this searcher has all the money he needs for the best education of these children—and in the evenings he can admire the play of lights under his fountain.

In his laboratory nothing more happens.

BOOK FOUR. THE HIDDEN HUNGER

BABCOCK

BABCOCK

I.

THERE IS A KIND OF HUNGER other than the hunger of the face gaunt for lack of food, of the lean belly hurting for want of something to fill it. There is the hidden hunger that lets folks starve to death while they are eating plenty.

Babcock of Wisconsin was first of all modern men to find this hunger that doesn't gnaw at men and beasts but only strikes them down with strange ills, maybe kills them. Babcock is certainly a most gay old man. The outstanding thing about him, aside from his roaring laugh that may explode at most dignified and embarrassing moments, is the way he has always kicked fame in the face.

He has lived his own life as a merry searcher, as a hunger fighter who never took himself seriously.

He would be the first to deny that he was the first fighter of this new mysterious hunger, for this science, too, has had forerunners as anonymous, as prehistoric, as the first men who turned tricks to fill empty bellies. After all, the first fighters of the hidden hunger must have been shaggy slant-browed fellows who foraged for every kind of food, who had sense enough to eat everything they could swallow without gagging at it. Was that a work of their brains? Was that some crude science of theirs? Who knows? There was nobody to set down the record of the why of their aimless and enormous foraging.

But of this there is record: that Stephen Moulton Babcock, whose science was always a sort of private vaudeville for himself and his friends, first asked the question: Is there a hidden hunger? He was lucky to live in these days when, what with the so-called advance of civilization, men have come to be finicky, have gone from the fields and woods into

267

the cities, have eaten fewer and fewer kinds of food. So this new hunger has loomed, in a dozen shapes grotesque and deadly—in the pitiful bent bones of babies, in the mysterious wasting away of children born healthy, and in consumption maybe, and in the dreadful red death of pellagra surely. Babcock—beginning with a slightly dirty and not at all dignified joke—was the pioneer who set a new kind of hunger fighter sniffing off on the trails to conquer these terrors.

But to listen to this smiling, ancient man, you'd think he'd had very little to do with the digging out of the mysterious things that lack in some foods—that are present in despised foods to guard us from death. "Hart and his able assistants deserve all the credit," laughs old Doctor Babcock as he talks of that fantastic experiment that began in 1907. He laughs a young man's laugh, and from his talk it is plain he is just as interested in Babe Ruth, and in the lamented Christy Mathewson whom he adored. He is fundamentally as excited about a new home-run record as about being called the first man original enough to see that a cow might still be hungry though she was eating enough to satisfy three beasts of her own kind and weight.

Not a single word has Babcock ever published about this basic discovery; all the glory of it went to the youngsters around him. Humor and work, jokes and experiments— these were continually mixed up in Babcock's life, and for him the finding of a new fact was immensely more fun than the recording of it. "His work has always been play for him," says Harry Steenbock, one of Babcock's boys who was later to trap the health of the sun's rays. Babcock has never allowed himself to be serious, businesslike, or bothered— and to this day he refuses to have a telephone put in his house. The hidden hunger is only one of his many discoveries; his curiosity has no limits; he has put his finger into nearly every pie of science. He *has been* famous. And the astounding thing about this once more obscure old man is that his curiosity doesn't seem to grow old with his body. He's now eighty-four, but you may still see him walking to his laboratory, up the hill, at Madison—and here he's still busy asking original, heretical questions: he's turned himself into a physicist now, and is busy propounding a new theory—unpublished of course—as to the nature of matter!

That highbrow question is far enough off from his first comical feeding trials with the two pure-bred cows of the Station Herd at Madison, who starved, to the great and very proper disgust of W. L. Carlyle. But in this day of specialists Babcock has stayed a primitive, and why shouldn't he experiment at anything?

In this humdrum day of efficient science Babcock has kept the spirit of old Antony Leeuwenhoek.

II.

IT was lucky Babcock was born on a farm, because it very early seeped into him there that just because you're a chemist, you shouldn't try to explain everything chemically. Before he went up to Tufts College and Cornell University, he fed stock with his father on their Oneida County farm upstate in New York, and his father had only the knowledge of common sense and experience. Not knowing it, maybe, Stephen Babcock went up to the chemical halls with his dad's small-word science tucked away at the back of his head. Babcock had an incessantly active head on him, was not satisfied with what they could teach him at Tufts, couldn't even learn enough chemistry at Cornell, and finally went to Germany where the great whales of chemistry were finding new chemical facts instead of simply teaching old ones.

These were the last days of the eighteen-seventies, and they were piping days in chemical science. Food, drink, clothes, war, life itself was going—according to the chemists' faith and by the chemists' art—to be turned topsy-turvy in test-tubes. Babcock sat in the classes of great-domed Teutons, who were going to figure out to the last ounce on a piece of paper the grub a man needed to do twelve hours of work. There was the famous Baron Liebig, who was positive he would soon brew a milk in his labora-tory, an ideal artificial milk better for babies than the nat-ural stuff that drips from mothers and cows. That hand-some scientist, adored by scholars from a dozen countries, had ambitions to concoct artificial foods to make farms things of the past. Liebig would revolutionize agriculture, not in the field—but in his laboratory! Babcock sat, with his eye open, drinking in such hopes and dreams from men who'd known Liebig personally. He saw brainy men drag-ging grains and green feeds, roots and every kind of rough-age off farms into their dens that were heavy with assorted chemical stinks. Babcock helped them stick those natural foodstuffs into their beakers, retorts, chemical ovens. Amid the fumes of strong gases fit to knock a mule-driver off his pins, happy in these outlandish workshops, Babcock helped the German chemists to analyze, speculate, weigh, compute, prophesy—

His one eye wide open, this New York State boy fol-lowed the reasonings of these chemical sharks as they got the knowledge of the feeding of beasts and men down to a simple diagram. Exact! All foods are nothing but proteins, fats, carbohydrates, salts—and water. Simple! And on the foundation of that they'd be building up presently a complete ration for man and cow in their laboratories, mak-ing a million pounds of beef from their new artificial grass, making a million pounds of German infantrymen from new artificial cows. . . . It was inspirational, no less.

Diligently Babcock picked up German, listened to lec-tures by big-bearded men with that curious bird-like alert-ness that he still has, with his head cocked to one side. He had the honor to shake hands with old Friedrich Wöhler, who first made in a test-tube what savants had always before thought could only be made by God; Wöhler had synthesized urea—up till his time the mysterious product of those living laboratories, the kidneys of beasts and men. Babcock's chemical religion was stoked up by his study with Bunsen, a gorgeous old chemical potterer, a chemical magician, whose thoughts soared from the gas stoves that he had invented for housewives to the unattainable chemistry of stars a million light-years away.

Babcock came back home, full of the very latest wrinkles of the exact analysis of foods, believing the new gospel that the exact mixture and balance of proteins, fats, starches, and salts would produce just the right amount of stuff and energy to form the tissues of pigs, chickens, heifers, and babies, and to make them run. What, according to this lovely science, were bulls and babies, excepting so many animated boilers and steam-engines? And what news this was, for Babcock to bring home to his northern New York chemists, feeders, farmers. You see this tall young American unknown, bending over standard formulas and tables that'll teach everybody to fatten hogs by arithmetic instead of by experience. People, horses, heifers? They're chemical machines—no more. Babcock came back upstate in New York to recite the amount of fat, sugar, and starch a cow needed in order to have the oxygen she breathed burn that food to give her the energy she must have to keep her going. Plus that, all she needed to do was to swallow the right amount of protein to make up for the wear and tear on her muscles, her sinews and the secret marrow of her bones. You fed one amount of all these things to a cow while she rested; you fed exactly this increased amount should she have occasion to gallop three miles.

Alas for the curiosity that was so much a part of him, there seemed nothing much more left for this boy to learn about the rationing of cows to make them moo, have calves, give milk, do all the deeds required of respectable cows for the carrying out of their cow destinies. But wasn't this too simple?

While he'd been in Germany, cutting his scientific eye-teeth in laboratories where a few arrogant men put the theories of their brains against the human experience of nobody knows how many thousands of years—imps of doubt played at the back of his head. Was it just a matter of chemical formulas? Didn't the source of food, the *kind* of food matter? What had the barbarous men and women of the days ten thousand years before colleges were invented—what had these folks done to make themselves grow, keep their bodies energetic, healthy? Of course they'd just eaten everything they could swallow. Not knowing why on paper, or even scrawling the science of it on cave walls, they knew enough to shin up trees and get eggs out of nests, to tame wild grasses and eat their seeds for cereals, to get meat by their arrows, to tame female meat on four legs in order to get the milk from it, to claw dirty-handed in the ground for roots and tubers.

Babcock pondered: these aboriginal folk had never had to figure out formulas for making themselves grow or go. They just went. And from what was known of present-day savage folks who haven't gone beyond these aborigines, their babies grew and weren't bow-legged; consumption was unknown among them; their teeth were so strong dentists would starve to death trying to make a living among them. And the uncivilized people ate everything—from all over the place!

Babcock wondered: unscientific people fed their chickens, cows, pigs, as many different foods as they could find. And if these dumb beasts were fed too few things, the animals had the sense to forage for varieties of food themselves. But here were the chemists. They said it didn't matter where a cow's food came from, so long as she had the right amount of protein to take care of her wear and tear, and enough fat, starch, sugar to give her energy. It was simple. But was it right?

III.

WITH a German degree of Doctor of Philosophy, but not at all dignified by it, Babcock came back to upstate New York, took a job at Geneva at the northern tip of Lake Seneca that runs like a blue finger pointing south between austere long hills. He was appointed chemist of the Experiment Station there, and his boss was Doctor Sturtevant, that self-made scientist who immortalized himself by sticking into their proper, if terribly changeable classes, all the different sorts of Indian corn.

Of the first conversation of Sturtevant and Babcock there is no written record, but roughly their talk went on this wise:

"Doctor Babcock, will you please get ready to do the chemistry of these food-digestion experiments that I've been planning for our dairy-cows here at the Station?"

But this was right up Babcock's alley, was what he'd just got down cold in Germany, what he could do better than any man in America, no doubt! "I was elated," said Babcock, long afterward, with a laugh. Here was a chance to find out by chemical science—superior to mere common sense—whether a given ration was good for a cow or no. And into Babcock's very bare little laboratory came baskets of corn on the ear, crackling bundles of good corn stover, messy bunches of hay—in short, all the food Sturtevant wanted to try out on his cows cluttered Babcock's sanctum, and into his glass vessels, porcelain pots, into his beakers and crucibles went samples of these foods.

Babcock computed—or believed that he did—the exact amount of protein in that ration, by finding the amount of nitrogen in it and multiplying this amount by the figures 6.25. The precise amount of fat in this hay and corn he got at by extracting the ration with ether. With care he estimated the crude fiber of all this feed. And its minerals he found by burning a weighed sample, and weighing the ash that was left after burning. And now—

The question was: How well would these precious cows of Director Sturtevant *digest* this ration?

Into their mangers in their barn Babcock had the hired man put samples of this same stuff he'd just analyzed. How much of it would they use? How much of it would they take into themselves for the building of their bone, muscle and sinew? How well would they digest this ration—whose chemistry he'd so exactly determined?

The hired man labored; grotesquely he carried into Babcock's laboratory what came out of these cows after they'd eaten this food. Exactly, with a chemist's glorious disdain for unbeautiful angles of his labor, Babcock tested these discharges by exactly the same tests and weighings he'd applied to the good foods from which they'd come. Exactly what was left, of these fats, proteins, starches, sugars, and minerals? How much of each of them had the beasts used? How efficient were these rations of Sturtevant's? Babcock— who had lost one eye when a boy by the sting of a bee— cocked his head to bring his good eye to bear on his tubes. Great were the smells and acrid were the fumes in which he labored. . . .

In precise columns, on paper, Babcock set down two rows of figures—the exact amounts of the chemical things his cows had taken in with their food, and the precise amounts of the same things that had come out of them. These last figures he subtracted from the first ones, and the answer?

The answer was the amount the cows had digested—of course!

The good Director Sturtevant stalked in every now and again, proud of these experiments that would undoubtedly tell them a lot about the best food for their prize cows. And he approved of Babcock as he watched that young man's industrious back—bent over those figures. But meanwhile, odd things were happening in Babcock's head. He is industrious enough, thorough enough, persistent enough surely—and dozens of times he has done these experiments over, when suddenly one day, he straightens up from his desk, his forehead knots up into wrinkles, he gives a puzzled grunt—

He scans the figures for the protein and what-not that had gone into his cows. He compares them with the rows of figures for the stuff that they've discharged. What's this? Look at these figures for the ash—for the mineral part of their excrement! What the devil does this mean? The amount of mineral in their discharges *is much more* than the amount they've taken in with their food!

He jumps up. "But this changes everything! What'll all these figures amount to, if I leave out the ash from my calculations—if I neglect the minerals altogether?"

It was a heresy. What would the great Germans who had devised the digestion tests say to any chemist who "neglected the minerals"? It was a hunch, and unorthodox. But Babcock got out fresh sheets of paper, began his calculations all over, set down the figures for the weights of the proteins, fats, sugars and starches that the cows had eaten. By their side he put down the figures for the outgo. But he left out the ash, the minerals—from both places.

Alas: what went into those excellent cows was exactly the amount that came out of them! But impossible! Cows digest hay, corn grain, corn stover. Everybody knows they assimilate a lot of it, use it. . . . Impossible! . . . Babcock did his calculations over and over again. Not impossible—but correct. There was not a thing wrong with the cows; their food was okay; but everything was wrong with the silly chemical science. Babcock smiled; why—these digestion experiments didn't tell a thing about how much or what the cows digested. And he burst out into a roar of a laugh. "And when Babcock laughs," wrote famed chemist Louis Kahlenberg, "he laughs all over."

With an appearance of proper respect Babcock took these

two silly sets of figures to the office of his boss, Dr. Sturtevant, laid them down on that good man's desk, and asked, with a straight face:

"Please tell me, Doctor, which one of those rations you would judge best for the cows here on the Station?"

Sturtevant, judicious as becomes a director, with scientific authority, scanned them, put the 3.25 in this row over against the 3.24 in the row opposite. He tried to be judge of whether 6.76 of this, for a cow, was better than 6.79 of that. "Well, Doctor Babcock, I must confess that one of these rations looks to be just about as good as the other."

"All right, sir," came back Babcock. "But one of those sets of figures is for what our cows ate, and the other is for what they dropped!"

And he had the nerve to chuckle, and then laugh.

There sat the excellent Sturtevant, amid the ruins of his experiments of months, and he couldn't believe it. This was tommyrot; Babcock must have weighed things wrong; made mistakes in his tests, didn't know how to cipher. From Sturtevant there came an authoritative sputtering of the kind that issues from authorities when authorities are wrong but still are—authorities. But by now Babcock had stopped laughing.

Down on the desk in front of his boss he put papers with rows of figures for exactly the same digestion experiments, made not by himself but by the greatest German chemists. "See—just leave the ash out of *their* figures. Now take a look at the two rows. Here's food. There's excreta. Which —according to the figures—will make the better ration?"

Sturtevant was stumped.

Babcock now went around, not preaching against these nonsensical digestion experiments, but getting laughs out of them. For years these tests had been dished out to up-to-date farmers as the last word in the most efficient way to put meat on cattle; the chemists never for a moment questioned these digestion tests: weren't the biggest chemical guns in Germany back of them? But now Babcock got up in the sober meeting of the Association of Agricultural Chemists: "I can make up a mixture of different things, none of them'll have the slightest food value, but when you examine them by your chemical tests, they'll have exactly the same composition as any first-class food—by the figures of the tests!"

"Name such a mixture!" challenged one of the leading chemical bigwigs.

"Just try analyzing soft coal—the same way we analyze for nitrogen, for sugars, fats, whatnot!" laughed Babcock.

And the noted Harvey Wiley, later the crusader for pure food, had to admit Babcock had them stumped.

But how to tell just how and what parts of a ration were good for cattle, and what parts might harm them? Babcock revolted—for who knows what irrational reason?—at the notion that animals, people, were mere engines needing exactly this and that for fuel and just so much protein for wear and tear. He had a hunch rations weren't at all so simple as that. He knew a bundle of alfalfa or a green leaf of maize must have, hidden in it, a hundred chemical compounds, unknown. Wise as the Bard was Stephen Babcock, and this gnawed at him, that there were more things in heaven and earth than were dreamt of—in even the exactest chemist's philosophy. Babcock was not for a moment predicting that there might be mysterious lacks in certain foods —that the absence of some "x" might have dreadful consequences for beasts. His hunch was not then so definite as that, he simply knew that next to nothing was known outside common sense farmer knowledge about what was good, what might be positively bad in the food of beasts and men. How to tell? That drummed in his active head.

He knew how to start, and with an experiment so simple any chemist would probably snort at it. Try one kind of food, from a single kind of plant, or even a single part of a plant. Try feeding that one thing to a beast and keep it up

a long time—try that on cows! Then just watch the cow—
and you'd find out what that food lacked. But that experiment was too original, too confoundedly A B C to get any
notice whatever. Try it on cows? Who'd give Babcock a
cow?

IV.

SEVEN years later, in 'eighty-eight, Babcock went to Wisconsin, and in less than five years his name was known in
every creamery and cheese factory in America, in Europe,
and in the Islands Down Under, and in nearly every dairy
farmer's home. Famous he became for his little fat test
for milk. Babcock's boss at Wisconsin was Dean W. A.
Henry. "What our state needs more than anything is a
simple, practical test for the amount of fat in milk," complained the Dean to Babcock. "The creamery business all
over the country is going to pot. The butter factories are
paying the farmers by the pound for milk. You see what
that means! The fellows who bring in thin milk, even the
crooks who skin the cream off their milk, or water it, get as
much as the farmer whose milk runs five pounds of fat to
the hundred."

"Well—" from Babcock.

"Well—we should pay 'em for the fat, but there's no
simple test for it. The honest men are kicking, aren't
taking their milk to the creameries any more."

As if he were some magician Babcock was expected to furnish that test like bringing rabbits out of plug hats. In a
year, he actually did do it, but that's another story. Only
if he hadn't been an extremely stubborn man, as well as a
gay one, he might never have got it. For the whole secret
of his discovering this famous fat test lay in his refusing
to be buffaloed by the outlandish milk of the Jersey cow,
Sylvia. He'd invented several tests that looked pretty good.
Henry urged him to publish them. But none of these tests
would take *all* of the fat out of the milk of this cursed

278

cow Sylvia. "Oh, let her go. Put out the best test you've found so far!" urged Dean Henry. "After all, there aren't many Sylvias."

"No," smiled Babcock. "No test ever leaves this place under my name until it works for every last cow I try it on." And that was that. But he kept on dumping more and more, and yet again more, of sulphuric acid into the milk of the annoying Sylvia—until all of a sudden he got enough acid into that milk to get out all the fat without doing anything else whatever to it. And that made an amazing simple test for the fat in the milk of all cows; so he tumbled on to this test that beat all his other ones to smithereens—by being stubborn.

"In the hope that it may benefit some who are striving to improve their stock and enable creameries to avoid the evils of the present system, the test *is given to the public*," wrote Babcock at the end of his paper—and he didn't put those last words in italics. Benefit? This jovial man turned the hit-or-miss guessing game, alas! often the skin game, of milk selling, into the prosperous business of American dairy farming. And ex-Governor Hoard, a God-fearing man, said: "The Babcock Test has made more dairymen honest than the Bible has ever made."

And the State of Wisconsin gave Babcock a medal, designed and struck by Spinx and Son of London, "recognizing the great value of his inventions, and his unselfish dedication of these inventions to the public service."

He wouldn't patent anything.

So Babcock and Henry worked for Wisconsin, Henry with his ears pricked up for folks' needs, Babcock never caring particularly, full of merriment, of high, unprofessorial horseplay. In his shirtsleeves he toiled, up on the fourth floor of the Old South Hall in Madison, tinkering, always looking in his own odd, different way at every question. "Cheese-curing methods are all mixed up," Henry would tell him. And while at work fussing with milks that were turning into cheeses, Babcock found that cheese cures itself, by a ferment, and not by microbes as Pasteur and the big scientific bugs of Europe were claiming. But this was all fun, no matter how much money cheese factories might make from it, and never for a moment was Babcock, like Pasteur, making ballyhoo of his benefactions.

His friend Henry, though really a botanist, had written a fine book on the science of stock feeding. He was an earnest man, whose beard, says one record, "was genteelly elaborate, and so tidy I should guess he curried and brushed it with considerable care, if not a little pride, for it was no common possession."

Babcock wasn't sure at all about the food science in Henry's book, was always going back to that old joke he'd played on his first boss, Sturtevant—in that matter of the figures for the food and the dung of cows. They would argue, with violence. "I don't believe in your fine book," Babcock would say, and he was always insisting there was only one way to find out the good or harm of those hundreds of chemical things hidden in oats and grass and maize. "Try one food at a time, for a long time, on cows!" But he had no cows. So he kept working on cheeses. Babcock's beard wasn't curried but Henry and Babcock were excellent friends.

Henry, with the dignity that seems to be inherent in Deans, met delegations of worried farmers. He was conscientious, not light-headed or sportive, and you could find him any day up to his eyes in letters, trying to answer why this dairyman's heifers weren't thrifty on this marsh hay, why those Nebraska farmers' cows weren't calving right the year they were fed wheat meal and straw during the corn shortage, or why those shotes got stiff-legged, rheumatic, towards spring. Henry never missed trying to answer— though God knows here were conundrums. In the middle of trying to dictate his answers—guesses! but honest ones —Henry stops, frowns, his stenographer has lost her place.

She smiles foolishly. It's a gusty bellow of Babcock's laughter cascading down from three floors above. Henry'd go to the head of the stairs, and shout: "We can't hear ourselves think down here!"

They were excellent friends. "If I could only get hold of a few cows," Babcock kept saying. "Hold 'em down to one source of food . . . what would happen . . . feed 'em on just one kind of plant. Practical feeders don't know—they feed everything at the same time!"

But this was no chemical science—and Babcock was hired for a chemist. But he kept arguing, twitting Henry on his best-selling book, "Feeds and Feeding," putting up unanswerable arguments that reduced Henry's ideas of balanced rations to worse than nonsense. Then, twenty years after his first joke on Sturtevant, Babcock got his cows.

Or rather, to be accurate, he got the loan of two cows to experiment with, but not to keep, mind you, 'til death did them part. One day in the midst of one of those skirmishes between the handsomely bearded Dean and the merry chemist, W. L. Carlyle listened in. It was that same Carlyle, brown-skinned and of clean-cut face, with very light gray eyes, who was then Professor of Animal Husbandry, who is now famous as manager of the Alberta ranch of the Prince of Wales—and no dude ranch will that ranch be, either, so long as there's Carlyle to manage it.

"But you can't tell which part of your feed does what to your stock, Carlyle, can you?" grinned Babcock.

"Just come down and see whether there's anything wrong with my Station Herd," was all Carlyle could offer in answer.

"Yes—but the rations you feed your beasts are mixtures of a thousand different chemical things. Your cattle are good, but mightn't they be better? Mightn't you be feeding bad things—masked, covered up partly, by good ones?"

What would Doctor Babcock advise? How would Doctor Babcock go about it to feed stock, Babcock the chemist,

Babcock thirty years away from the smell of a barnyard?

"Just let me have a couple of your cows, and I'll start a little experiment," begged Babcock.

Carlyle, though Scotch, gave Babcock the two cows, and should be honored and remembered for this generosity.

Right away the chemist told Carlyle and Henry his plan —so simple he could unfold it all in a couple of sentences. Limit each cow to just one natural food—feed one of them nothing but food coming from the oat plant, for a long time, say for a year; and the other one nothing but corn. . . . There might be a big difference in the way those two cows behaved on those restricted rations!

Again dreadful argument in that Old South Hall. Dean Henry got out his own bible, which was "Feeds and Feeding"—written by himself—to prove that such a diet wouldn't give the critters the proper balance of proteins, fats, starches, sugars, salts.

Never worry, laughed Babcock. There would be exactly the balanced amounts of those chemical compounds required by the most authoritative science. It's perfectly easy to balance a ration for protein, for energy, even if it does come from one plant. And Babcock proved it to Carlyle and Henry.

Carlyle? That practical man thought this was a perfectly fool experiment—and can you imagine any practical feeder thinking differently? Time out of mind good stockmen had fed their beasts mixed rations. More fundamental still—any beast will forage mixed rations for himself. Oh—there was trouble ahead for his precious cows, and Carlyle would keep an eye on them, even if they were Station cows, and not his very own. Couldn't be throwing state property around that way.

"But this has never been tried before!" insisted Babcock, who was delighted with his extremely simple originality, and his eye twinkled at Carlyle and Henry out of his genial face cocked to one side, and his good humor flowed over his colleagues, engulfed them, conquered them.

The fool experiment was on.

v.

WHILE the dairy-farmers of Australia and New Zealand Down Under, in thanks for his butter-fat test, sent the gay Doctor oil paintings of contented cows, while the World's Fair Exposition at Paris sent him an Award of Merit, Babcock—never concerned about his merit—began to make free with Carlyle's pure-bred cows. Cow No. 1 got oats to eat, rolled oats, oat straw for roughage, nothing at all but oats and salt and water. Her sister got nothing but corn.

Cow No. 1 promptly got thin, slumped down—and in three months gave up the ghost.

A far-away look came into the eyes of Cow No. 2. Her ribs showed and she threatened to follow her sister—but this was too much!

Carlyle took his one cow back, brought her back on the regular Station ration to look alive once more—no more such monkeyshines with stock the college needs for breeding, for the teaching of cow-judging!

So Babcock's first try for the spotting of a hidden hunger, flivvered, washed out. All he could do was to mull over his surprise at this swift, dreadful result of eating nothing but food from the oat plant. And then too, he had doubts to nurse, to mull over. After all, those cows, full grown, were used to mixed diets, and they hadn't taken too kindly to eating oats alone, corn alone. . . . Their appetites had certainly fallen off. . . . But surely they'd eaten enough for their requirements of protein, energy. . . . But had they? Damn it! The barn records of exactly how many pounds they'd eaten weren't complete, weren't sure. And—in contrast to his gayety—there never was a searcher more

283

austerely exact than the Doctor. But could he swear these beasts had eaten absolutely *enough?* Might they not just have plain starved? Babcock didn't publish.

VI.

SIX years more, and then his real chance came. Cows came to him now, times were changing and the world was beginning to believe in cow experiments—even experiments that killed valuable cows, and now Babcock rejoiced in cows galore, sixteen fine cows he got the chance to fuss to his heart's content with. Youngsters had come to Wisconsin, who appreciated the exploring spirit in the eternal youngster that the Doctor was. The brilliant young chemist, E. B. Hart, trained under wise and jolly V. C. Vaughan and the hawk-eyed F. G. Novy, at Michigan, came from Geneva to Madison. Babcock had hired Hart to work on milk, but the moment Hart heard of the Doctor's old fool experiment of holding cows down to just one kind of plant-food, this young man was all on fire to take a whirl at such a test. Then with Hart there was Humphrey, the new Professor of Animal Husbandry: these two youngsters seethed with modern ideas. . . . Babcock was no longer ahead of his time. . . .

"Let's try it out again," urged the two of them—they had the fire of exploring youth in their voices. Hot they were to try out the fool experiment right up to the hilt, to the death and damnation of every cow in the Station Herd if need be. They schemed, figured, planned, hounded the easy-going but enormously experienced Babcock. And that man, at last, though up to his eyes in the testing of a dozen other fantastical chemical notions, listened, laughed, said: "All right, boys—go ahead and try it!"

Twenty-six years after his first joke, Babcock at last had the use of sixteen husky heifers. Five months old, grade shorthorn heifer calves Hart and Humphrey bought, each one full of the pep such a calf should have, and they were

HART

hungry, Lord! they lived to eat. "And that's what we want," smiled Babcock. "We've got to be sure they eat *enough* of these monotonous, one-plant rations. Can't have folks saying they simply starved because they stuck up their noses at what we tried to feed them." But these particular heifers? They were young enough to be satisfied with a bellyful of anything.

Into four lots Babcock's boys divided the sixteen short-horn calves; one lot got nothing but corn—corn meal, corn stover, corn gluten. The next had to live on a diet of wheat —wheat gluten, wheat meal, and wheat straw for rough-age. The third entry of four in this strange race—toward

285

health or toward death, who knew?—began eating oats, rolled oats, and oat straw.

"And now, Hart, let's take these last four," said Babcock, "and feed them a mixture of all three of these plants —one-third the amount of corn, of wheat, of oats, that the others get. They'll be the controls, the check lot." These mixture-fed shorthorns would beat the rest hollow, be the thriftiest, milk best, breed best, no doubt of it. . . . The folk wisdom of ten thousand years was behind that bet.

So these sixteen calves began their strange, momentous lives in the basement of the University Dairy Barn at Madison. Every day they were let frisk about in a paddock as bare of a spear of grass or even a weed as the boys' side of a schoolhouse playground. . . . There would be no catches, no loopholes, in this experiment. The excellent William Voss was put in charge of the feeding of them, kept track to the pound of just how much each one would eat. And by Babcock's exact calculations, each one was swallowing the same amount of protein, and of sugar, starch and fat for energy. Then the old Doctor faded from the picture, let his boys do the rest.

For six months nothing at all happened, excepting that his first fool experiment with Carlyle's cows looked wrong, for every one of the sixteen beasts ate lustily, and seemed to grow as any calf should. There was just one funny business, that William Voss reported, and that Hart and Humphrey puzzled their heads over: the four wheat-eating calves wagged their heads about, as if they were annoyed by something. In the yard and in the stalls they kept sticking out their tongues, they'd open their mouths and keep rolling up their tongues and then unrolling them most queerly. . . . But that was all. . . .

One year: it was now May 1, 1908. All sixteen of them were still putting on pounds—in spite of the diets of such deadly sameness. Why not call it a day? What use going on?

But Babcock, though not a physician, had the sense of the old, outlandishly patient natural historians, observers of Nature before the days of efficiency. "Keep at it, boys," urged the Doctor. "Make it a lifetime of these creatures. Make the experiment like life itself!"

And it's to the honor of Hart and Humphrey that they showed no undue impatience, in spite of their youth. They had endless faith in the hunches of their chemical maestro. But would this test get them anywhere? Wasn't Babcock, for once, barking up a wrong tree? The gentle-voiced Hart and the walrus-mustached Humphrey looked at rows of figures: see—only a few pounds difference in what any of these sixteen beasts weighed. . . . True, the corn-fed beasts did look sleeker, fuller through the barrel. . . . And weren't the wheat-fed creatures a bit sluggish, and wasn't their build a little gaunt, unnatural? But what was that to put down as the result of an experiment? Science must show results, tangible results in figures—clean-cut comparisons!

But they stuck at it, adored their "Doctor," which is still Hart's one name—spoken with the utmost reverence— for Babcock. And Babcock, now past sixty? Oh, he was up to his ears, behind doors in a little room from which now and again came laughter, in experiments—on water. Why experiment on such an utterly well-known, simple, chemical compound as water? No—but this was not common water— but the strange, unthought-of water that all beasts *make* in the tissues of their bodies to keep them alive. "Metabolic water" was Babcock's name for it. And he fed clothes moths on old cast-off fur boas, nothing more, and he found the fantastic fact that these millers have got to make water in their bodies to keep them alive. They never had a chance to drink; they lived on fur that was almost bone-dry; but from the condensation of chemical compounds, from the union of complicated chemicals in their bodies came water: the bodies of these arid creatures were made up of water, more than fifty percent—and nearly all of it came from inside them! Dabbling with such unthought-of, original questions, that was what the Doctor always was doing. Poking his finger into pies of the unknown—into questions he alone seemed to have the sense to see. And he did not forget those dieting heifers.

The sixteen of them had grown up now, were ready to do their cow-duty in life. "Breed them," the old searcher told Hart and Humphrey. "Make your experiment like life itself. Maybe, when you put your heifers under the strain of forming young inside them—then anything that might be wrong in one of these rations will show up!"

From May to August of 1908, as the heifers came in heat, Humphrey married them, one and all, to the fecund and amorous pure-bred Guernsey bull, Coralette's Son. Life, new life, flowed from this able bull into each of the sixteen heifers. That winter there exploded the surprise that lies just around the corner in so many fool experiments—

Behold the corn-fed heifers. They come toward their first ordeal of motherhood, batting never an eye. Within six days, within two days, even right on the dot of their reckoned-up time they bear their babies, four fine heifer-calves these new mothers drop—four children weighing all the way from sixty-seven to eighty-five pounds, and vigorous. The calf of corn-fed mother, No. 556, gets up onto its sturdy legs in less than an hour, and sucks. "Lived: strong and vigorous," Humphrey and Hart mark down for all four of the children of the cow-mothers who've eaten nothing but corn-meal, corn-stover, corn-gluten.

But where are the calves of the cows who have lived on nothing but wheat? Pregnant each one of them had become by the noble Coralette's Son. But, better than a month before their time, things begin to go horribly and mysteriously wrong with them. The wheat-fed mothers are strangely in a hurry to get their calving over and done with. Here's the baby of wheat-fed cow No. 561—it's a miserable little creature, come sixteen days before its time. This little heifer manages to breathe, yes, but four days go by and still she can't bring herself to stand on her wabbly legs. Her breath is too fast, and her blat? It's no blat at all to speak of— better call it a moan. Humphrey and William Voss, tender as good stockmen are, feed her from a bottle, but when she's eleven days old she has convulsions, and on the twelfth morning of her life Voss finds her dead.

Here's another one of those wheat-eating mothers, bearing a calf weighing forty pounds, and it lives just two hours.

Way ahead of term is born the wretched child of the third wheat-fed cow, and breathing feebly for half a day, it too passes on.

The calf of the fourth and last wheat-fed cow is a little bull, weighing forty pounds—born dead.

Here they stand, old Stephen Babcock and his boys, agape at something utterly new in the science of living things. Face to face they are, with a new fact there was no way under God's heaven of ever foretelling—but a fact that Babcock had felt!

"Make it like life itself," he had said. "Maybe when you put those heifers under the strain of forming young inside them . . ."

That was his hunch.

Like voyagers peering at some unearthly sight looming up at them as they round the bend of a river never before passed down by men, these two chemists and that stockman stand there.

Face to face with a new x they are. There's an x, a chemical something that's lacking in wheat—wheat that lets heifers grow, become sexually mature, conceive, and then bear offspring mysteriously lacking the spark of life. And this virtue that lacks in wheat is present in maize, hiding somewhere in grain or the leaves or the gluten of maize, giving cows the unknown wherewithal to bear living vigorous young. What is it? What is this x?

These were great days in Stephen Babcock's life, but to have seen him you'd never have thought it. He was pleased, yes, and he was at his pranks a little more than usual, maybe, but he never touched this fundamental experiment, this terribly important science his boys, Hart and Humphrey, were toying with. For himself, for his own instruction—and amusement—he kept on playing with millers, with bee-moths, with those beings that so grotesquely existed on food with next to no water, that made their own water for their own internal mysterious uses. Faithfully he visited the college baseball games, to those who were interested he took pleasure in reciting the batting averages of his big-league favorites, and he was prepared to prove to all doubters that Christy Mathewson, "Big Six," was one of the greatest living Americans.

This new x? This new thing on earth not dreamt of in any chemist's, any doctor's philosophy? Said Babcock: "Hart and his able assistants deserve all the credit!"

The calves born of the mothers fed entirely with oats were just so-so, three lived out of four, and those three were not too chipper. But the children of the control cows, of those checks, of the ones that had been eating corn, wheat, and oats—rations any common-sense man would have said were the best of the four? Not so good were these calves—only one lived out of four. So it couldn't be *variety* itself that was needed. . . . Already the grand calves from the maize-fed mothers had shown them that monotony of diet wasn't necessarily bad. But what was wrong with the calves of the mixture-fed mothers?

Hart and Humphrey went to their searcher-father, the Doctor.

"Well," mulled Babcock, "maybe your mixture-fed beasts don't get enough of the something that's good that's in corn. After all, they're only getting a third as much corn as the corn-fed mothers. . . . Or, if there is something that's bad hiding in wheat—possibly they didn't get enough of the good in corn to make up for it. . . . Then again, it isn't necessarily a poison that makes the wheat diet bad for the pregnant cows—maybe wheat lacks something that corn happens to have. . . . We don't know." And Babcock could only smile, shake his head, say no more than that. Nobody knew, here at this birth of a new science. They were in new country and had to break their own trails. . . .

"We'll make this experiment like life itself"—that was a refrain Hart and Humphrey had now learned from the Doctor, and so on into its third year went this strange test. After the way of modern searchers, these young men became ambitious to get to the very bottom of the old chemist's simple fact of the hidden hunger, wanted to probe into the chemical structure and the very atoms and molecules of it. They imported a cunning young chemist, E. V. McCollum, who must be an expert, because he had a doctor's degree from Yale University—which is far east from Madison. McCollum was to help Hart dig into the chemistry of this hidden hunger of mothers that robbed their newborn offspring of life. Then there was young Harry Steenbock, fresh from a farm in northern Wisconsin. Hart, gentle but full of the divine curious enthusiasm of a searcher, used to walk home evenings in those brave days with Steenbock, and Hart started strange fires under the blond thatch of that tall austere young man. What was it that lacked in wheat? Or what was it that made wheat poisonous? And what was it that lacked in the bodies of those dead calves born before their time? Hart, McCollum, Steenbock, took apart the blood, the urine, the most intimate tissues of those dead calves, studied those limp, wet, lifeless little creatures from stem to rump, and what did they find? Perfect little machines those calves seemed to be—there was lacking only a something to make them go.

Did life lack in wheat? But what was the spark of life?

BUT maybe this weird fact of the virtue in maize, the lack of it in wheat, was only a chance result? Maybe something else had killed those calves a-borning? There was only one way to see. And in 1909 Humphrey bred the four sets of corn, wheat, oats, and mixture-fed cows again. Never for a moment were their rations changed, and it was absolutely sure they were all of them getting plenty to eat—any fool could figure that out from the book, "Feeds and Feeding." More than enough protein each cow had, and more than enough sugar and starch for energy. And salt? "They all got salt ad lib," wrote Hart.

But now trouble and disaster began to overtake certain of the cow-mothers themselves—beginning with the ones who for two years had had nothing but wheat. These creatures, the first innocent sign of whose worries had been that rolling and unrolling of their tongues, and the wagging of their heads, now began to stump about on stiff legs; up on their feet, they'd grunt trying to get down—once down on the ground, they'd groan trying to get up, and it was all William Voss could do to prod them back up again.

October, 1909, one of those wheat-fed cows up and died, of anthrax. . . .

January, and Voss found another of the wheat beasts mysteriously dead in her stall one morning—halter-strangled? Maybe. But then again—she'd been going down hill terribly lately. The beasts had been eating plenty, both of them, but there was just something—lacking. There was excitement in the little old laboratory at Madison—but not as much as there deserved to be, for, from Babcock down, this crew of men didn't seem to know, to realize the dark new gorge of the unknown they'd tumbled into. Here they were, down under the researches of Pasteur, digging at foundations below all of microbe hunting. Anthrax? Anthrax was due to a germ, it was catching. Why hadn't the corn-fed cows caught it? Might it be that food, some mysterious x in food—would make it needless to worry about vaccinations, about the assaults of microbes? But who blames Babcock, or Hart, or Humphrey, for not thinking of that? They were forerunners—bewildered by too many surprises in this new unknown. . . .

On the morning of May 27, 1910, three years from the start of the fool experiment, eleven remained of that herd of sixteen who'd started out so bravely. It was no chance, no accident. The second calves of the two wheat mothers that were left, saw the light, blatted dismally, died. But the corn-fed mothers? Okay—never fear, and four fine vigorous calves the four of them brought into the world again. . . .

"There never was a time we talked with the Doctor," said E. B. Hart, with that glow in his voice that comes when he mentions his merry old master, "never a time he went out of the room without leaving us some good idea, some new experiment."

So now Hart and Humphrey switched around the rations.

They took a prosperous, thrifty-looking corn-fed cow, put her on nothing but wheat.

One of those two miserable rheumatic wheat-fed critters they fed on nothing but corn. And so on with the oat- and the mixture-fed beasts, and William Voss came into the laboratory from the barn to tell Hart: "We've got good luck. They're all eating their new rations fine." Excepting, Voss had to admit, it was a little hard to get the corn cows to eat nothing but wheat at first—which would make it seem that cows may be smart, without science.

The result was astounding: poor old wheat-fed No. 570 began to live on her corn stover, meal, gluten at a moment you'd say she was ready for the slaughter house. Less than a month on corn and her legs got easy, and in two months her ribs hardly showed at all. Three months—it was a result like a patent medicine testimonial, only it was true—and you'd say she wasn't the same animal! And all the forlorn oat, wheat, mixture cows, changed to the corn ration, perked up, got new pep, more fat,—and brought forth vigorous calves.

There's no doubt now. There's an x, there's a life-giving something in maize. But the thrifty corn-fed cow that they'd switched to wheat? It was like that old experiment of Babcock's with the first pure-breds of W. L. Carlyle. In three months she looked sad, got stiff. By September she lay down and couldn't get up. Dr. Hadley hurried in, as veterinarian, and administered stimulants—whatever they were—but the creature died on the fourth of October, despite having eaten plenty—of wheat.

"What's this x? Is it a poison in wheat? Is it a lack of something good in wheat that's present in corn?" the young men asked Babcock.

But how could that old searcher answer them? He could only cock his head to one side, and scratch his thinning, grizzled hair, and chuckle, and tell them he didn't know, tell them that was for them to find out. . . . During the last twenty years since this basic experiment that told of the hidden hunger, literally hundreds of searchers all over the world had looked for this x, for the other x's that presently began to be discovered all over. But the real nature, the chemical build, of not a single one of them has been found to this day.

Meanwhile, pondered the Doctor, how about buying an automobile? He'd been reading of the adventures and triumphs of Barney Oldfield, he'd even gone pretty fast, as a passenger, himself. How about driving one of these things? They were getting mighty reliable. . . .

VIII.

so Babcock passed to other questions, having done his job of pointing out a basic one. He had started Hart, the serious Steenbock, the ambitious E. V. McCollum on their life work of mapping out the foods that lacked this x, the foods that caused the hidden hunger. Here they were, young men full of hope, digging away to find foods that satisfy the hidden hunger, and rob it of its terror. And the splash of Babcock's experiment made rings of ripples that reached to laboratories all over the world, and in every country men began fumbling for those mysterious unknowns in food, the lack of which makes men and beasts with full bellies so dangerously hungry. While Hart and Humphrey were counting the dead calves of those wheat-fed cows, an Englishman, Hopkins, discovered he simply couldn't get white rats to grow on a diet of pure proteins, fats, sugars, salts. But when he added a wee bit of milk, up went the weight of these beasts with a bang.

Here was a diet whose lack made puppies' bones soft, bent them, sent them staggering about, grotesquely bow-legged. Here was another that turned the mouths of guinea-pigs sore, and loosened their teeth, gave them scurvy. And all these discoveries came about by the use of the same sort of simple experiment that the Doctor had devised—holding down the diet to one or two or three simple sources of food, and then waiting to see what was lacking. Libraries now began to be filled with the science of the hidden hunger. . . .

While the laboratories buzzed and these searchers sweat, in 1917, Doctor Babcock, now seventy-four, bought himself an auto—and has since driven it forty thousand miles, and who blames him for being a little proud of that, since he has only one eye?

"There's nothing I regret more," said Prof. E. B. Hart, "than that the Doctor's name was not at the head of our paper." That paper was the famous Wisconsin Agricultural Station Research Bulletin, No. 17—where the curious adventures that revealed the hidden hunger now lie embalmed and buried.

But the Doctor's name on that paper? He wouldn't have permitted it, cared not a snap of his fingers for it. "All the credit is due my able assistants," he tells every one, and he chuckles, and is positive that having his name at the head of immortal but forgotten bulletins is not what he has been after in life.

So he remains an "unwritten book," as Harry Steenbock calls him, and most of his work, too, will be buried with him. Though what a book might be written about the queer flashes of insight that played through the clouds of his mirth and buffoonery—and what theories might be spun about why there's only one Stephen Babcock in this twentieth century, when Réaumur, old Antony Leeuwenhoek, Spallanzani, and so many searchers with the Doctor's many-sidedness flourished two and three hundred years ago. But of course he wasn't exactly like them—for they were after immortality, as reward for the truths they found.

A few years ago, a respectful reporter for *The Breeders' Gazette* had the honor to pay a call on the Doctor. "I had never before had the opportunity of meeting so eminent a man," wrote that honest reporter, and confessed he shook a bit at the knees. Respectful, the interviewer opened his mouth to begin asking questions about this distinguished man's science. Babcock gave him a handshake and a smile that took the tremble out of this visitor's knees. And behind the Doctor's jovial face there struggled a question that he'd been wanting, all that morning, to ask—anybody. Here, good luck, was a fellow from Chicago—he'd know.

"Are you reading John L. Sullivan's life, written by himself, that's running in papers all over the country just now?" asked Babcock.

Then the old searcher began, with a fire in his eye that makes him young at eighty-four, to regale his visitor with his own yarn of the deeds of John L., to expound what a grand bruiser this immortal John L. must have been.

Such is the finder of the hidden hunger. This man is the father of the vitamines.

STEENBOCK

CHAPTER TEN. THE SUN-TRAPPER

STEENBOCK

I.

GREEN FROM A FARM in north Wisconsin, Harry Steenbock had grown up as a sort of laboratory powder monkey in that long adventure with the shorthorn cows, in that famous experiment cooked up by Babcock to spot the hidden hunger. In the age of innocence of the vitamine science, before the hidden hunger had been split up into A, into B, into C, into D, into E—and so on *ad infinitum*—Steenbock had cut his scientific eye teeth under the genial eye of the merry Babcock. Steenbock was enormously sober, in both senses of the word; was cut out for a professor, was the very type and apotheosis of the plodding German searcher, seemed marked for nothing more than thirty years of obscure hewing of wood and hauling of water in this new field of the hidden hunger. Yet it was Steenbock who trapped the life-guarding x of the sun's rays.

Before he turned this trick, Harry toiled for sixteen years, himself hardly seeing the sun. He worked amid villages of white rats with beady pink eyes, among colonies of piebald rats with cauliflower ears and warts on the ends of their noses, between cages of sick rats with rheumy eyes, and down-at-the-heel rats with next to no eyes at all. During all these years he chased will-o'-the-wisps, and went home nights absent-minded, foolishly hoping he might at last become famous for finding the exact chemical formula of the Vitamine A—and there was as much chance of that as there was to discover the chemistry of mother love.

He tested, measured, estimated the strength of this A, of this mysterious guard against the hidden hunger, until he must have become sick of his own appalling accuracy. He became entangled in scientific bickerings with other professorial probers of the hidden hunger—about how much

Vitamine A there actually was in yellow sweet potatoes, and how little there seemed to be in the white leaves on the inside of a cabbage. For fifteen years any practical cow feeder, any doctor of humans, would have pointed his finger to his forehead at these ultra-scientific doings of Steenbock —and would have agreed that the two or three thousand dollars a year he was getting from Wisconsin University was certainly as much as Harry was worth. He seemed as far in the clouds as any medieval scholiast fatuously arguing about how many angels could be put on the point of a pin. Then suddenly Steenbock came down to earth—where he probably always had been anyway—and, in a two-plus-two-makes-four sort of experiment, shoved a tray of hog millet under the garish light of an Alpine sun lamp.

By this trick he trapped the x that comes zipping down from the sun. This experiment made his fame.

II.

WHILE there is no question that Harry Steenbock was in on the ground floor, had a head start in the vitamine chase because he'd been an apprentice in the old Doctor's cow experiment, he was very soon lost in the big parade that this experiment started. He began his searching, unknown among those hundreds of doctors, chemists, animal husbandmen, and every sort of biologist who surged at this new science, argued, fought with one another, even stole facts and ideas from each other in their madness to discover new kinds of this mysterious x in every sort of food. Harry Steenbock was then an anonymous prospector in the middle of this gold rush to a scientific Klondike: these were already the days when science was beginning to lose a certain deliberateness, a dignity that marked it in former less progressive times.

With Teutonic system, Steenbock started files of journals and scientific reprints of the battles of this vitamine war, bent his sober eyes over them, wrinkled his high forehead, found out how all over the world searchers were discovering hidden hungers that folks had known of for ages. From Europe came the news that a little chemist, Casimir Funk, had rediscovered what the old Dutchman, Eijkman, had stumbled on. At the very time when Doctor Babcock was trying to beg, borrow, or wheedle cow victims from the authorities on which to try out his hunch of the hidden hunger, this Eijkman had sent pigeons to a nervous death that was exactly like the human ill, beriberi, when he tried to get them to live on nothing but polished rice, milled free from the husks and the germ. Along with Babcock Eijkman is certainly father of the notion of the hidden hunger. Now the serious small Casimir Funk—I think he's a Polish Jew —dug out Eijkman's old fact, cured sick pigeons of their nervous sickness with nothing but the husks of rice. For this life-saving stuff in the rice husks Funk invented the name vitamine.

But even before Eijkman's time, some plain Japanese navy officers had saved their men from the beriberi death simply by putting more kinds of food into their rations.

Harry Steenbock read news from Norway, from a fellow named Holst, who found that if he fed guinea-pigs on nothing but grain, their gums became sore and their teeth got ready to drop out with a trouble exactly like the old disease of human scurvy. But good news—Holst found a something, an x, in turnips and dandelions, that would cure the sore mouths of these sad little pigs. Here was a new vitamine, discovered by science, made respectable and famous by science.

But then long before some obscure British navy man had kept scurvy out of his sailors with lemon juice—and from time out of mind the north country men had cured their sore mouths with raw potatoes and tea made from spruce trees.

Vitamine chasers even beat Harry Steenbock in his very

own laboratory at Madison. There was E. V. McCollum, whom Babcock and Hart had brought from Yale to analyze the urine, the blood, the tissues and bones of Babcock's sick shorthorn cows. In the very same laboratory where Steenbock was cutting his fingers, burning his hands, and finding out how many things he himself thought he'd discovered

had been found by other men long before, the tall McCollum—aided by lady scientists—had unearthed a new x, in butter fat. Without this virtue, McCollum's baby rats refused to grow, no matter how much of the purest protein, sugar, and starch McCollum and his scientific ladies might feed them. And here came news of another fact other folks had had the good luck to find ahead of Harry Steenbock. McCollum's old teachers Mendel and Osborne at Yale University, who had nearly broken their hearts because their white rats had insisted on dying though fed on the very purest of purified foods, discovered this same mysterious growth-x in cod liver oil. With his old teachers McCollum had to share the findings of this x—called Vitamine A—this fantastic virtue that could cure the sore eyes of their mal-nourished little rats. And here was something still more fundamental: so long as they dosed their rats on the pure-food diet with this nasty oil, they didn't die of pneumonia!

But of course, long before the days of laboratory science, Dutch, French and Norwegian fisher-folk had dosed their babies with cod-liver oil during the time of the gray winter fogs when Father Sun was taking his winter vacation.

So Harry Steenbock, who was nothing if not a conscientious plugger for facts, was left behind while old folk-facts were rediscovered all around him. But back in those early exciting vitamine days of 1913, Steenbock had the chance to make all this new science look drab and commonplace; in those early days he had the chance to trap the fantastic x that comes down from the sun. He was helping the mild-mannered E. B. Hart, the chemist whose toil with the shorthorn cows made Babcock's hunch of the hidden hunger come true. Hart was a man whose way of beaming through his spectacles would make any boy slave for him. There is gentleness in Hart's talk; there is benevolence in the look of him. Hart it was who started Steenbock on his trail. He had no great ambition. "Don't tell much about me. I've always wanted to stay in the background," said Hart, and he meant it. But he was forever simply experimenting to find ways of how best to feed the cows, goats, pigs, and chickens of Wisconsin to make them give more milk, put on better lard, lay more eggs for the already prosperous Wisconsin farmers. Hart was obsessed with the notion that all beasts must have plenty of lime in them, had the common sense to see that lime was as basic for the build of a goat—or a baby—as good steel is for the frame of a sky-scraper.

The benevolent Hart and the earnest Steenbock acquired a nanny-goat, and after the manner of all biological experimenters went at their work of treating this innocent creature pretty rough. "What is it puts lime into a goat's bones, and what is it makes her hold the lime there, once she has it?" asked Hart of Steenbock. And from the month of April until the 30th of July, these two lime-pioneers kept this martyr goat in a tight cage that held her near as motionless as if she'd been put in a strait-jacket. They fed her a dry, miserable diet of bran, of rice, of wheat gluten, of desiccated oat straw that made her want to spit cotton. They measured exactly how much lime she took in. They soberly collected and weighed all of her excretions, put them in a variety of porcelain pots and heated them in chemical ovens—and calculated precisely how much lime went out of her.

For better than three months, on this ration that must have made the wretched beast's tongue stick to the roof of her mouth, the ordinarily merciful Hart and the cool Steenbock watched this she-goat go down hill, lose lime. She lost more and more lime, excreted much more than she took in; she got stiff, she grew stupid, and wouldn't look up when they called to her; she became wabbly and weak. "She'll soon be collapsing," Hart said to Steenbock. And to Steenbock this was interesting—for Steenbock, any goat, cow, or rat, was a machine with which to find facts.

But to save her at last, they took their nanny out of her

abominable cage, put her out on a pasture of June grass.
A little better than two weeks they kept her out there in
the fresh air, in the light and the warmth of Father Sun,
and with all the green stuff of the field she could stuff into
her belly. Then just when she was beginning to appreciate
the new freedom, they stuck this heroine—whose name is
not recorded—back into her old narrow pen once more,
back on to that old diet that was not even tasty to the per-
verted appetite of a most undiscriminating, paper-eating
goat. What astounding thing had happened? Of course, out
there in the field she'd picked up her strength, had become
able to prance about, answered to her name—any sensible
person would have predicted that the sun and green feed
would have done her good. But here she was back in her
tight cage, on that fearful diet—and she gobbled it. She
kept on gobbling it. Her eyes became brighter still, and she
was much less dumb. Hart came in, looked saucer-eyed at
this creature whose first stay in that metabolism cage had
nearly killed her. When he came in she looked up happy and
snappy when he called her name. She fleshed up. And lime?
Even that bad diet gave her a lot of it, but now instead of
losing it in her discharges, it seemed to stay in her blood
and her bones: in fact she was a completely different nanny-
goat—chemically. So for weeks she kept on thriving in her
narrow prison.

It is astounding to think that both Hart and Harry Steenbock failed to guess what had happened. Here their goat
has been out in the fields, with plenty of green grass, and
under the good June Wisconsin sun, and eating grass on
which that sun shone—and this had worked a magic change
in her. But the thoughts of searchers are as mixed up, as
helter-skelter, as chancy as life itself, and there is nothing
more entertaining in the comedy of the history of science
than the way searchers pass by in a dream, with the most
striking facts right under their noses fairly yelling to be
discovered. . . . Here were Hart and Steenbock, hot on

the trail of the basic physiology of lime, wise in their belief that lime is fundamental to healthy life. Before their eyes was an experiment that gave them the chance to pin down a new mysterious x—an x that gives children strong teeth, keeps them from bow-legs, helps miraculously in the healing of the dreadful tuberculosis of bones. Carefully they recorded, even published their experiment, with no other comment excepting the remark that it was mysterious how this goat's vacation had improved her lime metabolism— and they went off industriously wool-gathering at other experiments, and the history of this deservedly notorious goat was lost for years in a limbo of half-forgotten experiments. Such is science.

III.

OF course E. B. Hart, and Steenbock too—since he'd been brought up on a farm—knew that stockmen, watching their cattle pick up strength in the spring, believed in the power of the sun to fight off the ills that come from life in the dark. But then, Hart and Steenbock were scientists, searchers first and last, and the better searcher you are, the more thorough your faith in science, the more convinced you are that the beliefs of plain folks are mainly a tangle of superstitions—holding a grain of truth in a bushel of nonsense. . . . So who can blame them for not going on with their strange and enormously significant experiment with that nanny-goat? The very fact that a farmer had a belief in the magic of the sun would steer them away from trying to work with it. After all, so many other things beside mere sunlight, had happened to that goat in the field. But there were other homely facts that might have made them stick at it. For without the help of farmers, chickens themselves look for the sunlight at the break-up of winter. Pigs bask for the good of their bones in the spring sun without pigherds to lead them there. But then—how would a pig know the sun was good for his bones? It is not—alas—from brooding over the hopelessly mixed up and mysterious doings of animals in nature that scientists usually get their start, their inspiration: it's from the man-made ideas of the science itself. . . .

But then came the war to Germany, and scant food for the German children during the war and just after it, and the suffering and the need of the German babies that followed this starvation which they suffered in the name of liberty, democracy, the rights of small nations, and because of the patriotic folly of their own fathers and mothers. The soft bones of those children, and their tortured cries in the night, revived the experiment with the Wisconsin nanny-goat of Steenbock and Hart. Of course, there is every chance that the German doctor, Huldschinsky, whose feelings about the suffering of these children wouldn't let him sleep nights, had never heard of this experiment of Hart and Harry Steenbock. This Huldschinsky was nowhere up high among the scientific hunters of the hidden hunger—indeed he was completely unheard of. But it was a desperate time, and the moaning of these post-war children rang in his ears.

Well—why didn't Huldschinsky get to work and cure this rickets? There was cod liver oil. . . . "Oh, yes, I know that'll put lime in these kids' bones, will stop their pain, will cure their rickets," admitted Huldschinsky. He knew the lore of the fisher-people—too plain to be called science—of how for hundreds of years they'd been using the pale yellow oil from the livers of those savage fish of the North Atlantic, to put strength into the ribs and legs of their youngsters. "But who's going to pay for the cod liver oil?" asked this worried German baby doctor. "Not the fathers and mothers of these kids—the parents are near to starving, themselves. Not our hospital—it hardly has the money to keep open."

"But it's said that sunlight is good for bones, too," they

told Huldschinsky. "Here's the report of an English doctor, named Palm, an excellent fellow who for some reason is no longer a medical missionary. Palm tells about there being no rickets in countries where the sun shines bright. "Why don't you get your babies out of that hospital to the seashore, or up in the mountains?"

Oh, indeed—Huldschinsky didn't have to be told. And he himself knew the tale of a wizard, named Rollier, who sat on the side of a magic mountain, at Leysin, Switzerland, high in Alps. It was well known that there this magician took children, men, women, miserable wretches far gone in consumption, with their bones rotten from the secret gnawings of the tubercle microbe. No medicine out of bottles did this Rollier use, nor any knives and plaster casts. No—he changed these doomed folks into clean-limbed copper-colored savages, simply by putting them out in the sun.

Oh, there was salt and bitterness in the voice of Huldschinsky: "How nice it would be if our babies had the carfare to go to the seashore sun—or away from the stink and fog of Berlin to the sun of that magic mountain!" This fact of the power of the sun was a Job's comfort, no more.

By reason of the need of these miserable young ones, and because of the despair in him that their need had caused, Huldschinsky took a shot in the dark. He went through his wards. He picked out four of the most fidgety, pain-racked, and feeble rickety babies. He took those four soft-boned children—their hospital charts were marked: "Extreme rickets"—and he did nothing at all to them but bathe their backs and sick pot-bellies in a violet bath of a sun-lamp's light. The manufacturers might call their newfangled lamp a sun-lamp: but were its rays the same as those of the sunlight? Was the virtue of the sun's rays there? Nobody knew. Nobody had tried, excepting maybe a fanatic Dane, named Finsen, now more than half forgotten. But Huldschinsky set up his electric lamp, whose strange flame burned in an atmosphere of the vapor of mercury. Its light was an outlandish violet that hid in it burning, searing, powerful invisible rays that were beyond the violet, and these poured out from this lamp through glass made of quartz.

His rickety, wretched, continually crying and puling babies, Huldschinsky rayed the first day for just one minute, with the lamp not too close to their backs and bellies. Then five, then ten, then fifteen, then twenty minutes, all the time scared of burning them, or in some other unknown mysterious manner playing hob with them—he got them used to bathing in this unearthly light, unhurt by the invisible strange power of it. They smiled—for the first time in their pitiful short lives. They began to work their arms, kick their little legs out strong. They lost their fidgets and in the nights the wards were no longer sad with their wailing. With rheumy eyes and runny noses these babies had seemed always in danger of passing out under a swift attack of pneumonia. Two months of the eerie light of the lamp: they were strong. And the X-ray pictures showed lime piling up in their bones where you'd have sworn there had been next to no lime at all. What was this secret lime-saving x in the light of the sun lamp? Huldschinsky didn't know; it is highly probable that he didn't much care; he had a way now to save his rickety babies—cheaply. It was only as a by-product that this man started searchers the world over hunting for the strangest x of the hidden hunger—the x of light.

What happened to the lime in a baby's blood when his belly and back began to turn brown under the noiseless blows of the swift invisible nothings that zipped out of the lamp—or the sun? Under the caress of these rays, that could be so dangerous, why did the lime decide to go into the bendy bones to give them strength? Who knew? An army of searchers set off to try to find out. This happened in the year 1919.

IV.

STEENBOCK, absolutely conscientious at reading every recent adventure of the hunters of the hidden hunger, heard of the miracle of Huldschinsky's cure of rickets as soon as any, but it seemed to awake no memory in him of his old adventure with the long-suffering nanny-goat who'd stopped losing lime after her vacation in the pasture. In those days you'd say he was stubbornly going just the opposite way, seemed the very opposite of his good friend Hart, who was practical, who was always trying to make chickens lay more eggs, goats give more milk. Steenbock, on the other side, was of the breed of men who must find out, get to know, sniff out facts and truth—devil take the consequences and let somebody else fiddle the practical stuff, as F. G. Novy used to grunt, with a sardonic chuckle.

Steenbock's hair thinned at the front and made his high forehead positively dome-like; his gray eyes peered absently from behind heavy black-rimmed spectacles; he seemed to forget the hidden hungers of cows and goats; became ultra-expert on the hidden hungers of rats, who if they were starving, what of it?

He had spent too many years weighing, measuring, trying to trap the unknown will-o'-the-wisp in butter fat and cod liver oil that makes baby rats grow like so many Canada thistles, saves them from blindness, prevents them from developing cauliflower ears, guards them from that sudden pneumonia that knocks them off when their food is too pure. . . . He had even gone off on a fool chase, on the hunch that he might actually be able to diagram the exact chemical formula of this vitamine whose lack in foods stopped beasts from growing, in the hope that he might be able to make in his laboratory this x whose presence in food had the power to guard his rats from ferocious sub-visible beings. . . . With that hunch and in this hope he used untold gallons of alcohol, barrels of ether, and slaving in their dangerous fumes he made stews, extractions, decoctions, filtrations, distillations of alfalfa, sweet potatoes, yellow corn, carrots, rutabagas, beets, dasheens and God knows what other roots and tubers, in the fantastic belief that Vitamine A might be nothing more than the yellow pigment in them. But what chemist in the world could have made that pigment? In this chase Steenbock went up a hundred blind alleys. And when he thought he had the whole business settled, while his hopes were at their highest, some nasty critical little scientist came along and announced that Vitamine A might be found in plenty, in stuff that had no pigment whatever.

In barking up wrong trees he worked with an intensity that his mild manner belied, and he used up thousands of white rats, could be called a rat-murderer on a grand scale, doing to death untold legions of these unhappy creatures whose diets—minus that x—sent them down hill deformed and sightless. His vast mistakes had their uses: for he became most expert of all searchers in the world at this comical work of measuring that x—of whose presence he could only be sure by the way the *absence* of it killed his beasts. And in chasing wrong theories he discovered dozens of valuable facts: hit upon the way this growth-giving what-is-it may be destroyed, by bubbling air through butter-fat while it was boiling. Steenbock looked timid, you'd take him for nothing more bold, as he walked along the campus, than a Professor of Ancient Greek Art or Creative Listening. But by dangerous extractions amid the fumes of petroleum ether he collected the Vitamine A out of yellow corn. In such a concentrated state he got it that there were vast quantities of it, enough to save the lives of heaven only knows how many rats from peril, and here in spite of himself he came to the verge of something practical. He was, finally, abominably critical. He took delight in doing over the experiments of English, German, American hunters of the hidden hunger. Never laughing aloud like his old mas-

313

ter, Babcock, he took a precise and very faintly savage joy
in proving them wrong—by the austere method of sets of
figures, and very sparse, dry comments in his scientific
papers.

He became a master of rat-husbandry, or a master rat-
physician, if you will. Bending his tall body—that even
from the rear has a studious attitude—over a baby rat that
frolicked, seeming perfectly healthy in its cage, Steenbock
would spot an eyelash dropping off the lid of that youngster. The next day there'd be a few more lashes gone and
maybe a touch of red to the rims of the rat's eye. "He should
have one-tenth percent more cod liver oil in his ration,"
Steenbock would tell one of his assistants. So he became a
hair-splitter in the measuring of the hidden hunger. It
seemed useless; but he came to know nearly as much of
the wants and symptoms of these beasts as the oldest rat
mother in the swarming cages of Steenbock's villages—as
much as a mother who ate her own babies by instinct to
satisfy the gnaw of her hidden hunger.

Never realizing it, he started towards his day of days,
towards his outlandish trapping of the x of the sunlight,
by putting himself a most philosophical question:

"Can the rays of the sun—or of the mercury vapor quartz
lamp—do all of the things cod liver oil, or butter-fat do to
guard against the hidden hunger? Are a rat's sore eyes
cured by the sun's rays? I know that cod liver oil can put
lime in the bones of beasts or babies, just as it can guard
them from pneumonia. Well . . . is the x in the oil of the
fish liver only some other form of sunlight? Or is it exactly the same thing?"

These questions weren't original with Steenbock; and indeed, to have known his work back in those days, you'd
never have thought him a true son of his scientific father,
old Doctor Babcock, for so many of Steenbock's hunches
had turned out wrong. You'd say he was the ablest searcher
to be found for mere precision—but certainly no great

shakes for insight. Other people before him had puzzled at these same questions, and a quiet, strictly polite hurly-burly of argument raged across the ocean between English and American laboratories. "Does light cure the eye disease? And does it have anything at all to do with pigs and babies growing?" Everybody agreed that cod liver oil had those virtues—but light? Such was the scientific row, a sort of punctilious battle royal conducted on paper. . . .

In Madison, Steenbock got ready his rat villages—in this agricultural school where folks were supposed to be paid to help the Wisconsin cow- and goat-farmers. With a sort of thin-lipped care he studied the report of the lady hunger fighter Hume in England—this woman claimed that the x of light and of cod liver oil must be the same. She'd fed her baby rats on a ration with not quite enough cod liver oil in it; they'd stopped growing. Then she stuck them under the sun lamp rays—and up went their weight once more.

"Yes—but those rats, though they grew, just the same developed bad cases of sore eyes," muttered Steenbock. And everybody knew that cod liver oil and butter-fat prevented sore eyes.

Then Harry's old friend, E. V. McCollum, now scientifically famous at the Johns Hopkins University, used Steenbock's old trick. He bubbled air through good fresh cod liver oil while he boiled it. He fed it to rats—and they didn't get rickets: but they did get sore eyes. . . . It was very confusing.

It was topsy-turvy. And to a sensible man the whole argument might be considered a lot of nonsense. So long as the sunlight kept babies from rickets, put lime in their bones, fought off tuberculosis, and so long as cod liver oil helped rickets too—what the devil did it matter that cod liver oil prevented sore eyes in white rats? And who cared whether these mysterious vitamines were the same in both places? And who'd ever find out whether they were—since

315

the chemical formulas of all vitamines were utterly and for all time unknown? And what could the rays of the sun coming from ninety million miles away have to do with what's in butter or in fish livers? A plain man would yawn and say: "Hooey!"

V.

NOT Steenbock: though he was plain enough, to all outward appearance; but he was touched with the inward queerness of a real searcher; so now, jumping into this fool scientific battle royal, he took eight baby rats that were twenty-some days old. They had just been weaned from mothers who had been fed diets with exactly so much of each of the known vitamines in it. Steenbock put these four babies on a ration of just so much casein for protein, so much of the dextrin from corn starch for energy, a mixture of various salts, an exact little quantity of yeast that supplied them with the x to guard them from inflamed nerves. He put into this diet, what's more, a definite amount of agar-agar for bulk and roughage. There was not a speck of the Vitamine A—so far as he could tell—in their ration.

For a week, on this scientific breakfast and supper, this octette of little creatures gained a wee bit. That was as it should be, Steenbock told his helpers: the young ones had taken in some of the growth spark with their mother's milk —stored it up. . . . But that was only for a week, and presently one after one they begin to fail, to hunch up into ruffle-haired small balls of rat, to look dilapidated, fit only for the cleaner. The corners of their lovely pink eyes begin to get dirty, and the brightness of their eyes films over with a mysterious cloud. Steenbock straightens up his long thin body from his inspection of them, looks at his helper Nelson. "Nelson—now's the time." There's the click of a switch, and the faces of the two of them change weirdly to a sickly, purplish gray in the light of the rays streaming down from the bell of the mercury-vapor quartz lamp.

This is precisely the right time: and for ten minutes a day—excepting Sundays, as Steenbock always meticulously sets down in his records—they give four of those eight sick little beasts their bath of light.

Without mercy, they leave the other four, without light, as checks. But there can't be mercy in this remote strange world. . . .

Like magic the light-bathed ones grow again. Here's one, in spite of this diet that lacks the growth spark in cod liver oil or butter-fat, doubling his size in three weeks! Here's his brother who in the same time has gotten nearly three times as heavy. And on the charts of the four of them, Nelson carefully marks four heavy, upward mounting lines —the queer laboratory shorthand of their growth curves, like this: ∫∫∫∫

But is light a food? It's impossible. It's true though. Then the horn-spectacled searcher thrusts his lean face close to the top of the cage of these four light-bathed little rats that have grown so nicely. "Look," he tells Nelson, "they've grown, but they've still got their sore eyes. They're getting worse, here's one with his eyes completely shut."

And then, in spite of the light baths—they stopped growing! The whole kit and caboodle of those eight little brothers and sisters, rayed or not, lost weight. Down hill they went together toward the predestined end of their obscure rat lives, and gave up the ghost within a few days of each other—victims all of the hidden hunger.

The experiment was clear—à la Steenbock. It was clean-cut, as only that serious man's exact searching could make it. It was plain as the nose on your face: light from the sun lamp could do *part* of what cod liver oil does to appease the hidden hunger. . . . It could make rats grow for a time. But it couldn't do all. It failed to guard them from blindness, death.

All right—but will cod liver oil that's been boiled while air bubbles through it—will that make rats grow, just as

317

the light rays have done? With Nelson he goes at it, with all the pernickety precautions of the first experiment. Four of them get the heated and air-bubbled cod liver oil, instead of the light bath, and in addition to the deadly, restricted diet. Four others get nothing but that diet that's sure doom to them. It's a perfect repetition: the first four grow—for three weeks—then they all eight of them go down hill, go blind, turn up dead, together. . . .

Steenbock, tiresome in his exactness, a veritable Leeuwenhoek in his disdain for the published results of every other searcher in the world—no matter how eminent—has found out for himself. Now—

VI.

STEENBOCK, who believes so completely in logic, whose faith—if he has one at all—is that there's a rime and reason, an order behind the outward clotted confusion of Nature, makes a mistake. And by this technical bull of his he finds a truth that no orderly reasoning in the world could have predicted. He is only trying to be extra careful. "The environment in which we put our experimental rats must be exactly alike for all of them," he tells Nelson. "It is wrong for us to keep our light-rayed rats in one cage and the checks in another. They should all be kept together—under precisely the same conditions!" And so, he discovers that these outlandish beasts can *catch* growth from each other—as folks catch colds!

Steenbock had a prim and dignified disgust for any chaser of the hidden hunger who would say: "There's *some* of the growth-x in butter-fat," or "There's not very much of it in rutabaga." Let him read such a loose statement and it was a kind of reflex for him to set up an experiment to ask: "Just how much?" And now he put four rats on the usual diet of purified foods—casein for protein, dextrin for energy, and all the rest. To this ration he added one percent

318

of butter-fat—exactly weighed. Was there enough x for growth in this one percent? You'll agree this was sickening. You have a right to ask: "What of it?"

But the four rats ate this ration—and there was not enough of the x in that one percent of butter-fat. They gained a little, then started down hill as if they were getting no growth-x at all in that one percent of butter. . . . "Now, to prove there isn't quite enough of it," murmured Steenbock. And into this same cage with these four downhill little rats, who were no longer growing, he dropped two companions, same age, same weight—and these youngsters, too, had been trying to gain weight on the very same ration, including the butter fat. Only—in addition, they'd been held ten minutes, each day, under the violet light of the sun lamp. And these two young fellows were growing. . . .

"Now our comparison will be most exact," said the irritating man from north Wisconsin. "The surroundings of the rayed rats and the four that are not rayed are exactly the same."

And then, by all that is wrong, and cock-eyed, and hopelessly unexpected in the mixed-up world of a searcher, the four little downhill un-rayed rats began growing! In less than a week after their light-bathed companions had been put in their cage, the un-rayed ones started to pick up flesh, gain, grow. And Mariana Nelson, and the assistant Jones, had to draw new strange kinds of lines on the growth-curve charts. Before the two little visitors, bathed in the light, had gone into the cage the stories of the four miserable brothers could be told as follows: ⌒⌒⌒⌒ But now? Here now was the new happy record of their short, obscure rat existences: ∫∫∫∫

But this was wrong. This was unscientific. This was against all rules. Who'd ever heard of one beast catching growth from another? It was contrary to all human experience, it was beyond what a crazy man might imagine. And Steenbock was certainly far from crazy—in fact he was hardly crazy enough, you'd say, when you think of the essentially insane notions that are at the bottom of so many jumps ahead in science.

Again and again Steenbock tried that experiment, refusing to believe it, rubbing his eyes at the figures of the fantastic growths of these rats who invariably caught growth simply by living in the same cage with light-bathed pals that were growing. He looked for loopholes in his tests and couldn't find any; he kept doing them over until you'd believe his assistants would walk out on him and stage a scientific mutiny. But he couldn't make this grotesque result untrue. It was true; so long as he kept the rayed rats in cages by themselves, their un-rayed pals went downhill on the one percent butter-fat diet. The moment all of them were put in the cage together, up went the whole bunch together—light-rayed or not! . . . And you understand—the rayed ones were in a different room, far away from their brothers, while they got their bath of the eerie light. . . .

In the midst of this Alice In Wonderland sort of science, that was happening to a man whose thoughts were as dry and precise as Euclid, came stranger news still, from England. The unbelievable tidings came from the darkened rat rooms of the English lady scientist, Hume. This woman published abroad that if you simply held an empty rat-jar up—rat homes are glass battery jars—and let the rays of the sun lamp shine into this jar, and if you then put a baby rat into it—he'd start growing! Though he was on a ration that completely lacked the growth-x. And this searcher Hume, whose imagination was immensely more nimble than Harry Steenbock's, asserted that the air in the jar had been made active, had become mysteriously growth-promoting, simply by letting the violet light shine into that jar. "Because," explained this lady-scientist, "when I've rayed my jar, and then blown all the air out of it with a pair of bellows, and *then* put the rat in—he refuses to grow!"

The whole business sounded fishy to the common-sense Wisconsin man. He'd been getting fantastic results himself lately: there was that business of the rats catching growth. But he wasn't going to believe the nonsensical results of others—particularly. . . . Well, after all Hume was a woman scientist. . . . But how could his rats catch growth? Was it possible that the little fellows that he rayed, *gave off* those rays afterward to the ones who had not been in the light? This was a Mother Goose sort of a notion—but it is to Steenbock's credit that he entertained it. . . . But Hume, with her sun lamp putting growth into the *air* of a rat jar? Nonsense. . . .

"Look here," said Steenbock to Archie Black, who was another one of the many slaves his thousands of experiments required—"Look here, Hume doesn't say whether or not she left the bedding, the shavings, in her rat jars when she rayed them. . . . And did she leave the food in? And when she blew out the air in them with her bellows, didn't those bellows blow out the shavings and the food too?"

By such ponderings, by such hole-picking in the work of searchers four thousand miles away, he edged towards his day of days. Along with Archie Black, Steenbock stalks, head bent, into a room that is dark, into a room where no ray of sunlight can sneak in anywhere. Archie sets up two rat cages. Bright pairs of eyes gleam in a half darkness as the lusty young rats swarm up and down the sides of the cages. They seem beautifully bursting with life, fit to live for three years, and they're only twenty days away from the start of their little experimental rat lives. Steenbock hesitates. A day or so before he's talked over this experiment with Black. "It sounds so foolish that I feel reluctant to ask you to do it," Steenbock had explained, in his queer, faintly pedantic way of talking. "I hate to ask you to waste your time at it," he went on.

"But why not?" Black had answered. There was this about Steenbock: outwardly he doesn't seem at all to have what's variously called personality, or magnetism, or the what-is-it made popular by the lady-philosopher, Elinor Glyn. But there is no record of his laboratory slaves ever refusing to follow him, to work too hard for him, to repeat over too many times those tests that his exasperating pernicketiness kept them eternally repeating. So that very day, Steenbock had sat down with his unquestioning Black, and together they'd doped out a ration for these swarming, just-weaned little creatures that were now before them in the darkened room. From his sixteen long years of feeding rats to spot their hidden hungers, out of dozens of experiments that turned out flivvers, out of a hundred disappointed hopes and from the ruins of his own theories he had figured out this ration. Simple it was, and it consisted of common hog millet, of casein, of a mixture of salts. It was a subtle diet, amazingly, delicately balanced, and it had in it, hidden in that millet, just enough of the vitamine, the x that would ward off the sore eyes, that would guard the baby rats against pneumonia. . . . But it wouldn't make them grow. And, believe me, that combination of foods wasn't a thing to be cooked up out of your head or found in a week or a month or a year.

Now Steenbock burned his bridges behind him.

"We'll give this hog millet just about ten minutes under the sun lamp—ten minutes will be about right—don't you think?"

Snap goes the lamp switch. Over the table there spreads the strange violet glow. Three, five, seven minutes they wait, talking of this and that. Now everything's ready, and under the gleaming bell of the sun lamp Black shoves a dish, a porcelain dish with hog millet in it, spread out in a thin layer. Twenty-three inches, exactly, away from the weird glowing heart of this dangerous, life-giving light is this dish of millet. For ten minutes the inert millet is bathed in the light while Black and Steenbock wait, in this room where the purplish light throws their own giant shadows grotesquely along the walls.

For ten minutes invisible darts hurled out through the quartz glass from the violet-hot vapor of the mercury shoot down into this hog millet that won't let baby rats grow. Remote child of the medieval alchemists who fatuously tried to turn lead into gold, Steenbock stirs the millet while the ultra-violet energy bombards it. Now let this idiotic experiment proceed—presently to be lost in the limbo of all fool tests that have failed. Here are eight rats, in two cages. Four of them start out, eating the precise diet of common hog millet, casein, and a mixture of salts—and their millet has not been rayed by the lamp. They eat lustily. You think from all they eat, and being as how they're only twenty-some days old, they ought to grow. They try. They can't seem to. Their growth curves rise on Black's charts, just a little bit, half an ounce maybe—then down they go. But here, in another cage close by, are four baby rats who are swallowing every day the same ration exactly—same amounts, proportions, weights, everything, and the most skilled chemist in the world could never spot the difference in their food from the food of the first four. . . .

But the millet of these last four has had a ten-minute bath of ultra-violet rays. . . .

Well—these fellows won't grow, either, mulled Steenbock. What effect can light have on millet seeds?

Why then was he trying the experiment? Well, you see, Steenbock didn't know whether this woman, Hume, had blown all the food out of her rat jar before she'd rayed it. And then there was that experiment of another fellow over in England, named Goldblatt—a good old Anglo-Saxon name—and this Goldblatt had put living rats under a sun lamp. This Goldblatt had then killed these rats, had taken their livers, and fed them to young rats failing to grow on a special diet. And presto—they'd started to grow! Though their mates, who ate livers of rats not rayed, went down hill.

But how could this lead Steenbock to his foolish test of light-bathing hog millet? This was another kettle of fish. Maybe light rays *can* start things going in an animal's living body—make its liver build the growth spark. . . . But millet? Millet's a dry seed. What could light do to the dry seeds of plain hog millet?

On to the scales go the squirming, lively baby rats, those four who have been swallowing the light-bathed millet.

But they're growing. Their curves for growth ⟋ ⟋ ⟋ ⟋ all four of them, are on the up and up. Black shows them to Steenbock, and together they peer at them, and can't believe their eyes, and they weigh the rats again, and by the beard of Pasteur—they are growing!

From right off the bat the little scoundrels took on weight, for six weeks they grew, for seven weeks they shot up—doubling their weight. One of them, at the end of seven weeks weighed three times as much as she'd weighed at the start—and all from an invisible, unweighable, completely intangible nothing, that had entered the millet during its ten short minutes beneath the sun-lamp's bell.

So Steenbock trapped the sun.

VII.

BUT if this little magic of the bath of the millet in the light of the quartz lamp would turn that lowly grain into a food to make beasts grow—what would this mysteriously changed food do to bones, soft bones that lacked lime? Through his years of failure he'd found ways to give his eternal rats any kind of a hidden hunger, and now Steenbock fixed their food so they'd get bow-legged, big-wristed, pot-bellied, soft-boned exactly like human babies who were kept by their poverty or the ignorance of their parents away from the light of the sun. He raised sundry little rats on the

clever diet, called No. 3143, of his old friend E. V. Mc-
Collum, who, aided by his lady assistants, had become one
of the world's foremost fighters of the hidden hunger. Yellow corn, wheat, and wheat gluten were in it, and gelatine,
common salt and the carbonate of lime, and you'd swear this
would be enough to defeat any beast's hidden hunger. But
Steenbock's animals ate this ration—and it was to laugh
what strange rats they became!

They were rather plump, and looked perfectly thrifty,
and there was plenty of the unknown x—called for conven-
ience Vitamine A—in the yellow corn, to guard them from
sore eyes or an untimely death from lung trouble. But they
didn't want to walk. Steenbock's boys would try to stir them
up, but they made never a try at the quick, prize-fighter's
sidestep rats execute so prettily. They occasionally shambled
about, flat-footed, and often when the tall searcher came in
to look at them, there they lay, the wise rascals, on their
backs with their feet up in the air—keeping off the soft
bones of their legs that couldn't stand their weight. Lime
was not in those bones—rickety they were, like the bones
of slum babies.

Of course, cod liver oil would cure them. And surely
a few baths in the light of the sun lamp—or better still in
the good sun of Nature—would put lime in these rats' legs.
But now Professor Steenbock will try magic. Professor
Steenbock takes that rickety diet, No. 3143, that mixture of
yellow corn, wheat and all the rest of it. For a few minutes
he lets the glow of the sun lamp bathe this food—and when
he's finished that, what chemist would tell the difference,
what genius could ever detect faintest sign of a change in
this provender? But Steenbock feeds this light-bathed food
to his rickety rodents. In less than two weeks—no need of
sun, no need of cod liver oil—into their weak bones goes the
strength-giving lime from their blood. And they'll box with
each other, and stand on their hind legs to try to bite Steen-

325

bock's finger, and dance a jig, and swarm up the sides of their cages. So Steenbock traps the sun. . . .

VIII.

HERE was his chance to rush out and be practical. Why not give the world this magic? But it was not in Steenbock's make-up to be jostled or hurried. He'll clean up the last points in that old scientific battle royal first, find out all about why his rats caught growth from the rayed ones, and explain finally the mystery of the so-called activation of the air in the rat jars of the lady scientist, Hume. (Although quietly he is very thankful for Hume's mistake—or how would he ever have thought to turn his lamp on that millet . . . ?) He smiles, his eyes twinkle ever so faintly from behind his black-rimmed spectacles. With Nelson—faintly chuckling—he plans vast experiments in the interests of science and to knock this idea of Hume's into a cocked hat.

With the fiendish ingenuity of a Spallanzani, with Spallanzani's barbed humor in his experiments, he solved at last how it was his beasts had caught growth from the rayed ones. He got together cages he'd been keeping his rats in. These little prisons had screen bottoms, wide meshed, to let through the dung of the beasts and the remains of their food. Those screen bottoms *looked clean*. But he turned the violet rays of his sun lamp on to those screens, then put these rayed screens in cages and let baby rats run on them —while he fed them a ration sure to give them rickets. But they grew, strong-boned, perfectly healthy and sound-boned —while their pals on soiled screens, not rayed, lay on their backs and waved their feet in the air! And when he rayed new screens, never soiled by food nor the discharges from rats? When he let young rats run on these, in two months you could hardly get them to budge, they were swollen-wristed, and shambled around—peplessly. Was it the air that had got the power from the light? He permitted himself another small smile.

Now everything was clear. Of course, in those old puzzling experiments where he'd kept the rayed beasts in the cages with those not exposed to the light—it was simple to see what had happened. Those not rayed had walked over screen bottoms soiled by the excretions, the discharges of the rayed beasts. So they'd soiled their feet, and of course rats like to lick their paws. . . . And so they picked up just that faint trace of x they had need of to grow, from their light-bathed brothers—by swallowing infinitesimal bits of that growth-x. But it could not be. By simple tests Steenbock proved it was so. . . .

But now he had to be practical. For there he stood, ready with the magic of the rays of his lamp, by the utterly mysterious play of those rays to turn tasty foods—not like the cod liver oil that children gag at—into bone-builders, into carriers of the growth-x, nearly as powerful as the cod liver oil itself. He'd learned how few foods have in them the x that has the power to help animals put lime into their bones. . . . After all, cod liver oil could hardly be called a food. . . . It was sure that what stood mainly between babies and the peril of rickets—and worse dangers maybe—were the ultra-violet rays of the sun. But now he'd nailed down these rays, caught them, trapped them on millet, yellow corn—and what else?

With a thoroughness that can best be described as Steenbockian, he went out to find what things might be so marvelously changed by the light. And if you'd wandered into his laboratory, you'd have found that strange house of science cluttered, even in the hallways, with bell-shaped Alpine sun lamps pouring down their light on great dishes, trays of thinly spread-out food. . . . And every now and again some helper appears from behind a mysterious door—to stir up this rolled oats, or that wheat flour, or whatever the food is on which their tall chief wishes to try his magic. And the results are beyond his wildest hopes. Here are rolled oats, for the oatmeal that children want in the mornings. Rolled oats by itself has no power at all to put lime in the bones, lacks entirely this x of the light. Some British searcher had even claimed that this oatmeal might help to bring on the rickets—though there he was wrong, as the searchers of that land are prone to be, fully as often as the hunger fighters of other countries. But Steenbock sticks a tray of rolled oats under the sun lamp, leaves them there for a little while, has one of his boys stir them up now and again—and does absolutely nothing else to them. They take on the strange virtue of cod liver oil—and what's most wonderful, they keep it. Here this dreamer has gone a step ahead of those fisher folk—without whose discovery of the cod liver oil Steenbock would never even have got started.

Here are great cans of fresh cow's milk, rich in lime, but powerless to put that lime into a baby's bones. Upon this milk in thin layers Steenbock turns the rays of his lamp, and changes it, anchors an x there that'll put strength into the teeth of children, and sturdiness into their legs. Here he's gone a step ahead of Huldschinsky—for how many fathers and mothers can afford one of those expensive sun lamps, for baths for their children when Father Sun himself is hidden, or low down in the southern sky, and powerless, in winter? Into milk Steenbock can put part of the sun. . . .

Then there's wheat flour, good hard high protein wheat to make the staff of life: but on that bread alone any child would go down hill with the hidden hunger. Steenbock plays the light of the sun lamp on that flour—and imprisons part of the secret of growth in it. . . .

IX.

so Steenbock has trapped part of the sun, gone a little way toward the sublime medicine of that Swiss wizard, Rollier, who, a hundred years ahead of his time, makes doomed children, and men and women with death in their bones, over into bronzed healthy human animals. Rollier is wisest of all, is simplest of all, never splitting hairs. He uses all of the health that comes down from the sun. But the rank and file of humanity can't live its life bare-bodied or prancing about in breech-clouts on the side of Rollier's magic mountain. Civilization is against the sun: the years may be long and slow before men will return to the basic sense of taking all of the sun they can get. But into food Harry Steenbock—who is not a physician—has put a part of this age-old virtue.

For these deeds, Steenbock—whose pay was certainly a good deal less than ten thousand dollars a year—was approached by rich makers and sellers of food. There was a great hurly-burly of newspaper publicity for Steenbock, in the best modern American manner. It was not because he'd found something to put strength into the bones of babies, or something to make them grow—it was because a chemical counselor of a great food company had told newspaper men that Steenbock's trick would be worth millions to concerns like that company. . . .

Steenbock resolved to patent his process. "I was merely attempting to protect the public against . . . exploitation," he wrote. "In a very secondary way, I was moved to patent my findings from the standpoint of personal pride in my profession. Too often had I heard the remark that college professors are not practical-minded enough to sense the value of their work. I felt this criticism very keenly. . . ."

He tried to get Wisconsin University to patent his trick of trapping the sun. The University was slow, didn't know whether it would or no, whether it could or not, and anyway if the University did take out a patent, there'd be no funds with which to defend it.

Then a big breakfast-food company offered Steenbock a

contract, to buy out his idea of putting the bone-building x into rolled oats. In England their rolled oats were being talked against because the British scientist—wrongly!—said they actually produced rickets. In Europe countries were actually legislating against their importation. It was a wonderful contract Steenbock was offered, it was real money—

"I replied . . . it should be sent to Dean Russell in order that he might realize in what light my discovery was held, and that possibly the University would be more favorably inclined to act. . . ."

The food company sent on a tentative contract. It specified an initial payment of five thousand dollars and yearly payments thereafter, increasing up to sixty thousand dollars a year and totaling for the life of the patent to something over nine hundred thousand dollars.

But the poor old University couldn't see its way clear to do anything. So with his own money, six hundred and sixty dollars—which was a great deal for him to spend—Steenbock went after the patent applications for a year on his own hook. Then the good and enthusiastic Dean Slichter dug in to help him, and finally certain alumni heard of this fantastic Steenbock and the gold-mine he'd stuck up his nose at, and finally the Wisconsin Alumni Research Foundation was incorporated under the laws of Wisconsin. To this foundation Steenbock unconditionally assigned his rights. "In this connection allow me to say," said Steenbock, "that the Research Foundation is organized without profit to any of its members."

If it should make money—think of all the white rats that Steenbock, Hart, and all the rest of them will be able to buy. . . .

"You undoubtedly appreciate," wrote Steenbock, "that I have been commended for my action in this matter, which has been merely from a sense of duty."

His present automobile is a couple of years old. It's still

pretty good. But—and here's the one bit of fire, of wildness I've detected in this strange, professorial man—he invariably drives it as if he were in an airplane, with no other motor cars, no pedestrians within a mile of him. Like a Jehu he drives, and a little absent-mindedly, talking maybe about some new kink of the hidden hunger that he hasn't solved. So his Chrysler may not last many years more.

Knowing him now as we do, it is perfectly certain he'd consent to ride a bicycle if he can't afford to buy another. He'll be happy so long as he has a chance to be surprised out of his wits at seeing one of his white rats grow when he never expected it to, as a result of some fool trick he himself had not thought would work.

GOLDBERGER

GOLDBERGER

I.

STEPHEN BABCOCK found the hidden hunger with a laugh on his lips, never dreaming at all how deadly this hunger might be. Even when Hart and Humphrey were telling that gay old man of the limp lifeless calves born to those wheat-fed mothers, Babcock's face didn't become completely solemn—after all these were only dumb beasts who had missed life through the hidden hunger, and wasn't the proof of a hunch held for twenty-five years enough to keep any one smiling? Of course, those pain-racked babies whose soft bones made them cry for the x of the sun or of cod liver oil, were no laughing matter—but before long Babcock might chuckle again, for what is more beautiful than the prevention or cure of the hidden hunger of rickets, by the rays of the sun, by a little oil from those fish, or by the light-bathed food of Harry Steenbock? It is hardly likely that Babcock had more than a dim notion of the deadliness of the human ill, pellagra. It is certain he never suspected that within a few hundred miles of him there raged a most dreadful hidden hunger of humans. For pellagra every year lays away thousands of folks under the sod in the South of our American land.

II.

WHEN Goldberger was six, and on his way over from Central Europe to the East Side of New York, pellagra had never been heard of in Dixie. What with doctors who were not up-to-date, what with folks who were thousands of them too poor to call in even a cheap doctor, this ill of the red rash wasn't definitely known there, though it had been killing off poor peasants in France and Spain for better than

335

two hundred years. Goldberger's father wore a long orthodox beard; his boy Joseph grew up on the swarming sidewalks where the song is "East Side, West Side." The whole family from the grocer father down were hard-working after the manner of immigrant Jews. And the patriarch, Joseph's brothers, and Joseph himself, all pitched in to put this gangly-legged boy through school and into City College. It was young Goldberger's dream to be a mining engineer. Doctors? They were mainly soothsayers, bunkshooters—this was the youthful opinion of Joseph Goldberger.

Meanwhile the physicians of Europe were filling ten-pound books with theories about pellagra—this plague of the sore mouth and the flaming skin. Complicated cures and medicines were everywhere recommended, though here and there you might find obscure family doctors, in the Landes of France or in the mountains of Spain, who said: "Feed a pellagrin well, and he'll *do* well." But these were after all only plain practicing doctors, and the cause of pellagra lay deeper than that, asserted the scientists of the famous schools. They filled scientific periodicals full of forbidding words, with arguments that this fatal disease might be due to the bites of buffalo gnats, or to some still unknown microbe, or to the eating of spoiled corn, or to eating any old kind of corn exclusively. And the poor folks went on dying.

By the chance of having an enthusiastic friend, Joe Goldberger was converted to the study of doctoring; one of his East Side boy friends deviled him into attending a lecture by Doctor Austin Flint, the younger. That day Goldberger sat, with a new look in his eyes, listening to Flint tell his youngsters about the human heart, show them the machinery of the endless pumping toil of that organ by means of a live, beating heart—of what unfortunate animal remains unknown. Eight years, and this Joe, instead of mining gold romantically, was an unknown cog in the machine of the United States Public Health and Marine Hospital Service, along with the pompadour-haired George McCoy, along with Edward Francis who proved how dangerous it may be to get your hands into the insides of a sick rabbit. And down South, the plague of pellagra—though it doubtless had been killing people there for years—was suddenly discovered, scientifically.

There now began to be published, in American medical journals, reports of persons with sore mouths, with rashes that broke out looking only like a mild sun-burn, but that turned into sores to make them look like lepers. And some of these people died gibbering, insane, and certainly thirty to forty out of every hundred that came to clinics and hospitals with pellagra died, one way or another. "Like a mushroom pellagra is coming up overnight, spreading everywhere," wrote one of Goldberger's mates of the Public Health Service, the able Lavinder. Lavinder toiled at it, showed how terribly prevalent this plague was below the Mason and Dixon line—but explain it? Who had learned anything about this evil mystery, in two hundred years?

The doctors of the South were many of them sure this was a contagious pestilence, for here were villages, that seemed to be suddenly swept by it. Who can blame the folks of those forlorn white-washed towns of the cotton belt for getting scared, for fumigating, for quarantining by the aid of shotguns—for throwing nothing less than a panic? Thousands in South Carolina, Georgia, Mississippi, were being consumed by the red flame of this strange skin rash—and who would deny it was spreading?

In 1914 Joseph Goldberger got orders from the red brick laboratory on the hill over the Potomac in Washington, to take the train down South, to be in charge of pellagra investigations. "In Charge of Pellagra Investigations"— Goldberger could now write that title after his name. And he knew just about as much as a babe in arms would know of this weird disease. Surely there's no denying that Goldberger was something of a shark at certain diseases that raged in the subtropics. He'd come within an ace of dying of the typhus, while he was showing how that plague may be given to monkeys by the bites of lice that have feasted on Mexicans who were doomed. He was an excellent bacteriologist, and well I remember him, back in 1914, eager, thin-faced and with slightly curling hair, talking diphtheria to the formidable F. G. Novy—nestor of American microbe hunters. It may be said, though, that Goldberger's skill at microbe hunting, and his fire for it, might have easily steered him off the track of finding out anything whatever of this red death, pellagra. . . .

But Goldberger got off the train in Dixie, and immediately began to show what a queer fish he was. He began at what every trained medical scientist would tell you was the wrong end of the problem; he put the cart before the horse; he started trying to wipe out pellagra before he'd found out its cause! Was that science?

He stalked, stoop-shouldered and lanky, among the sick folks of those miserable little towns down there, shooting alert sidewise looks out of his brown eyes. And he pestered doctors, farm-owners, and down-at-the-heel tenant farmers with questions about this red ill. Long into the nights he read the science of it, and went to sleep confused. He didn't buy monkeys and guinea-pigs; he didn't do the formal thing of trying to find microbes in the sores of these farmers and millhands. Never a high-powered microscope did he unlimber; not even a low-powered hand lens did he use. In short, to show fully how unorthodox was his searching, it is a matter of record that Goldberger set up no kind of laboratory at all. He didn't wait for the disease to be brought in to him, on trays holding jars that contained the sick interiors of dead folks. Instead he went out to the disease in the living.

He made a tour of State Insane Asylums, and, arriving at the South Carolina State Hospital, saw nobody knows how many crack-brained inmates there. He examined their reddened hands, squinted at the rash, shaped like a butterfly,

that decorated their noses, and he saw plenty at their last
gasp with one toe in the grave. . . .

III.

"HOW many of your nurses, attendants, orderlies, or doctors catch pellagra?" Goldberger asked the Superintendent
of this asylum.

"Why—none of us ever do," said that worthy man. "It's
only the patients ever die of it, or have even a touch of it."

Yes, mulled Goldberger, somewhere he'd read that before. Hadn't that been pointed out by some searchers who'd
fumbled with this plague in an institution in Illinois?
Strange. . . . He chewed this innocent-looking little fact
over, and was presently off for the State Sanitarium at
Jackson, Mississippi.

"Yes, we've had ninety-eight deaths from pellagra among
our patients here in the last couple of years," said Dr. Harrington, the Superintendent. And heaven knows how many
of the inmates now showed the beginning of it, and were
getting worse—what could he do about it? No, admitted
Harrington, not a nurse, nor an attendant, nor a doctor
had had even a touch of the rash. Goldberger then asked a
simple question, got a quick answer—

"Of course, our attendants have to handle, wrestle, sometimes fight with these sick folks. Sure—the nurses even sleep
in the same ward with dying pellagrins. . . ."

Lonely and hook-nosed, Goldberger was off from Mississippi for the asylum at Milledgeville, Georgia, muttering
to himself, as a result of these simple things he had seen, the
following piece of horse sense:

"Pellagra can't be catching."

So he took a jump over what might have been years of
peering through lenses—and he got to Milledgeville. Here
were plenty of demented folks, made still more miserable
by this breaking-out, by this what-is-it that gnawed at their

339

skins, by the evil that turned their bowels to water: and again he asked questions, and after preliminary politenesses, talked of nothing but pellagra with the Georgia doctors. And he argued:

"From what the best books say, and from what I've seen," said Goldberger, "the big difference between folks that die of pellagra and those that never get it, is that pellagrins are poor!"

Possibly true, answered the Georgia doctors, but still, there were cases. . . . And they smiled to themselves, wondering how such a hunch could ever help Goldberger's researches along, and they unquestionably wondered why this tall Jew didn't set up a laboratory and begin shooting stuff into rabbits after the manner of all regular scientists.

"No—here's something more," persisted Goldberger. "The big difference between rich and poor is that the poor don't get the right stuff to eat!"

Oh, nonsense—it couldn't be that easy. Pellagra was a million times more mysterious than that. That hunch surely didn't explain how pellagra was killing folks in the Milledgeville Hospital, the authorities told Goldberger. "Look at our nurses, and orderlies here. They never get pellagra. But they eat in the very same room with these pellagrins that afterwards die. They eat food that comes up from the kitchen on the same trays. Why—they eat the very same food!"

And Goldberger, the Government theorist, the so-called expert, was invited to laugh that off, and by this information they expected him to be demolished. . . . Why didn't he set up a laboratory?

The peering public-health man had, however, this merit: he didn't just listen—he looked. He went into the dining-hall amid a clattering of dishes, he stalked down this room where the demented ones sat in grotesque rows at the business of feeding themselves to keep going the spark of their hopeless lives. And with Goldberger was Doctor Lorenz, who was stationed there to probe that last terrible outburst of insanity attending some pellagrins to their graves. Lorenz and the Government man sat at their unconventional science in this dining hall. And the gaunt Goldberger watched the trays of food, crowned with a cloud of steam, come up from the kitchen. He saw the waiters fill the plates of the patients from the identical trays that furnished their own grub—but he saw something more.

Goldberger caught what ninety-nine searchers out of a hundred would have said was an insignificant nothing, noticed an event you yourself would say was absolutely unimportant, and he nabbed this truth because he was first of all a human being, alive to human kinks and quirks, aware of human weaknesses. He looked down those rows of crazy ones, then he turned to Lorenz, with his very small, quick smile.

"You're right, Goldberger," said Lorenz, excited. "See! By George! You're right—who'd have thought it?"

Goldberger was right. It was the attendants, the nurses, who got the nice cuts of meat, the glasses of milk. "And look," said Lorenz, "a lot of those patients aren't even eating the gristly meat they get!"

"Yes—and watch that bright fellow, that kind of patient you call a stealer. . . . Look at his neighbor—dull . . . just paws at his food a little . . . sort of half puts his spoon to his face. . . . There! the stealer's snatched his meat. . . . And look how many of 'em are just going through the motions of eating!"

So they sat there, talking in whispers, and their eyes went back to the tables off in a corner, where the nurses and orderlies were busy getting on the outside of food—choice food off the same trays. "Who'd have thought to look for it?" said Lorenz.

"Why—it's human, natural. We'd do it ourselves if we were in their place," answered Goldberger. Wise, like Max Steuer, he was to human weakness.

341

He had hit his trail. He was at the beginning of a road up a mountain it would take him ten years to climb. These inmates weren't being mistreated, mind you, not at all. But they were getting, most of them, mighty little or no fresh meat, next to no milk—it was a pretty narrow diet of corn-meal mush, hominy grits, cane syrup, most of them were living their darkened lives on. . . . Goldberger counted noses, watched, and those were the folks who day after day turned up missing, took to their beds with the rash across their necks and knuckles, went toward their last homes with foreboding pains in their bowels and bones.

But, oh—it was a slender thread of fact, and who would believe it? The authorities at Milledgeville smiled a little, but it is to their everlasting honor that they didn't kick Goldberger out, that they let him go on with his simple observations, that in the end they helped him with his strange experiments. In those days Goldberger was like some modern Wandering Jew, now here, now there, all over the southland, and now bold in his own belief, he hit the trail once more—back to Jackson, Mississippi. He pulled up at a desolate little Baptist Orphanage there, presented his credentials. One hundred and thirty of those fatherless, motherless young ones could at this place be set down as pellagrous. He went down to a poverty-stricken Methodist Orphanage, and here seventy-nine of those homeless brats were down with the red ailment that made them so listless. And with nothing but his thin thread of a fact seen in the dining-room at Milledgeville, he now set out to stamp out the red plague from these children. . . .

IV.

IT was the summer of 1914, a year when 1,192 persons are recorded to have died of pellagra in the State of Mississippi —and in that state the records of the cause of death were not then too complete. Goldberger began making a sort of kind-hearted nuisance of himself around those two orphanages. He pried into the breakfasts of those raggedy kids, into their mischiefs, into their most hidden comings and goings. With his helper, Waring, on hot southern nights, he pored over the records of the sick ones. And in those records there appeared a fact—it was certainly surprising—and that fact was this: that the children between the ages of six and twelve—and hardly a soul among the older or younger ones—were down with pellagra. He mulled over it, got nowhere. . . .

The science of Goldberger and Waring consisted in making friends with everybody, getting the nurses to trust them, the waifs themselves to crawl up on their knees, the big boys and girls to tell them their troubles. And all the while Goldberger kept puzzling at his strange fact—were the six- to twelve-year-old brats, those with the red rash, kept apart from all of the others? Not a bit of it. These orphanages were a hurly-burly of lisping tots, mischievous brats, and boys and girls already past puberty—all in a heap, overcrowded was no word for them. Everybody had a splendid chance to catch this pellagra, but only this one bunch had it. But food—the kind of food—what is it they're eating? That was the notion that buzzed in the brain of Goldberger, who was a theorizing sort of man, looking at these experimental animals—Southern poor children—with his brain as well as his eyes.

Sidewise from his brown eyes he saw this fifteen-year-old boy sneak a long swig of milk from the cow he'd just been milking.

He got growing-up girls to confess they stole into the pantry, nights after supper, for milk and a piece of meat, maybe—and who could blame them?

He watched the older children at their suppers and dinners: the older ones all had some kind of little job to do to earn their keep—and these actually were served fresh meat several times a week.

343

And here was something nice, something the trustees of this poor waifs' home were to be congratulated upon: the tots, those up to five or six, got a couple of good mugs of fresh milk a day—little youngsters must have their milk, and the authorities could afford to keep just enough cows to see that they got it.

"But those six- to twelve-year-olds?" said Goldberger with his faint smile, and a quick cock of his head, "why, those six- to twelve-year-olds were just roustabout children!"

But how?

"Well, they were too young to work and do chores, so, since there was only just so much fresh meat to be had, and that not enough for all, these kids who didn't work didn't deserve any. . . . And they weren't babies any more—so they didn't absolutely need milk, you see. Yes, they were just roustabout, useless children," and Goldberger permitted himself a soft-spoken chuckle.

But these roustabouts weren't actually underfed?

"No, no—they weren't starving, you understand. They had plenty of corn-bread, hominy grits, biscuits—molasses. And then there were gala days once a week when everybody on the place had fresh meat."

Now the hawk-faced man concentrated on these six- to twelve-year-old children, followed them 'round, watched them try to grow, and they were growing some, there's no doubt. And he watched them try to play, and they did drag their spindly legs about the grounds in an imitation of playing—a kind of slow-motion-camera sort of play it was, with rests under trees, rests too often for eight-year-old boys and girls. They were gentle players, and listless. And pellagra? A good lot of them had the red breaking-out, and the nerves, the funny irritated restlessness that went with their listlessness, and pains at night, and worried dreams. . . . But it wasn't so serious—not nearly so serious as with the grown-ups, thank the Lord. Children take a long, long time, many

344

years, to die of pellagra—it goes away in the fall, somehow, and comes back in the spring year after year. . . .

Goldberger started his first experiment. These orphanages were maintained in a reasonably dirty and miserable condition, for want of funds to pay for help. Crowded was a polite name to call them, but he didn't try to change their sanitation at all. He simply went to the grave trustees of poor children's homes, and spoke soft to them!

"Would you object to feeding fresh meat and plenty of fresh milk to *all* of your children here—if the Government, if the United States Public Health Service, pays for it?"

The grave trustees looked at the hawk-face as if he were Santa Claus: "Would they object?" Just let Dr. Goldberger try them!

So, in the middle of the month of September, 1914, those youngsters began to have the luxury of two seven-ounce cups of milk each day. They began to live like so many little lords—on nice cuts of fresh meat four times each week. Every child under twelve had at least one egg a day—for breakfast. And they were to have beans and peas all winter. And they did. And it was like Christmas all the time for them.

The next year, 1915, was the very devil of a year for pellagra, and 1,535 souls in Mississippi are down in the records as having died from it—and who can tell how many perished forgotten? But let's go to those orphanages. Here is Joseph Goldberger, that big doctor who got them the meat and the milk, walking among the children at the Baptist and the Methodist orphanages, and they're always tickled to see him. And Goldberger and Waring go over every single one of those kids, their faces, their hands, the young skin of their naked bodies, and it is beautiful:

At the Methodist home, where seventy-nine last year suffered from the flaming rash—not a single youngster has so much as a sign of it.

At the Baptist home where one hundred and thirty last

345

year were red-skinned, listless, one lone child had a possible touch of it. . . .

But it couldn't be! Do not the highest authorities say: "Once a pellagrin, always a pellagrin"? Maybe the kids of last year were gone, and these were new children? But no —they were nearly all the same ones he'd seen last year. Maybe the children aren't hit quite so hard by pellagra as the grown folks, but then it keeps coming back, worse and worse, 'til at last—well, let's not think of it.

But this year of 1915 was a new kind of year at those children's homes. The trustees were not grave now, nor solemn: they clustered around the Government doctor, and they laughed, and tumbled over each other to get their words to him: "Why—they're different children! They're bright now—bubbling over, raising the very dickens. They're hard to keep in order. It's remarkable."

And no pellagra—in a state where thousands of poor folks were tired with it, red with it, rotten with it.

But it couldn't be that easy. And who blames the eminent medical men, the celebrated scientific authorities of our American land for shaking their heads, maybe even pointing their fingers at their foreheads when they heard the wild notions of Goldberger? He was a man of excellent reputation, the name of the Public Health Service was back of him, and they'd been waiting for him to send news from the southland of some horrible microbe, or a spoiled-corn poison, or a bug like the buffalo gnat, or some drug with an unpronounceable name that would cure pellagra. But here he'd only been down there a year, and was saying: "Fresh protein food is the one sure medicine to prevent or cure." And he hadn't even given a letter to a new vitamine that might be the answer to what he claimed was a hidden hunger. Of course, these authorities hadn't been down there at Jackson, to see the children of these orphanages, before and after—but anyway—

No great discovery could be as *surface* a one as that. . . . Not so easy.

v.

BUT Goldberger for all his kind brown eyes and his gentle speech—that oddly keeps just the faintest touch of the New York East Side—was mulish. No laboratory slave he, just because it was the fashion to do all science in laboratories. And now he went, this bad pellagra year of 1915, to Governor Brewer, of the State of Mississippi, and asked him a most unreasonable, ticklish, and dangerous favor. With introduction from the State Health Officer, Galloway, Goldberger went:

"This plague of pellagra I believe to be nothing at all but a lack of the right kind of food among your folks. What they're not getting is fresh protein food, meat, milk, eggs. . . . But, Mr. Governor, I've got to prove that, convince the whole world of it. Now I can't use animals—so far as we know, animals don't get pellagra—" In some such words as these the polite searcher opened fire on the Governor, who was, well—like all Governors.

"Well—"

"Give me the use of some of your convicts, out at the Rankin Prison Farm. There's never been known to be pellagra out there—and that would be the ideal place to try to produce it. That's *the* place for us to get our proof!"

But the Governor wanted to know just what this wild theorist would do with those convicts. After all, human life, you know—and all that sort of thing. . . .

Goldberger was gentle, deferential, smiling, and plausible, oh, devilishly plausible. He would just feed these experimental animals, no—these convicts, the food commonly eaten by the poor Mississippi folks, on the tenant farms, or in the mill villages—

The Governor was undoubtedly acquainted with the conditions in those godforsaken places—pellagra was killing off the people there by thousands. And, finished Goldberger: "Your convicts will get plenty of cornmeal, white flour, white hog meat, cane syrup—good quality every bit of it. And I'll see there's an expert cook. They can stuff themselves if they want to—"

Here were these two men, bargaining, arguing, for a foolish experiment that had one chance in how many thousand for success. In how many thousand? In as many thousand as any test tried by imperfect human brains—which is not many. Here they threw dice for possible disgrace to themselves, for danger and even death for their convicts, and for the future good of humanity—who knew? The Governor might have asked: "But if my convicts do get pellagra from your diet—can you stop it? Mightn't they go on from bad to worse, and die?" Their deaths would then be on Goldberger's head. . . .

Calm on the outside, inside the hawk-face there raged a fire of sureness. Of course they wouldn't die. If they got it from his diet, that would prove he was right, and then he'd take them out of all danger by feeding them milk and fresh meat once more. That satisfied Brewer, but could Goldberger be sure? What if pellagra started out from bad food, but what if the deadly end of it were due to some germ, some multiplying poison? Could Goldberger control that—once it got started? Faith never asks too many questions, and now there was due and legal pow-wow with the lawyers of these convict *volunteers*, which was the double-edged word that was used to describe them. It was stipulated by the men through their lawyers that the test was under no condition to last more than six months. And, dead or alive, they were to have their freedom at the end of that time. So presently, Goldberger coops up twelve prisoners on the Rankin Farm, hale men and hearty, every man jack of them having sworn he'd

G. H. WHEELER

never had so much as a touch of pellagra. Into a most sanitary and shipshape house he puts them. And behind the mild-faced Jew's back there is laughter, the convicts and their lawyers snickering long and secretly: wasn't this a cinch, wasn't it a graft? Here was this Government guy, asking them to live like lords for six months on plenty of first-rate white bread, good corn-pone, grits, sweet potatoes,

349

salt pork, cane syrup, cabbage. And for that they were to go free! And there were murderers, lifers in that gang of twelve. This was something soft.

For two months those twelve were kept on the regular prison diet in that clean little house, with all the sanitary. conditions of a well-kept hospital. And wasn't this rich— all bedbugs, cooties and crab-lice were removed from them, and the new little house didn't have any at all, which was a different kettle of fish from the old jail, where it was hard to sleep, where the crab-lice would have liked to get up in your eye-brows! These twelve bozos felt fine, were fit. And they made trouble for Dr. G. A. Wheeler, Goldberger's stocky, open-faced helper, who has the look of a very able top-sergeant, the kind of top a dough wouldn't want to get gay with. Wheeler had to bawl them out, make them toe the mark, there was only one thing wrong with the unruly lot of them: they were rarin' to go on that so-called pellagra ration.

On the nineteenth of April, 1915, that grind began, and at noon sharp of that day they were served their first meal of hard-times grub, cooked by Mr. Decell—hired especially for this purpose.

It was a grind—but it was better food than thousands of poor folks through Dixie lived on their lives through. The mornings of these twelve volunteers meant nothing but bis-cuits-mush-rice-gravy-syrup-coffee-and-sugar. Their noons brought them cornbread-collards-sweet-potatoes-syrup-and-grits. For supper they were looked in the face by grits-biscuit-mush-gravy-syrup-sugar-and-coffee. For variety, the cunning Mr. Decell would switch breakfast for supper or dinner for breakfast. It was a grind.

But freedom was just over the hill for these twelve; so they whitewashed fences and told smutty jokes, they ran the ram-saw mill with good cheer and made quips, about that fool of a Government Doc, and about their freedom just over the hill. And Wheeler, and guards with guns

—always with guns loaded and ready—watched them. Wheeler, especially, like the hard-boiled top-sergeant kind of a man that he was, watched them with both eyes all day and with one eye all night. He'd see to it there'd be no monkey business by these bozos—no fresh meat, no greens, no milk would they bootleg on him if he could help it. . . . More helpless than rabbits in a cage were these twelve volunteers, and more closely watched than any guinea-pigs ever have been.

Freedom crooked a finger at these men, and for a month and a half they were as chipper as could be, but then things began to go pot with them. Volunteer A— W— comes to George Wheeler, whining: "I feel weak an' bad all over, Doc,—dizzy, an' shaky. Lyin' awake all night—just cain't seem to sleep nohow. . . ."

"Cheer up, you've only got four months and a half to go—" something like that Wheeler maybe told him, but here comes Volunteer E— H—, who was in jail for life for rape.

E— H— told of trembly spells in the night, his clothes had gotten baggy on him, he had a misery in his muscles, and pains ate from his muscles right down into his bones. . . . "And I keep havin' the blind staggers, Doc," he complained. And E— H— was interrupted by another fellow, a crony, who stated that he felt weak and all broke down, and that crony had a buddy who was just weak and no 'count. And Wheeler narrowed his wide frank eyes, and looked at these men, at their hands, at their knuckles, at the backs of their necks and saw—nothing.

But what was happening? Here was the jolly convict W— McD—, who weighed 189 pounds at the start, and used to laugh, and swell up his biceps, and tell them he could lick the whole kit and caboodle of 'em with one hand tied. W— McD— has stopped his kidding, and there he sits in the corner in a desolate heap, moaning. His arms jerk, his face twitches. He complains to Wheeler: "Doc, there's a big knot of something in my stummick— right here." And other days this former life-of-the-party, W— McD—, gets very nasty, and behind Wheeler's back doubles up his fists. Wheeler sits on a sort of powder

352

magazine—where anything may happen. But what's happening?

Others have red, sore tips to their tongues, and still others show him cracks at the corners of their mouths, and every man jack of them complains of strange pains that shoot from the small of his back to the front of his belly. . . .

And Goldberger comes, every now and again, comes fagged, gray-faced from his incessant prowling up and down through asylums, mill villages, orphanages, wherever this death of the poor and lowly may call him. And Goldberger and Wheeler look at the knuckles of these their experimental animals, at the backs of their hands and the backs of their necks, and see—nothing. And the weeks are passing, and where's the pellagra? Together these two companions in this criminal research for the good of humanity hold secret council about the ticklish business that goes on here in this little prison house. What if these doings leak out? What if the American nation were to get up on its ear at the news that Government doctors were actually trying to give helpless convicts—human beings after all— the deadly malady of pellagra? Already one of these men had to drop out of the experiment—too sick, and the rest were thin, nervous, so haggard it was hard to look at them, bad men though they might be. . . . Look at them there at the ram-saw mill, two of them hardly able to lift a little log. . . . But where was the red rash?

Months went by, and the prison farm harvest was gathered and the mocking birds long ago had stopped singing, and the land lay oppressed under the dank and glittering heat of a Mississippi August. Day after day Wheeler stripped these broken-down experimental animals, stripped them down to the buff—and peered.

It was a ticklish business—and one day Wheeler's military sternness let down, and he allowed them each four ounces of fresh beef—one day in those long six months a bite of beef for an oasis in that long desert of fat-back and sow-belly. October it now was, and the test drew to its end, toward failure, when one morning, at the roll-call, at the inspection of these miserable creatures—they'd long ago stopped trying to go through the motions of working— Wheeler noticed something queer. Here was a volunteer, stripped. From top to bottom Wheeler peered at this fellow —though you'd say what was the use? Everybody admitted the rash showed *first* on the knuckles or the back of the neck. . . . But Wheeler examined this fellow, and here, on his private parts, on the under side of his scrotum of all places—was something. Here was a rash, a strange breaking out, that had the same shape, exactly, on one side of the scrotum that it had on the other—like a butterfly it was shaped, exactly like the butterfly rash of pellagra. . . . Nervously, but never letting his nerves show, Wheeler passed to the next fellow, and there it was again, and here again on another—'til he found six of them that showed it. Yes, and here were two more that showed red spots, that seemed to be turning to a sort of copper brown, on the back of their hands. . . . And here was yet another, with twin streaks of sunburn red on the right and left sides of the back of his neck. . . .

Wheeler telegraphed Goldberger.

And over across there behind the stockade, on the regular prison farm, what of all the rest of the prisoners over there? They were dirty, they were crowded, they were bitten by cooties and bothered by bedbugs, and they had their fresh meat and milk, regularly—and never a single one of the hundreds of them showed a sign of pellagra, no rash, no sore mouth, no jumpy nerves nor midnight fear. It was a perfect experiment.

From Memphis, Goldberger called the pellagra expert, Dr. Haase, and to St. Louis he wired for the celebrated skin doctor, Engman—both of them could tell pellagra blindfolded, you'd say, to know their experience. They

354

came. They examined. They reported: "Six out of eleven of these convicts show undoubted pellagra."

So the eleven volunteers, embezzlers, murderers, committers of the ultimate crime of rape, earned their freedom. "Stay for a couple of weeks, and we'll cure you up," Goldberger urged them. And he hurried to Jackson to tell Governor Brewer his triumph, and begged that good man to let him have his prisoners for a couple of weeks more—but Brewer had given those convicts his word. And on the way back to the farm, Goldberger met a truck driving fast for Jackson, and on that truck were his freemen. So they were all marked in the scientific records: "November 1—passed from observation," and God knows what became of the lot of them.

But they were human beings, after all, animals with sure instincts—and can you imagine them, sick, weak, skin-and-bones though they were, doing anything else at all but making a beeline for a good plate of hamburger steak and onions?

That day Goldberger wrote a formal letter to Governor Brewer: ". . . Science and humanity will for all time owe you a profound debt of gratitude. . . ."

So, that year of 1915—the year that 1,535 souls are recorded to have perished of pellagra in Mississippi—the hawk-face, and G. A. Wheeler, and certain unnamed outcasts, blew away its mystery.

VI.

NOW Goldberger's real troubles began. But it cannot be so easy, the cause of pellagra cannot be that simple, so rose the cry from the eminent searchers, committees, commissions of scientists—who were sure there must be a microbe at the bottom of this red plague. Objections rained around Goldberger's ears. The convicts had developed the rash on the wrong part of their bodies—so he hadn't given them pellagra. And if it was pellagra they'd got, then it was only a relapse from a former attack of it—so Goldberger hadn't given them pellagra. And if he'd given them pellagra, it was by some chance microbe he didn't know was getting into them—so pellagra had nothing to do with bad diet. . . . He read. He mulled these objections. He never answered in words. He pulled up his belt, and tightened his lips.

Now up rises Goldberger, quiet and gentle, and turns into a desperado. No arguments—except maybe in the secrecy of his home with his good wife. No discussions, excepting with certain hard-boiled death fighters up there in the red brick laboratory on the hill over the Potomac in Washington. If there is anything at all to this germ theory of pellagra, if the men who are razzing him now are right, Goldberger will take the one sure way to find out. His plan is appalling, revolting, and by the prevailing scientific beliefs and theories—excepting his own—dangerous. But he laughs, and not nervously either. "There's not a bit of danger. It's absurd to suppose so. I'll prove there's no danger!" And all of his young men, Waring, Willetts, and G. A. Wheeler, and the cool devilish rest of them tell him: "We're with you, Goldberger."

Danger? He laughs. But does he know?

Of course there was Eddie Francis, since become famous for his seven years' fight against tularemia. Francis had tried down in Savannah to give pellagra to monkeys, and he'd failed. Seventy-four monkeys to say nothing of three baboons Francis had injected with the blood, with the excrement, with the spinal fluid of sufferers at the gate of death with pellagra. . . . Absolutely nothing came of it. . . . No microbe, then—but wait. Who could say from that that there was no microbe? Maybe monkeys just don't take pellagra. . . .

Don't think for a minute that everything was on Goldberger's side of the argument. Was he fooling himself?

When you think of the imperfection of the best human brain, and the immensity of the unknown that surrounds the most perfectly devised human experiments—mightn't there be loopholes? Here were three well-known scientists of the Thompson-McFadden Commission—Siler, Garrison, and Ward MacNeal. Hadn't they worked for years down in South Carolina? Always these three men had found that sufferers from pellagra *had been in contact with other cases*. What's more, they had made maps of the desolate little villages where the red plague raged. And those maps showed that the farther you got away from a given central, pellagra-stricken house, the fewer were the houses where you'd find the red rash and the nervous weakness. There were, so it seemed, centers of this disease, centers it spread from. This was what science called epidemiological evidence—and who could deny it was powerful? And this careful Commission had worked in the Spartan Mill Village, where the sanitary conditions were frightful, and that place was shot with pellagra. In this desolate huddle of hovels from which the whitewash was long since worn off by the weather, there were no sewers at all. They'd put in a modern sewerage system, and right off, the death from the red skin, the tiredness, the jumpy nerves stopped spreading—so it seemed. Why—pellagra was a plague like typhoid fever, unquestionably spread about by sick folks' discharges; it was infectious, it must be caused by a germ. . . .

"No," whispered Goldberger, and his lips were a thin line in his gaunt face. "Maybe baboons and monkeys are naturally immune—but we all know one animal that isn't. . . ."

With his good helper and faithful, with G. A. Wheeler, Goldberger went to Spartanburg, South Carolina. On April 25, 1916, the two of them drew blood into a clean sterile syringe from the arm of a woman who was broken out and very sick with her first attack of pellagra. Wheeler took off his shirt. Goldberger shot a sixth of an ounce of the

357

SYDENSTRICKER

blood, still warm from the veins of the sick woman, under
the skin of Wheeler's left shoulder. Goldberger took off his
shirt. Wheeler shot a *fifth* of an ounce of the sick blood of
the woman under the shoulder of Goldberger.

For two days the arms of these adventurers were stiff.
. . . That was all.

But Goldberger was a glutton for proofs. The Commission has said that pellagra spread like typhoid fever, from
the bowels of suffering ones. Well—

358

On the 26th of April, 1916, alone, he faced it.

He would just be sure the natural acidity of his stomach wouldn't hurt this alleged microbe of pellagra—so he swallowed a dose of baking soda. Now then, ready. . . . Here he stands, alone in this most grotesque of laboratories—the washroom of a Pullman car. Out of his pocket he takes a little vial. Into a pill mass with wheaten flour he makes up the contents of this tube—the intestinal discharge of a woman very sick with a true case of the red disease. He swallows this dose. "And maybe the scales from the skin rash are contagious, too," says Goldberger, who is a thorough man. So for good measure he makes himself a powder from flour and the scaled-off skin from two more people sick with pellagra. He swallows this powder. . . .

For a week Goldberger had a rocky time of it—upset in the stomach. Was this the first sign of the working of the microbe? He went about, looking at his knuckles, at his nose, at the back of his neck in a mirror—nothing.

And on the 7th of May, he felt a great deal better, and much more cheerful, because on that day he had company, had what he now calls, smiling faintly at the memory of it, a party. At the U. S. Pellagra Hospital at Spartanburg, South Carolina, he held his soirée; and there were present sundry folks who believed in him. His wife, Mary Goldberger, was there—it was a nice vacation away from her family cares up at Washington. And Edgar Sydenstricker,

his statistical shark, and David Willetts, who had been curing the pellagrous folks in the Hospital at Milledgeville, Georgia, with fresh meat and milk as their only medicine—these men were both there. And Tanner mustn't be forgotten, and of course here was the eternal Wheeler—a hog for work and for punishment. All these were at this party.

From four sufferers down with the red ill, those four young men took the same ghastly dose that Goldberger had fed himself seven days before. In the interests of science and for humanity—but most of all because of Goldberger, these four boys ate this meal. And Goldberger? Of course he joined them in it. "What else would you have had me do?" he asked, years after, smiling. "It was simply a business of *noblesse oblige.*" And he was utterly modest when he said that.

For good measure all of them took injections of a quarter of an ounce of the blood of a pellagrous woman, dangerously ill. And there was in this party one woman, Mary H. F. Goldberger, aged thirty-five, housewife and mother of children. Into her flesh too went a dose of the dangerous blood.

About ten days later Tanner felt a sharp pain in a gland in his groin. It passed off. And the tall chief wrote precisely in his records: "None of the others experienced any inconvenience."

Is adventure dead? All that spring this brown-eyed man, soft-voiced and terribly persuasive, went up and down the Southland, from Carolina up to Washington, and back to Spartanburg, and down to New Orleans, inciting his cronies, searchers of the Public Health Service, from the Director, George McCoy, down to the cubs of the Service, to join him. He made the experiments better and better and three separate times his good friends tried to infect themselves with the blood and with those unspeakable meals—first recommended to the subjects of Hezekiah by Rabshakeh the Assyrian—from folks dying with pellagra. Always Goldberger was the first to take the dose. Seven times in all did he risk his own skin, and sundry times did he lead fourteen of his mates of the Health Service into the threat of the Valley of the Shadow, and Mary Goldberger, housewife, must not be left out of this reckoning. Bold fools they were, all of them, but now Goldberger *knew* that pellagra was not catching.

It was an excellent experiment. Eleven years have gone by, and none of them have experienced more than that "slight inconvenience" they all complained of the first few days.

VII.

WHY not now wipe out this hidden hunger? The simple facts about it, the truth of it was at Goldberger's finger tips, his scientific opponents were routed, and in the Public Health Service there were private hoorahs for him. Think of Walter Reed in Cuba, and his officers, and those privates whose names now are forgotten. In a very few years after that stern human experiment, yellow fever began to fade from the earth, 'til there's now hardly enough of the pestilence to put on the point of six pins. Why not the same with pellagra—here was a business of nothing more than the lack of a few ounces of fresh beef, or a quart of fresh milk a day. . . . But years went by, and the red breaking-out, and the gnawing pains, and the panicky tossing abed in the night—all these kept on in tens of thousands of weather-beaten Southern shacks you'd be polite to call homes. And is it a wonder Goldberger's hair turned gray?

At the two orphanages at Jackson the youngsters were safe now; there'd been never a case of pellagra for three years—what with fresh meat and fresh milk. What was still better, Lorenz, and the earnest David Willetts, had *cured* badly sick pellagrous folk with Goldberger's plain medicine of fresh meat and milk at the Milledgeville hospital. With the meat and milk they'd driven the rash, the pain, the frightened fidgets away from seventy-nine folks, presto—and for a solid year not a sign of pellagra had come back to a single one of them. It was perfect. . . .

But Goldberger, you see, in spite of the foolhardy way

361

that he risked the lives of himself, his mates, and his wife, had first of all good sense, and that was why his hair turned gray. He went up and down the Southland, himself forgotten, among those obscure sore-mouthed and red-tongued sick ones. Well-off folks hadn't ever heard of Goldberger; prosperous folks, thank heaven, didn't have to see these sufferers. He lived among these unknown thousands who were dying from pellagra, starving to a red death though they were eating plenty—on tenant farms, in mill villages. Is it any wonder that Goldberger lay awake, one hot southern night after another? This grotesque fact faced him, leered at him: "The surer it is that pellagra is only a hidden hunger, the more hopeless it seems to try to wipe it out."

For two years he went up and down through seven drab mill villages in the South Carolina cotton country, with the help of Wheeler, and the encouragement of that statistical shark, Edgar Sydenstricker. They spent two years at proving what they were already sure of: Well-off, prosperous families, with good incomes of, say, a thousand dollars a year or a little better, have none of this red-skinned death! There was a mockery in this, that you give the most ignorant imaginable folks an extra dollar, and they'll buy fresh meat, never worry, and milk for their kids, and themselves; and give them a little land and a little daylight in the evenings —and they'll make a fist at raising a truck garden. But where were the dollars, and where was the daylight?

Goldberger faced the high humor of this joke—at which Babcock would not have laughed—that, take away those fundamental, perpetual hard times, and there'd be no pellagra at all for him to work on, no problem, no experiments necessary!

But Goldberger, who, because of the desperate tricks he turned with the lives of other men and with his own, you might take for a Messiah, had no Messianic delusions. He had good sense, and he said: "After all, I'm only a bum doctor, and what can I do about the economic conditions of the South?"

The cold figures of that human adding machine, Sydenstricker, showed it sure as fate: the death from those pains in the bones, the strange exhaustion and the scaly skin, you could track down to the weather-beaten houses where the feast, day in, day out, is the famous Three M's—white hog meat, meal and molasses. Coldly their figures grinned at them, proved the saying of the old French doctor Lalesque: "These are the individuals attacked by pellagra, for it attaches itself to poverty as the shadow to the body."

So Goldberger didn't go around making speeches, painting pictures of the buried horrors that existed down there, advocating that poverty be abolished. . . .

VIII.

BEING blessed with sense, he began working again, groping, prying, snouting—instead of going on lecture tours preaching impossible plans for furnishing these hidden-hungry thousands with fresh meat and milk the year 'round. Why— it was absurd to propose that those folks should have those luxuries, which did not accord with their station in life. . . . There were plenty of hard-boiled people who'd tell you that if those poor whites down there amounted to a row of pins they'd get out of those villages and go where they could earn more and so get the right grub. . . . And myself I've sat listening while men of science told me Goldberger was foolish to try to find a cure for such low-down folks; they had bad heredity; it were better they be left to die—to be cut down by the natural selection that uses this red death as a scythe.

When you'd swear this monomaniac Jew was at the very end of his tether, he came across his happy accident, across a stroke of good luck that may cheat the fact of poverty itself. A report of the curious disease of black tongue—in

363

dogs—drifted before his discouraged eyes. It was a little scientific report by a pair of Yale professors, Chittenden and Underhill. Of this pair of earnest academicians, Professor Chittenden was famous for proving, on students—I believe they were Y. M. C. A. boys—that it improves the health a great deal to live on next to no meat, that you can be a bigger and better American by giving up the pleasures of steaks and roasts, and that in general the human race eats altogether too much anyway. Chittenden had no enthusiasm for full-blooded Gargantuan life. And now it was war-time. Chittenden and Underhill were patriots; and here was a chance to prove the same theory on dogs—which would make it look more scientific and applicable to humans. They were anxious to know whether these poor creatures wouldn't get along fine on daily meals of nothing but boiled peas, cracker meal, and cottonseed oil. And if the dogs could, then—

The dogs were willing to do their bit, but this bit was a bit too much—and they up and died! They curled up in the corners of their cages. Their tongues got red, then blue, then almost black, and sore—so terribly sore I'll spare you the reading of it. They drooled, then died. "It is a disease that has much in common with pellagra," wrote those two scholarly men.

For years, down at the Milledgeville Hospital where the authorities were so loyal to his hopeless work, Goldberger had been trying to keep the patients from dying of pellagra by feeding them diets not so confoundedly expensive as meat and milk. He'd tried soy-beans, peas, dried skim-milk —everything cheap. Failure—and in the midst of his tiredness, he'd come across some southern dogs, fox hounds they were, who were dying from a sore-mouth sickness exactly like the ill of those Yale dogs who'd given up their lives for liberty and democracy. Yes—here was a fellow who'd lost a valuable fox hound.

"How much meat have you been feeding her?" asked Goldberger.

"Been trying to thin her down for the hunt—she's been getting nothing but cornbread," said the Georgian. And here she was, dead of *black tongue*. No, wasn't catching, plenty of the other hounds had been licking around her, and they were okay. Yes—*they* were all on meat ration. . . .

Goldberger left the discouraging South with its dying ones, and anyway there weren't quite so many dying now, what with the years of the war and just after, with their higher wages. He went back and at last buried himself in the laboratory, that red brick building on the hill overlooking the bend of the dirty Potomac. "If the black tongue is really dog pellagra—then the food we fed our convicts back at the Rankin Farm in 1915 ought to kill dogs with the black tongue."

He tried. It killed them. And the diet was very close to the chuck prepared by the notable cook, Mr. Decell—except that there was a bit of cod liver oil added to it to keep the dogs from getting soft-boned.

Then an utterly unimportant waif of a thought came to Goldberger. He called together his helpers, got them up out of the not too aromatic dog basement. There was the pipe-smoking Lillie, and of course G. A. Wheeler, and his veteran assistant, L. M. Rogers, and to these Goldberger proposed a piece of exact, Steenbockian science. "Let's do this experiment over, and this time let's add yeast, as well as cod liver oil. Yeast has vitamine, has the x in it that prevents beriberi. Our dogs might stay in better shape, might grow better with yeast and cod liver oil—and we wouldn't get mixed up with other hidden hungers besides pellagra. . . . I mean black tongue. We might get cleaner-cut cases —more surely like human pellagra. . . ."

So, to kill their dogs, you might say, a little more artistically with black tongue, they sprinkle a little dried brewer's yeast into the Rankin Farm diet. To a new batch of pups—

365

surely doomed—they feed it. The pups flourish, confound them. They grow. When Goldberger and the rest of the boys come down into the smelly basement of the red brick laboratory on the hill, those supposedly doomed pups leap against the cages, yipping and yelling at their would-be tormentors. In fact months went by, and all the disease they got—was the mange! In short, these dogs barked and grew fat. And it is part of the comedy of science that Gold-berger and his boys didn't see for months what lay right under their noses. . . . The first bunch of beasts, that died so quick of the black tongue—*didn't have yeast.*

IX.

MAY 26, 1923, and the hawk-face is at the end of his trail, back down in Dixie, back at that Milledgeville Insane Asylum, where he'd first shot his sidewise glance at the difference in the food of the nurses and the patients sick with pellagra. He feeds the first dose of plain dried yeast to two people sick with the red skin rash, with the doom that starts out like sunburn, with the death that's the pen-alty of the crime of poverty. A couple of ounces a day of this ordinary yeast these two patients eat. In less than two weeks the flush fades from their skins; the sinister butterflies fade from over their noses. In less than a month they are well of every sign of pellagra. Excepting for this ounce and a half of yeast per day, they are on a diet that would surely have finished by putting them under the sod.

Mysterious in the dried, shrunken cells of this humble yeast sleeps the x that's the answer to this worst of hidden hungers. Twenty sick ones, with the help of Doctor Tan-ner, Goldberger feeds yeast that year at Milledgeville, daring a diet that would certainly do them no good, mind you, daring a diet those no-'count Southern thousands have to eat all winter, many winters. Only, in addition they eat a couple of ounces of this yeast every day. It was wonder-

366

ful. Those twenty—excepting one—got better as if they'd been suddenly turned into rich folks who could afford high-priced food three times a day. And on the 10th of May, 1924, ten years from the beginning of his long chase, all of these folks were alive, well, free from a single sign or symptom of the flaming sickness. All excepting one, who, sick to death from pellagra, had closed her eyes for the last time three days after coming to the hospital. Yeast can do everything—bar miracles.

Three years have gone by since that first test, and again and again, on more and more unfortunate folks the power of this plain dried yeast has been proved—it's more potent than the choicest lean beef, far stronger than milk, in the

mysterious x, in what Goldberger calls the Pellagra-Preventive, using for short the letters P-P.

And using his black-tongue dogs for martyrs, Goldberger has dug out this same life-guarding P-P in tomatoes. . . . But there's a nigger in this wood-pile: how are the poor white folks going to raise gardens for tomatoes—there's hardly time after the day's mill work is done. . . . And who is going to make them eat yeast?

This prosperous year of 1927, what with the cotton times that are not too good, and what with Father Mississippi on his rampageous flood, more folks are recorded to have died of pellagra than in any year since that worst of all years—1915.

And that is three years since the first tests of the yeast at Milledgeville. Who's going to do something? In war time the Germans learned to produce yeast—dirt cheap—in lots of thousands of pounds. And the yeast doesn't have to be fresh. It is marvelous how the mysterious pellagra-preventive x of the yeast *lasts*—it'll stand even boiling under pressure.

So this cheap yeast doesn't have to be fresh, and families who earn much less than a thousand dollars a year will still be able to spare the few cents a day needed to buy it. And Goldberger has found kinds of yeast that taste so well that even an invalid would smack his lips, and eat plenty. . . .

How will the Southern poor folks find out about this guard against the hidden hunger—this x that's within their means? Of course, there are those who say it isn't worth while saving them, and there are those who say they're so ignorant that—

But who, having seen their terror at this red death, and admitting they're human beings, will dare to claim that if these people knew they could save their lives by spending a few pennies a day for dried yeast—they wouldn't jump at the chance?

Here is the chance for experiment, on a vast scale that

368

Carleton would have loved—finally to see whether yeast will wipe out pellagra. For every remedy must have the hard test of practice—away from its discoverer's loving care.

Will Goldberger organize the yeast campaign, beg yeast, buy yeast, teach yeast to those who will otherwise die? No, I think not, for there never was a worse hand at ballyhoo. That strange searcher, hair gray, face lined, stands on the steps of the Hygienic Laboratory. He looks off up the river, climbs the steps to his little room close by the cell of Edward Francis, goes downstairs to his dogs, his diets, his rats. He has actually, with the help of that pipe-smoker, Lillie, made white rats sick now, with a hidden hunger you'll swear is the same as human pellagra. And he has the curing of them down to a beautiful science.

Just before he turns to go, leaving me with thoughts of his dreamer's face, he talks of poverty, talks of human ignorance. But he's sure the curing of those eternal ills is not his job. His last words as he turns to go I remember best of all:

"I'm only a bum doctor. . . ."

That is why to me he is lovable, altogether admirable, for, like all of the hunger fighters whose deeds are here recorded, Goldberger has the good sense to know what he can do and can't do. Like all of them—with the possible exception of Mark Alfred Carleton, though that Jayhawker, too, had his own admirable points you'll admit.

In Goldberger's deeds there is nothing extraordinary—he was a simple worker, excepting for that moment in the spring of 1916 when in anger at rivals who sneered at his science he risked the lives of himself, his mates, and his wife. But then all of these hunger fighters, Henry Wallace, Marion Dorset, and the rest of them, were plain men working hard at their jobs. As Angus Mackay put it: what they've discovered might have been found by any other set of men. That's one reason why this story is in no sense a

369

history of modern hunger fighting, since it has picked out only a few high lights from the mass of work of hundreds of other men. The adventures here told of are only a fragment of the recorded story of the modern fighting of hunger. On a grand scale it is a battle—though not considered to be one by the men themselves—carried on in the workaday humdrum lives of thousands of searchers who are persistent, quick-witted, and full of courage. Think of these unknown men and you may laugh at those prophets of doom who predict mankind's approaching starvation.

The men here told of stand out just a bit, maybe, because like the gay Paul Ehrlich they had a moment's brilliant good luck in their struggle with Nature. Goldberger had it. What if he hadn't sprinkled that yeast—with an entirely wrong intention—into the diet of his black-tongue dogs?

But Goldberger had something else besides good luck. To use what he'd found by happy accident, he had to have something that's common to most folks in their own line— and that's good sense.

END OF
HUNGER FIGHTERS

INDEX

371

INDEX

INDEX

INDEX

INDEX

375

INDEX